YOUNG MR. DISRAELI

DISRAELI THE YOUNGER   *From a Watercolour by Chalon*

YOUNG

MR.

DISRAELI

HARCOURT, BRACE AND COMPANY

NEW YORK

PRINTED IN THE UNITED STATES OF AMERICA
BY QUINN & BODEN COMPANY, INC., RAHWAY, N. J.
Typography by Robert Josephy

TO DERRICK DE MARNEY
AND
SOPHIE STEWART

In this book there has been no tampering with time and character. The story moves chronologically, and the people in it appear as nearly themselves as contemporary diaries, their own letters, and the considered estimate of political historians can show them. No novelist could possibly improve on the drama of Disraeli's life exactly as he lived it.   E. T.

CONTENTS

ILLUSTRATIONS

YOUNG MR. DISRAELI

I. BLOOMSBURY

SPRING sunlight lay warm on the grimy window-panes of Messrs. Swaine, Stevens, Maples, Pearse, and Hunt, Solicitors, of Frederick's Place, Old Jewry. It was honourable grime, for the firm was wealthy and old. Spruceness, in Law, is for the parvenu, and does not inspire confidence. The clients of Swaine, Stevens, Maples, Pearse, and Hunt could see at a glance that the five partners had been established in Frederick's Place since the Flood, and thereby must infer that they would still be there at the Millennium; which was good for business.

Dimmed by its passage through the murky glass, the bar of pale yellow light touched the slim bent shoulders of Mr. Maples' secretary, and made a faint warmth on his velvet jacket. He sat with his head on one hand, the fine fingers thrust upward through his dark, pomaded curls; an idle pen was in the other. Mr. Maples' correspondence, voluminous as a Cabinet Minister's, covered the desk; a stack of scrawled notes regarding replies was under the young man's elbow. . . .

Gentlemen:
   In response to your favour of the 10th instant—

> There is a sunny garden in the world,
> The azure flowing of a glorious river—
> Between green banks of vine-enamoured hills,
> Crowned with grey towers . . .

And there the pen had slowed and stopped, letter and poem alike at a standstill, while the sun lay warm on his shoulder-blades and the time drew near for Mr. Maples to sign his correspondence for the day—but his secretary sat shamelessly dreaming, enthralled in his own private magic

3

of words. "Vine-enamoured hills" was rather good. It had
cadence. It was original. . . .

The chime of Bow Church bells filtered into the quiet
room, and he laid away the scribbled sheet with a sigh and
took a fresh one.

Gentlemen:

In response to your favour of the 10th instant, my chief
desires me to acquaint you—

It was May, 1824, and Byron was lately dead at Missolonghi.

II

There was a great deal in Mr. Maples' correspondence
these days about South American mining stocks. Everybody
bought them, it seemed. The King of Spain was about to
lose his New World colonies before the wave of revolutionary
nationalism which had rolled westward from Greece across
Italy, dashed itself harmlessly against the restored throne
of the Bourbons in France, landed the restored Spanish
monarch in something very like captivity at Madrid, and
surged on across the Atlantic, where the United States of
America was already a bright and beckoning example of
consolidated independence.

It appeared that the vast mineral riches of an almost un-
explored continent were about to be released from the grasp
of a backward home government. New states were forming in
the Western Hemisphere, new peoples; young, hardy, pushing states, ready and anxious to be exploited in their untold
resources. Companies were being formed in England, with
glittering golden prospects of wealth which could be doubled
overnight. No matter how small one's stake in this new venture, one must emerge rich. It was Progress, on a grand scale.

There was a fellow named Powles, who was something to
do with the Anglo-Mexican Mining Association. In a word,
he *was* the Anglo-Mexican Mining Association. He brought
his business to Mr. Maples, and was frequently in the office.
It was fascinating to hear him. But it all sounded much too

good. Much too easy. The young man in the velvet jacket, copying out legal documents, answering letters, at his desk in the corner, could not help but hear. It left him singularly unexcited. They were too sure. They were all getting in too deep. Suppose there was a crash. Or suppose the colonies were whipped back into line by Spain. Or suppose there just wasn't all that gold in the South American continent. Then where would they all be? He would smile sardonically behind his pen. If *he* had had any money to throw about, he would have backed them to lose, as sure as he sat there.

The world was in a state of flux and change. It seemed the world would never be steady again. Napoleon was to blame for that, of course. One blamed the Corsican for everything, always. Amazing how one small man, one mighty ego, could so put his mark upon a generation, an era. They had buried him at St. Helena about three years ago, but his son was still alive, at Vienna. . . .

The world had been at war so long, and when peace came (they called it peace, to get rid of Napoleon) everyone had thought things would be—well, peaceful. But it hadn't worked out that way.

When that long, polite intrigue of Prince Metternich's known as the Congress of Vienna undertook to remould Europe nearer to Austria's desire in 1814, Louis XVIII of France was recalled to the throne of his fathers from an adventurous exile in Switzerland, Westphalia, Italy, Poland, Sweden, and England. He was sixty, and fat, and had gout, and his odd little wife was dead; a lonely, childless, bewildered, pacific old man. He did not mind that the victorious Allies seemed to humiliate France in the Treaty of Paris. He had lived among the Allies for more than twenty years, and they had been kind to him most of the time, and anyway had kept him from starving. Let them do as they pleased, then. The world had changed in twenty years. He was grateful for his throne—grateful for the scenes of his youth again, to die in. Let them do as they liked, about France's boundaries.

But his younger brother Charles, Comte d'Artois, had

learned nothing and forgotten nothing in those same twenty years, most of which he had spent quite comfortably in England; and he boasted of it. Louis had come to England late, as his last asylum, and he appreciated its easy-going national spirit. After Verona had asked him to leave, and Spain had refused to receive him; after he had been shot at at Dillingen, and had almost starved in three shabby rooms at Blanckenburg; after the bleak splendour of the château at Mittau, from which he was expelled into a Russian blizzard at the wilful caprice of Czar Paul; after camping out in borrowed palaces in Warsaw and drifting fruitlessly through Sweden—sick at heart and full of gout and underfed and always cold, and wanted nowhere, Louis had been allowed to land at Colchester. His brother Charles, refusing at Holyrood from his creditors, did not want him in England, but the English populace flocked to cheer the French king-in-exile; and though Louis was not invited to London, the Prince Regent gave him a pension and a country house to live in, and was considerate of his royal feelings. Warily, a little incredulous of his own good fortune, Louis settled himself into the tidy English countryside and began to notice things he had clean forgotten in his wanderings—such as small spring leaves against an April sky, and the smell of heliotrope in the sun. For nine years he pottered in his English gardens and read the newspapers and waited for something untoward to happen to Napoleon. And when that time came in 1814, and he was recalled to Paris, the Regent drove down in a carriage to congratulate him, and swept him off to London for a party at Carlton House, and saw him cordially on his way to Dover. It might have been partly that the English were glad of Napoleon's downfall, but certainly everyone seemed very pleased that Louis was to be King of France at last. He himself had never doubted his own destiny, and his royal dignity had never sagged beneath the weight of his misfortunes. Even at Hartwell in Buckinghamshire, among the lilac and the rose trees he had loved like his own, there had been a semblance of a Court. And the Regent had never ordered him to move on, or made him feel that he lived on charity. The

Regent had understood that a homeless Bourbon might still have his pride.

But Charles was arrogant, spoilt, and unchastened in spirit. His Holyrood exile had been enlivened by a charming Vicomtesse, for women adored and never deserted him. Charles had not starved in Blanckenburg and frozen at Mittau, and therefore could not appreciate England to the full. Charles had a poor opinion of the way England was governed, with a Parliament which actually intruded its own opinions on the will of the sovereign. He said he would rather hew wood than be a king like the English king. *That* was not power, said Charles. He meant to show them, now that the Bourbons had come into their own again.

This intention of the King's brother was causing friction in Paris in 1824. The world was so different nowadays. But Charles would not see that. He tried to behave as though the Terror had never happened. Louis was old and dull and very Bourbon, but he knew better than that. There would be trouble again in France when he was gone, for Charles was the heir.

In 1824 Metternich still ruled in Austria, with the Emperor Francis, good Kaiser Franz, pretty well under his thumb. His arbitrary policing of Europe included keeping a tight rein on Prussia, which had come off very well in the spoils of war and except for a few rioting students and hotheaded Liberals was settling down to consolidate its new territories under the well-meaning Frederick William III. The other thirty-seven German states, in various stages of royalist reaction, were watching each other jealously, each behind its own coinage and customs duties.

Alexander of Russia, once so visionary and so Liberal in his views and tendencies, was beginning to see eye to eye with Metternich concerning the defence of the divine right of princes—especially since Metternich was able to point out to him in time a certain disaffection of the Imperial Guard. The Czar brooded over the lapse of his youthful principles and the relentless ascendency of Metternich, but he no longer

cared to act without Austrian sanction. Alexander had no
son. That would make things difficult there.

Italy—well, Italy was in a bad way, what with the ubiqui-
tous Austrian intervention in the north, the nervous shuf-
flings of the House of Savoy in the South, and a general re-
coil toward mediaevalism. The Greek war of independence
against the Turks dragged on. Missolonghi—tragic, deadly
Missolonghi, with its swamps and miasmas that had killed
Lord Byron—still held out against the Sultan's Egyptian
allies; an endless, dreadful business, so heroic, so seemingly
hopeless, so—Greek. Spain was perhaps in the worst muddle
of all, with its obstinate, perjured King taking a hideous
vengeance as soon as the French rescued him from his pre-
dicament at Madrid, inviting revolution with every breath he
drew. The Powers had discussed sending an expedition to
subdue the Spanish colonies, but Canning as Foreign Secretary protested on England's behalf, and there the matter
stood. "Every nation for itself and God for us all," said Canning philosophically. Portugal's internal discord, with the
King warring against his own sons from under the protection of an English fleet, came as a sort of anti-climax, a petty
postscript to the general mêlée. Europe was one vast powder-
magazine, ready for the match.

And England? Why, England's King had retired to Windsor with Lady Conyngham in attendance, and drove about
in a pony chaise with a cockatoo on his arm, and went fishing
from the little Chinese temple at Virginia Water. His long,
meddlesome regency over at last, and himself duly crowned,
George IV abandoned himself to his eccentricities, and let
his ministers do the worrying. As a consequence, England
was going along very well indeed.

Lord Liverpool's Tory government was in its thirteenth
year, and seemed likely to last forever. To be sure, there were
certain problems like Catholic Emancipation, and the Irish
question, and a perennial thing called Reform. Castlereagh,
who as Foreign Secretary in the great days after Waterloo
agreed with Metternich in most things, had committed suicide in 1822, and was succeeded by his implacable rival

Canning, to whom non-intervention was a dogma and nationalism a religion. Wellington, who had a seat in the Cabinet now, was always quarrelling with Canning over the foreign policy. But on the whole things were very quiet in England. There was plenty of capital, and commerce was lively, and this South American mining boom looked like a further extension in that direction. England was prosperous, despite her national debt. England was the place to be, these days, especially if one was young, ambitious, and without a personal fortune. One was grateful to whatever gods might be that one had been born an Englishman. . . .

Mr. Maples' secretary dealt with the last of the day's letters in a somewhat less tidy script than when he had begun the pile several hours before. His wrist ached. The sun had crept past him long since, to lie high and thin against the filing-cabinet on the far wall—dust hung in.its dim path even there, but it had found the worn gilt on the backs of a row of calf-bound volumes on top of the cabinet, and lingered.

The last letter—and then he would be free for the evening. He was going with his father to dine with Murray, the publisher. That was always something to look forward to. One always met the literary celebrities of the hour at Murray's dinners. Not long ago Tom Moore had been there, lately returned from his long residence abroad, and missing the French wines. One envied him his easy scorn of England's inevitable port. He had even made an unworthy pun about the sudden transition from the wines of France to the port of Dover. . . . Moore had seen Byron in Venice, grey-haired, getting fat, and worried about his teeth. Odd, to think of Byron growing old. He would have hated that. Dead at thirty-six. Perhaps it was better so. Perhaps his glorious work was all done, and there had remained only a slow decline. Perhaps that fever-trap of a Greek town was the best way out for Byron. God knew, he had lived.

And Murray had had the colossal courage, or whatever it took, to burn the *Memoirs*. What a scene! That little group of survivors known as executors round the hearth in Murray's drawing-room, and those priceless pages full of un-

guessable indiscretions and revelations, and perhaps justifi-
cations, in Byron's own hand, being fed to the flames. It was
unthinkable. For the next thousand years, the world would
grope after solutions which Murray had burned with his own
hands. Was Byron laughing in the shades? How powerless
were the dead! All the more reason then for making use of
life while one had it. . . .

Tonight at Murray's would be important, for he had something to broach to the head of the foremost publishing house
in England. His first manuscript was nearly ready—it related
the history of one Aylmer Papillon, in a slightly satirical vein
—and he meant to ask Murray tonight if it would amuse him
(Murray) to be the one to launch a new author on a waiting
world. Murray might laugh, and turn it off with a tactful
jest. Or he might—yes, he might publish it. Everyone had a
beginning. . . .

—if you will communicate with Mr. Maples at your earliest
convenience.

I have the honour to remain,
Your obedient servant,
B. DISRAELI (Secretary)

He laid the last letter on top of the pile and rose like one
who casts off shackles. He was free. The evening was before
him. Some day no doubt it would be amusing to look back
at the time when he, England's most fashionable novelist,
had been a solicitor's clerk in Old Jewry.

III

He had never considered his position as Mr. Maples' secretary anything but a temporary roosting place in his ascent to
fame and financial ease. Of course his father had enough
money, but he wanted more than enough. And his father was
famous in a quiet way, but fame should not be quiet. That
was a contradiction in terms. Fame was what Byron had had.
One was recognized in the streets, one had great friends and
splendid enemies, and tragic love affairs. One's books were in

everyone's drawing-room, one's name was on everyone's lips, for praise or censure, it mattered not, at least they talked. One's smallest deeds and utterances took on stature, one was quoted, fêted, hated, imitated. . . . But Byron was dead. Who was to take his place?

It was necessary first of all to have a thorough knowledge of men and affairs, and a solicitor's office was a good enough place to gain that. His secretaryship included certain privileges not usually attached to that position. His father and Mr. Maples were friends, the association was an informal one. He was introduced to clients instead of being sent out of the room when they came in. There was a paternal air about Mr. Maples' references to "our young Mr. Disraeli."

It was a situation which had threatened to be awkward, for Mr. Maples had a daughter, young, attractive, unmarried. The secretary was invited to family parties, little dances, and receptions. His gallant manners and elaborate dress, in the Byron tradition, made him an addition to any drawing-room, and women made a fuss of him, to his unembarrassed amusement. He and Miss Maples were, to put it delicately, thrown together. He liked the girl well enough, but not—good Lord, *not* well enough! It was so obvious, what the elders all expected. In the beginning he wondered what Miss Maples thought about it, and the uncertainty lent a sort of mystery and fascination to her company. What was going on behind that smooth, parted hair, those smooth, round cheeks, that young, round bosom? Was she setting her cap at him?

He was charming to her, but wary. He paid all his compliments in public. If ever they were alone together the conversation became impersonal at once. At the same time his desire to know what was in her mind grew almost irresistible. Her cool virgin calm exasperated him. Already he had discovered that married women were much more interesting than young girls. They were not afraid of you. Or was it that you were not afraid of them?

Finally Miss Maples herself, with maiden self-possession, voluntarily shed the only real attraction she had for him, the uncertainty of her views concerning himself. Her mother was giving a small dance, and they had been dealt each other for supper. They found themselves in the conservatory. He had brought her an ice which she did not want, and both were aware that they had been consummately stage-managed. He felt sure that this was the moment chosen by her mother for his proposal of marriage. In a flash of what he considered real insight, he imagined the scene when he had gone, and Miss Maples had no pretty secret to whisper to her expectant parents. But his compassion for her inevitable embarrassment did not alter his determination that so far as he was concerned there should be nothing to tell.

There was a silence between them. Then she lifted her eyes to his, and for an awful moment he was afraid that she was actually going to do the proposing herself.

"Mr. Disraeli—do you mean to stay in Frederick's Place all your life?" she inquired astonishingly.

"Good heavens, no!" His reaction was unflattering in its promptness and emphasis.

"I hoped not," said Miss Maples.

He stared at her.

"We're friends, aren't we?" she queried then, with a becoming diffidence.

"Yes, of course."

"Then I can say what I like?"

"Of course."

"Well, then—" She clasped both hands around the dish that held the ice, her eyes on his. "I've felt for some time that I ought to say this to you. It's important that—well, that you should know how I feel. I think it's only fair to you. You're not—not at all a usual sort of person, you know. You're not—that is, you don't belong in Law. It's stuffy, and gouty, and dull. You'll—suffocate. You have too much genius for Frederick's Place. It will never do."

Still he stared at her, in incredulity and suspense. It was all so true. But fancy her knowing! And what was she driving at? She hurried on rather breathlessly, the forgotten ice melting in the dish warmed between her palms.

"I suppose I shouldn't be talking like this. It's not my

place to do so. I'm only a girl, and—I was afraid you might laugh at me. But I wanted to tell you—"

"Laugh at you!" he broke in, confused and pleased, but still a little uneasy too. "But you're saying all the things I've said to myself so many times—that I could never be satisfied with the Bar as a career, I mean. My father always cites me Philip Carteret Webb, who was a solicitor and an M.P. too. But it took him such a long time to do both! There must have been years of dulness before the fun began. I want to enjoy myself *now*, while I'm young. I must be great *before* I am old!"

"Then you must leave Frederick's Place."

"Yes—I must."

"I'm glad you feel that," she said with a little breath of relief. "I'm glad you realize that you'd be wasted there. It makes the rest so much easier."

"The rest?"

"Yes. You see—" Her cheeks grew pink. "Oh, heavens, we're neither of us babies or fools, *we* know what they expect!" with a jerk of her head toward the ballroom behind them.

A little chill ran through him. What on earth could she be leading up to? She too had felt the pressure of their elders' anticipation. Not many girls would have dared to confess that. But where was her courage taking them? He pretended denseness.

"Expect?" he repeated helplessly.

"Oh, don't be tiresome!" cried Miss Maples, and there were tears of mortification in her averted eyes. "They want us to marry! You can't have helped seeing that! And as long as there is any hope of it, they won't hear of George!"

"George?"

"That's the man I'm in love with. He's only a captain in the Devonshires, and he's only got his pay and a tiny bit from his mother, poor dear, but if father would see reason I should have enough for both."

"I see," he said rather blankly.

"Did you—do you really mean what you said about being an M.P. like that Mr. Webb?"

"Well, I—I had thought of Parliament, of course—" he admitted. Everyone thought of Parliament when choosing a career. But usually, in order to succeed there, one's parents must have thought of it first—one began with Eton, or at least the Universities—usually one had connections in one House or the other—or one's father knew a Duke who had pocket boroughs. . . .

Her small, worried voice was struggling on beside him.

"You see, if you should go on in the office, father would take you into the firm, because your father is his friend, and —and then you would be a good match for me. But if you don't mean to go on with Law after all—that is, if you intend to go into Parliament or something quite different like that—"

"Why, then I should be no more desirable than George!" he discovered, and was able to smile above a sudden devastating sense of chagrin.

Miss Maples did not see the joke.

"It isn't that I'm not terribly fond of you," she hastened to explain. And the truth was that in the beginning his unusual good looks and air of somewhat satirical admiration for her sex had quite dazzled her. But gradually she had found his tireless brilliance, his restless vitality, rather taxing. He was altogether fascinating, incomprehensible, and—uncomfortable. One always knew where one was with George. "And I hope we shall always be good friends," she added kindly, anxious not to hurt him by a preference for a penniless captain in the Devonshires. "But you see—it's only that George and I understand each other."

"I see," he said again, with that odd, enigmatic smile still curving his lips. His mouth was always vaguely disturbing, full and sweet, and ready to smile. Her glance lingered on it even now, even while she felt again the utter exasperation of his remoteness, the impression he gave of ageless maturity behind that youthful face—his *foreignness,* which she could only attribute guiltily to one thing: his race. There were times when she found him rather frightening, and this was one of them. And yet now, in the very midst of her confession about

George, she was visited with a desolation of doubt—would she ever see Mr. Disraeli again, after tonight?

"You—you aren't angry with me?" she entreated uncertainly, wondering with maidenly compunction if she had wounded him, prepared to believe that he was a little brokenhearted, ready to comfort and be kind—and also virtuously conscious that she had spared him the humiliation of an out and out refusal, if he— "You don't mind—about George, I mean?"

Still smiling, he took the dish from her hands and set it aside, and folded her fingers inside his own, protectively.

"My dear girl," he said, "I wish you all the joy in the world —with George." And then, in case it might appear to her that he relinquished that expectation of their fathers' too easily, he bent and kissed her fingers with a gentle resignation. "I shall be very grateful if you will allow me to keep your friendship," he said softly, with the odd, gallant formality which so became him.

"Oh, always!" she breathed, and her fingers closed impulsively on his.

In the sweet confusion of that contact his tremendous, bewildering magnetism ran through her again—and George in all the glory of his regimentals paled to stodginess before this low-voiced, smiling enigma in a royal blue velvet coat and brocade waistcoat, with lace at his wrists and the glitter of gold chains against his shirt frill. Everything which had once helped to make her decision against him seemed now to argue for him. Of course George was dear, and safe, and usual. But excitement, and adventure, and an unreasoning desire to throw one's cap over some windmill, and a most improper flutter of delight at the touch of a man's hand on hers—these were Mr. Disraeli. Puzzled, she lifted her eyes to his face. Had she chosen wrong? Should she have encouraged him, after all, and waited for him to declare himself; accepted him recklessly, surrendered blindly to his compelling mystery—and felt those lips on hers?

He rose and stood looking down at her, very tall and young and pale in the colourless light of the conservatory. The dancing had begun again, and the soft throb of a waltz came to them on scented air. It was the perfect setting for a love scene, and what had they been saying? He felt an artist's pure regret for wasted effects. He should have been kissing her, that pink-cheeked tremulousness in tulle and blond should have been in his arms, for him. She looked willing enough. . . . But no. It belonged to George.

He had never liked her so well, and he was able to see the humour of that. He felt suddenly very experienced and slightly cynical. Yes, undoubtedly she was a great dear, but all the same she had very nearly made a fool of him. No, no, he had not wanted to marry her himself—but she hadn't known that. He was having all the reactions of a rejected suitor, without ever having been in love, and one side of his nature, the ageless side, protested that this was hardly fair, but protested with sardonic amusement. It occurred to him for the first time that life was going to be very funny.

"Shall we dance this?" he inquired punctiliously, and recognized as he spoke that it was very apt—very sophisticated, it sounded, very like a fashionable novel.

She rose and stood facing him, her lips parted, trying to read a countenance he felt to be inscrutable. She was so young. Girls were such queer, helpless, piteous creatures. Here was he, quite master of the situation, and she, who had made it, not quite sure where she was. He hoped, with a prayerful sincerity, that George would be very good to her.

"Please don't worry," he said, and drew her hand through his elbow. "I'm sure your father won't be too hard on you, once he understands how it is. Shall I tell him I'm thinking of going abroad?"

"But then—if you didn't go—?"

"Perhaps I shall go," he said, smiling down at her with what he felt was appropriate melancholy. "But first—may I have this waltz?"

She followed him submissively, her hand on his arm, to the ballroom, wondering if it was to be their last waltz ever. . . . They danced well together, and he saw her mother watching, and felt a pang of pity for the girl he held, so valiant for her happiness in the face of such odds. Poor child, she was still too young for the battle of life. He was nearly twenty himself.

IV

Frederick's Place,
June, 1824

My dear Sir,

Until I received your note this morning, I had flattered myself that my indiscretion had been forgotten. It is to me a matter of great regret that, as appears by your letter, any more trouble should be given respecting this unfortunate manuscript, which will, most probably, be considered too crude a production for the public, and which, if it is ever imagined to possess any interest, is certainly too late this season, and will be obsolete in the next.

I think, therefore, that the sooner it be put behind the fire the better, and as you have some small experience in burning manuscripts, you will perhaps be so kind as to consign it to the flames.

Once more apologizing for all the trouble I have given you, I remain ever, my dear Sir,

Yours very faithfully,

B. DISRAELI

Thus ended abruptly *The Adventures of Aylmer Papillon on a Visit to Vraibleusia:* that "satire on the present state of society" which had so embarrassed and puzzled the good John Murray ever since its arrival in his office some weeks before.

Byron had once called Murray the most timorous of all God's booksellers, though Murray was not the only man in the year of grace 1819 who had found *Don Juan* intimidating. A kind and amiable man, with a colossal natural indolence and a genius for gracious living, John Murray loathed above everything else to read a manuscript. To his authors, big with the pride of achievement or driven by a need of ready cash, this was often the last word in exasperation. Murray invited them to his dinners, gave them delicious food, wine for gods, music, charming women, amusing conversation—but he would not get round to read their manuscripts.

Nearly everybody of literary distinction in England, Europe, and America was entertained in the drawing-room at 50 Albemarle Street sooner or later. You were likely to meet anyone there from Madame de Staël to Washington Irving. Canning and Southey came to Murray's; Scott had first met Byron there, both lame, and immensely taken with each other at first sight. There Tom Moore would sing his lovely Irish melodies after dinner, in his light, sweet voice which brought tears to the eyes of his hearers. The walls of the room were covered with portraits of its habitués, past and present. It was an honour to be added to Murray's picture gallery. He was not an immensely wealthy man, but his generosity was untold.

Murray and Isaac Disraeli had been friends for nearly thirty years now. In 1804 he had written to congratulate Isaac on the birth of a son, the first, to be called Benjamin. There was already a daughter, Sarah, and two more sons had come since. Murray was very fond of them all, and the girl, just turning twenty-two, was handsome and intelligent. But Ben was Murray's favourite. An inordinately sensitive man, Murray basked in the boy's ardent admiration. Isaac's son had qualities which his own lad lacked—most decidedly. Isaac's son was a much more exciting person, with his black curls and his fiery enthusiasms, than sixteen-year-old John Murray III.

He had published Isaac Disraeli's books for years. It was only natural, considering the literary atmosphere in which he lived, that Ben should produce a book himself. But a satire? On society? What society did Ben know except what he had seen at Murray's? Was this going to be an impertinence?

Always a slightly anxious man, Murray squirmed before the necessity of giving judgment on the manuscript concerning Aylmer Papillon. He didn't want to offend Isaac or discourage the boy, who might some day do something really worth while, like his father. But—*satire?* Murray contemplated its title again with aversion. Made up names and places, of course. But might not real people be behind them? No, no, it really would not do. But how to say so? Perhaps one ought to read a little of it, just to . . . He laid it aside on the end of his desk where it would be handy. Tomorrow . . . Just now he had to write some letters.

The manuscript lay there, reproaching him. It was legibly written. Perhaps a note now to the boy lest his expectations run too high. After all, the manuscript had been in the office quite a while. Murray's pen began to move cautiously. The title, he wrote, seemed a trifle ambiguous—and of course Ben realized the policy of the house was largely biography and poetry—but he looked forward with the keenest interest, naturally, to reading this first effort of his old friend's son— as soon as he could find time—very busy just now—in the meantime, he thought he would just get someone else's opinion—there was a very able man in the office, who really knew more about such things than he did himself—the manuscript would therefore be passed on to him until . . .

Result: this high-handed note from Ben desiring him to burn the manuscript, with an uncalled-for reference to that unhappy episode of the Byron *Memoirs*. Murray was still being driven to justify himself on that. As a matter of fact, he had merely acted on the wishes of the family. Those two women were to be considered, after all—Byron's unfortunate wife and sister. And there was a child, too—poor little Ada must be about ten years old now. Memoirs like those should never have been written in the first place, but it was like Byron's mad ego. Men like Byron must write memoirs. But someone had to see that people were not hurt by them. Someone had to preserve the decencies. . . . Not that Murray knew what was in the *Memoirs* himself, he had scrupulously refrained from reading them while they were in his possession. It had seemed the gentlemanly thing to do. Moore had read them, and thought that with a few omissions they would pass. But the women—one had to take their word for it. The family's feelings must be considered in these things. But it was a matter which Murray would have been glad to be allowed to forget.

Ben needn't have flown at him like this, anyway. Murray hated to offend people. He wished for the hundredth time that his friends would not write books, thereby creating these situations. Something would have to be done now. His eye, wandering vaguely, fell on a parcel of manuscript newly arrived in the post. Oh, yes, that *Life of John Paul Jones,* by an American. Doubtless not much good. Doubtless it wanted pulling together—an introduction added, perhaps. Why not ask Ben to do that—just to show him one had confidence in his ability—let him down easily. Somebody had to do something with the John Paul Jones manuscript, it was in a very untidy state. Ben at least knew how to prepare a manuscript. The boy was a scholar too, and could easily add whatever was needed. One might take it up with him. To-morrow . . .

V

To Ben, the abortion of Aylmer Papillon scarcely ranked as a failure, after his first impatient reaction to the startling fact that Murray had not instantly arranged for its publication. He had only dashed it off for fun. He could write another book, much better, as soon as he got time. Meanwhile, more important things were afoot.

His father, with a fourth *Curiosities of Literature* volume just published and out of the way, had plunged enthusiastically into his *Commentaries on Charles I,* and his eyesight, which always needed to be coddled, was showing strain. He had been working much too hard and steadily even for him, whose very food and drink were between book covers, and whose idea of exercise was the short walk along Bloomsbury Square from his house to the British Museum Reading-Room. The logical remedy was a holiday with Ben, somewhere quite away from his writing-desk. The most natural holiday, Ben at once informed him, was a trip abroad. The question, said Isaac, was to find a peaceful spot abroad where they would not be kept awake nights by squabbles between the king and his people—any king, any people.

Ben suggested Italy, but Isaac said it was too far and too

hot and one never knew what was going to happen there these days now that the Austrians had gone in. Ben said all the better. But eventually they decided on the Rhine valley, and God knew that would be bad enough, said Isaac gloomily, though things had been fairly quiet there lately. Isaac said your life wasn't worth tuppence if you set foot out of England nowadays; he who had been in Paris in 1788, with the Revolution brewing! He grumbled a good deal at being uprooted, and slandered every government across the Channel, and read his family extemporaneous lectures on the evils of the republican doctrine—but Ben had started packing.

William Meredith was going with them—a quiet, learned young man just down from Oxford, the son of another of Isaac's legion of friends. Meredith was being taken along to supply young companionship for Ben, whose private opinion was that Meredith was already years older than Isaac would ever be. It was true that the University sometimes sat somewhat heavily on Meredith's speech and outlook—pattern-minds, said Ben, fiercely individual himself; Oxford left them like peas in a pod—poured them into a mould—turned out a race of facsimiles—his figures of speech grew violent. His sister Sarah said that perhaps Oxford would wear off them in time. They came down with their boots very new and tight and shiny, said Sarah, with her own figure of speech—but the dust of the highway would collect on them very soon. Ben remarked that he would see to it that Meredith got a devil of a dusty march in Germany.

Actually, Meredith was so awed by this dazzlingly articulate family of Disraelis, with its floods of graceful hyperbole and its prodigal way of using three synonyms in a row simply because the words were there in the language and might as well be brought into line, that his own clipped University habit of trenchant understatement was swept away into comparative silence. The Disraelis talked for the love of sound and climax, not for the sake of the bare idea. Even Sarah could do it, piling up her sentences to a deliciously over-emphasized peak of well-phrased effect. Even Mrs. Disraeli, who was never quite sure what the others were talking about,

ran on and on in her own way, though she was likely to repeat herself, which the others never had to do. Meredith
would listen, entranced, to a family vocabulary several times
the size of the meagre set of over-worked words which sufficed
at Oxford for daily intercourse. It was a revelation to him.
Contrary to Ben's suspicions, Meredith had no conceit whatever. He was merely getting acclimatized, in a sort of delighted wonderment, to the rarefied Disraeli air.

The three landed at Ostend late in July, thought it a dis-
gusting place, and proceeded at once in a diligence to Bruges,
where the first of Ben's enormous letters to the beloved sister
left behind in London was sent back.

. . . Bruges is the city of cities. Perpetual palaces, not an
ordinary house. The city is three times too extensive for its
inhabitants, and you may lounge down magnificent pa-
rades, bounded on both sides by palaces and churches,
without meeting a single individual or being disturbed by
a single sound. In its decay, its splendour, its antiquity, and
its silences, it very much resembles our Winchester.

I never knew the Governor in such fine racy spirits.
Meredith and myself talk French with a mixture of sub-
limity and *sangfroid* perfectly inimitable. We are off to
Ghent tomorrow by canal after having passed a long and
luscious day at Bruges. Give my best to *ma mère* and the
dear young slave drivers. . . .

"He's homesick," said Sarah, smiling, when she had read it
aloud to the assembled family in Bloomsbury Square.

"With father there?" jeered Jem, aged eleven. "And
canals?"

"I say, can't you see old Meredith spouting French without
turning a hair?" grinned Ralph, aged fifteen.

"*Mr.* Meredith," said Sarah firmly, folding the letter with
loving fingers. "Of course he speaks French. He's been to
Oxford."

"Does everyone who's down from Oxford speak French?"
queried Jem.

"Yes," said Sarah, firmly.

"*I* remember Winchester," said Mrs. Disraeli. "We had a house near there for the holidays once—it was that hot summer—Jem was very small—three years old he was that summer—well, perhaps four—the sun shone every day, and the garden all dried up, and your poor father had to go about always in dark glasses—" She was off.

The next letter was from Antwerp, tacked on to the end of a closely written sheet from their father, who had got "a Sevigné fit," said Ben, and left him no room for his own impressions. They liked Ghent, with its busy river and its cathedral, where they heard a Mozart Mass. Best of all they liked its food.

. . . We ordered, of course, something cold, not to be detained. The hostess, however, seemed peculiarly desirous to give us a specimen of her cookery, and there was a mysterious delay. Enter the waiter. A *fricandeau,* the finest I ever tasted, perfectly admirable, a small and very delicate roast joint, veal chops dressed with a rich sauce piquant, capital roast pigeons, a large dish of peas, most wonderfully fine, cheese, dessert, a salad pre-eminent even among the salads of Flanders which are unique for their delicate crispness and silvery whiteness, bread and beer ad lib., served up in the neatest and purest manner imaginable, silver forks, etc.; cost only six francs, forming one of the finest specimens of exquisite and economic cookery I ever witnessed. We have had a good deal of veal stewed with sorrel, and not bad.

Antwerp delights us all more than any place we have yet been at. We have had a perfect debauch of Rubens, and Meredith and myself have destroyed the reputation of half the cathedrals in Flanders by our mysterious hints of the spuriousness of their Sir Pauls. The paper in this country is bad, the ink infamous, and the pens wusser. Love to Mère and all. . . .

"Veal stewed with sorrel," mused Mrs. Disraeli. "I must speak to cook."

"What is a *fricandeau?*" inquired Jem interestedly.

"They're overeating," said Sarah, smiling.

"Nonsense. Disraelis can eat anything," said the woman who had married one more than twenty years before.

"But poor Mr. Meredith will get indigestion if he keeps the pace," smiled Sarah.

At Mechlin, on the way to Brussels, the dinner was good, and the cathedral magnificent, the oysters small as shrimps but delicately sweet, and they found an old bookseller. The peas were singularly fine, but—

> . . . the idiots, imagining they could please our English taste, dressed them *au naturel! Peste!* The entrance to Brussels is very striking. The part in which we reside, the new town, is a perpetual Waterloo Place, a regular succession of grand places and Rue Royales in a magnificent style of architecture. Dinner excellent—frogs—*pâté de grenouilles*—magnificent! Sublime!
>
> The Governor is particularly well. We pass the evenings very agreeably in cafés, where Meredith and myself play dominoes and the Governor invents or discovers new ices, lectures on sorbettes and liqueurs, and reads the Flanders papers, which are a copy a week old of the Parisian copies of the English. We then rush home to Seltzer water and Moselle, sugar and lemon, an invention of a waiter and my father, and which, to use our favourite national phrase, if it is equalled by any cup in Europe, it is certainly not excelled.
>
> Brussels is full of English. Tomorrow we visit the field of Waterloo, not so much for the scenery, but, as Mrs. Young says, for the idea. . . .

At Brussels they hired a travelling carriage of their own—one left behind by a Hamburg gentleman in payment of his bill. In this they drove up the valley of the Meuse and over a mountainous ascent to Spa, through "a perfect debauch of scenery."

> . . . Pen and ink, and particularly the miserable materials with which I am scratching, can give you no idea of our

rich adventures. We rode on the Spa ponies to the distant springs. They are handsome little galloways; the Governor was particularly equestrian.

I have become a most exquisite billiard player; we shewed off to great advantage at the Wells and Aix, to which place we were off on Wednesday. We were all asleep when we entered the Prussian frontier, and the Governor mistook the customs officer for an inn-keeper and kindly informed him that we had taken refreshment at Limburg on the way. The rest of this scene, which was exquisite, when we meet. . . .

Cologne was next, where they rode about the city in an arch-ducal fiacre; Ems, "the very Castle of Indolence," a watering place without shops or houses, devoid of English, whose inhabitants dozed in acacia arbours and were rowed upon the river; Frankfort, where they went to the opera and the casino, and read the English newspapers and bought Dürer and Rembrandt prints; Darmstadt and more opera, attended by the Grand Duke himself in military uniform, beating time with one hand and watching the orchestra through a glass. From Mayence, arranging for the conveyance of their carriage, they began the voyage down the Rhine, sixty miles of the most beautiful part of the river, in perfect weather, bringing to a close a month which had exceeded even Ben's highest expectations.

To Isaac, it was the first long holiday in years—since his marriage—since those stirring days in Paris before the Revolution. He felt gay and carefree—coltish, in fact. He seemed to be perpetually kicking up his heels, like an old horse put out to grass. And he was finding the company of his eldest son very amusing. The boy was growing up—he had a mature brain and a witty tongue; one could talk to him, one could even listen to him. Isaac was astonished and pleased. He spent so much time in the Museum he had not noticed that Ben was no longer a child. Not since the first novelty of fatherhood had worn off, a long time ago, had Isaac been so conscious of having a son—a proud and pleasant feeling.

To young Meredith, self-contained, British to the back-bone, it was a charming interlude in his well-ordered existence across the Channel, necessary prelude to the more elaborate Grand Tour which he hoped one day to make, as well-educated young men did. He found it very illuminating, and the contagious good spirits of his companions surprised him into making jokes and uttering hearty laughter of his own. They even got him a little drunk, which was good for his soul.

But to Ben—it was the beginning of all things. He had been practically born in a library. His schooling had been quiet, but thorough, as far as it went. He had read in the original Greek parts of Herodotus, Thucydides, the Iliad and Odyssey, Sophocles and Xenophon; in Latin he was familiar with Cicero and Caesar, some of Livy and Tacitus. Since leaving school he had gone on browsing at will in Lucian, Terence, Demosthenes; stumbling bewildered but determined among Greek Metres, discovering Pericles with great satisfaction; Voltaire he quarrelled with, and questioned his good taste; he read Chaucer and Gibbon at odd moments at his desk in Frederick's Place, and discovered that there were classics in other languages besides Greek and Latin; began to cultivate the philosophers of modern Europe, and became aware of the whole enthralling pattern of modern European history.

In his father's library he had watched glorious lives unfolding page by page, dreamed enormous dreams, cherished high aspirations. But it had all been wholly visionary, a distant promised land of fabulous creatures and impossible adventure and achievement. Even at Murray's he had listened, as it were, like a child on the staircase, peeping in at the party.

Suddenly, on this magic first excursion abroad, he touched life with his own fingers as he meant to live it. The world outside Bloomsbury suddenly became equally real. People were actually speaking French and German because they had no other language to speak; Waterloo had been fought here, under his feet, across cultivated fields of ripening corn and little farms with gardens; the inn, where Wellington had slept with the powder stains still on his face, was standing there now, in the village. It had all *happened*. For the first time in his life he had no words for what he was feeling.

But as he watched the lovely banks of the Rhine slide away past his fascinated eyes on the last days of that journey, he knew with a sort of awe that his life had turned a corner and would never look the same again. He felt a deep, humiliated scorn for the inexperienced child he had been until now, grubbing in books for his sensations, playing at Law in Frederick's Place for his career, envying the things Murray's friends had seen and done—it was the existence of a puling infant! He had wasted time. He must begin.

First of all one must see the world. One must think internationally. Travel, obviously, was important. One must have money, then. Not money doled out by an indulgent father. Real money, of one's own.

One must establish great friendships, make the most of knowing famous men, instead of wagging at their heels like an infatuated puppy. Brummell had made himself the intimate of princes, by sheer impudence and dandyism. But Brummell had inherited a fortune. Still, there was Murray as a beginning. Murray liked him. Surely there would be opportunities at Murray's if he watched for them. His father was content with his note-books and a publication every three or four years. But that was not exciting.

The growing desire for immediate, tangible evidence of the brilliant future he had always imagined for himself consumed him. He had to be famous, rich, powerful—but nothing short of real greatness would do. The Bar? Miss Maples' words came back to him—"stuffy, and gouty, and dull." Even she had seen that. But Pitt had begun that way. The Services? All the Army men he had ever seen were either desperadoes or fools. But there was Wellington—a little man with a bad temper, and getting very deaf, but he could win a battle, and now that peace had come he could turn his hand to politics with the best of them. The Church? He thought of Wolsey. But the odds were against him. Fashionable novels? Scott was making money, with *Waverley*. Parliament? Canning was coming into his own at last at the Foreign Office, with poor Castlereagh out of the way, despite what the snobbish called "the lowness of his origin." Canning was splendid inspiring proof that one did not have to be born into the peerage to have a career in Parliament these days. Why, Canning's mother was an actress! To be sure, she had only taken to the stage to support a small family left penniless by the death of the father, who was a gentleman, though poor, and literary. Nevertheless people considered that Canning's charm and eloquence were honestly come by, from the stage, and therefore contemptible, and they labelled him "charlatan" and "adventurer." Canning's raw and sensitive spirit flared up and drove him to reply to the epithets. "I present myself unaccredited by patrician patronage or party recommendation," he cried. "If to depend directly upon the people, as their Representative in Parliament; if as a servant of the Crown to lean on no other support than that of public confidence—if that is to be an adventurer, I plead guilty to the charge; and I would not exchange that situation, to whatever taunts it may expose me, for all the advantages which might be derived from an ancestry of one hundred generations." That was rather magnificent, and Canning was a power in spite of his enemies, and his foreign policy was showing the world the way to the peace he so desired. His colleagues' jealousy of a brilliant, self-made career was complicated by their vague but growing apprehension of change. The exclusive privilege of the aristocracy to statesmanship was slipping. Even Peel—big things were expected of Peel, the Home Secretary, though he was a young man still. But even Peel's father was a cotton manufacturer, though wealthy, and Peel was duly sensible of his disadvantage in this respect, instead of choosing presumptuously to ignore it, as Canning did.

Great names, great deeds. They had all found what they could do best, and they were doing it superbly. Even Murray had found his niche, and there was no greater publisher. But Murray had inherited something to start with. If one

had money, or a business, or a title, the race was half won.
Canning, of course—ah, but Canning was a genius. . . .

V I

In September, immediately after their return home, Louis
XVIII died, and the worst happened in France. He was succeeded by his younger brother (aged sixty-seven) the Comte
d'Artois, as Charles X. Made even more fanatical as to the
divine rights of kings by the murder of his son the Duc de
Berri in 1820, Charles set out to re-establish a privileged
class, curtail the liberty of the Press, and create new peers
to outvote his opponents. "It is only Lafayette and I who have
not changed since 1789," was now his boast. He possessed to
the last degree the colossal Bourbon faculty of believing
blindly that he was right. And it was soon plain too that
France was to be ruled by priests again, through the King's
confessor.

Charles' accession meant that France would more than
ever support the Royalist cause in Spain, and French troops
were still in occupation there. Canning was determined that
if France had Spain at least it should not be Spain with the
West Indies and South America. He strenuously insisted on
England's behalf that every nation had the right to set up
whatever form of government it thought best, and to be left
free to manage its own affairs so long as it left other nations
to manage theirs.

The Powers regretted that his attitude tended to encourage the dreaded revolutionary spirit; the old-fashioned Powers in Metternich's train who still regarded the United States
of America as some sort of organized anarchy quite beyond
the pale. But Canning saw that Europe was clinging hopelessly to worn-out formulas, and he recognized a new force
in a changing world—constructive nationality. "We will not
interfere with Spain in any attempt which she may make to
reconquer what were once her colonies," he announced. "But
we will not permit any third Power to attack or reconquer
them for her."

When the Central Powers (meaning Metternich) proposed to send a "European army" to settle the undignified family brawl in Portugal, Canning promptly dispatched an English squadron to lie off the coast—a sort of intervention to prevent intervention. The Central Powers dropped it, with a protest.

Canning was fifty-two now. For years he had been labouring to free England from her continental entanglements or alliances, left over from the Napoleonic wars; to set her free to act as she saw fit, independently, for the principles she stood for. "England must move in her own orbit," he said, "without looking too nicely to the conduct of the Powers in alliance with her; must be content with her own glory, and by its example, excite other nations to arrive at the same advantages which her peculiar system has bestowed upon her."

Naturally, the Powers were aghast, and the elder English statesmen objected. Wellington, with years of foreign military service behind him, was so strongly in opposition that Canning sometimes thought of resigning. But things had to be dealt with. He held on, and his speeches became epochal, until it was said that he rarely delivered an important speech without making an enemy for life. "I hope I have as friendly a disposition towards the other nations of the earth as anyone who vaunts his philanthropy most highly, but I am contented to confess that in the conduct of political affairs, the grand object of my contemplation is the interest of England. Not, Gentlemen, that the interest of England is an interest which stands isolated and alone. The situation which she holds forbids an exclusive selfishness. Her prosperity must contribute to the prosperity of surrounding nations, and her stability to the safety of the world."

He had already dispatched consuls to South America to observe and protect English trading concerns from the hit-or-miss piracy for which there was no redress so long as Spain could not be said to be in control of her colonial possessions, and those possessions had no government of their own to be held responsible. President Monroe of the United States of

America gave unexpected support to Canning's attitude by declaring his conviction that the Spanish colonies in the New World must be left to work out their own destinies without interference from the Powers of Europe, and England's point was gained without a war.

The possibilities of trade with an established and peaceful group of new nations in the Western Hemisphere were enormous. El Dorado itself was supposed to lie in the Andes; gold, silver, and diamonds in unguessable quantities to be had for the mere mining.

So much gold and silver, it was said, would be speedily produced that when the national debt was paid the whole money values of Europe would undergo a drastic change. The madness for speculation began to spread from the trade to private individuals. The most preposterous schemes found dupes to support them, and the greatest gainers were the attorneys. Professional men living on incomes, old ladies with tiny legacies, young men with responsible inheritances, rich and poor, wise and foolish, all caught the fever. The banks were as bad as anyone, and began lending money on rash security, and discounting bills at long dates—the rate of interest dropped so low that it became very tempting to borrow large sums to speculate with. People too cautious to try for a prize in this wholesale blind grab were regarded as unprogressive old fogies, and they watched wistfully while fortunes were made by skilful buying and selling—and while high prices loomed ahead of them.

On his return to Frederick's Place in the autumn of 1824 Ben found that the rising tide of speculation and company promotion had penetrated even there. Young Evans, who held a similar position to his with Mr. Pearse, and who was the only real friend he had made in the office, was volubly of the conviction that their everlasting fortunes could be made at once. Ben learned, on going into the matter cold-bloodedly and in detail, that Evans had been listening to Mr. Powles. Evans had a friend whose father was in the Stock Exchange. It would all be so simple. . . .

A fortune was what Ben wanted more than anything in the world. But his original opinion that Powles and all his disciples were riding for a fall persisted, in the face of certain not inconsiderable evidence which Evans eagerly laid before him. So-and-so had made £1,000 on the rise, had he. Very well, but the drop was coming. If *he* did any speculating, said Ben with a knowing smile, he would speculate in the opposite direction.

Evans was much struck. Ben's ideas were opportunely underlined by the utterances of the Lord Chancellor, who had begun to be alarmed by the gambling mania which was sweeping England, and who alluded publicly to the South Sea Bubble episode of 1720, and threatened Government interference. Backed up by the unwitting Chancellor, Ben and Evans and Evans' friend took the plunge against the tide.

By the end of the year, with the madness still raging all around them, they were £100 down. In January the independence of Buenos Aires, Colombia, and Mexico were recognized by England and things went on soaring. The three partners found themselves in debt to the extent of £1,000. In spite of the Lord Chancellor, even Ben began to have misgivings.

Meanwhile Murray had bethought himself of the John Paul Jones *Life,* which had encumbered his desk the whole of the time Ben was abroad. Ben undertook the job lightheartedly, regarding it as child's play; spent a few days investigating the surrounding material—of course the fellow was a plain pirate if you came down to it—and dashed off a neat and non-committal introduction.

> The revolt of the Anglo-American colonies had produced in the mind of Europe a similar effect to that which is the consequence of the revolt of Mexico and the States of South America. The same passions were excited in the 18th Century, governments were placed in similar situations; and new interests then arose as are now arising.

And so forth. One could go on like that for hours. . . .

By entering into the Cabinets of Europe at the latter end of the last century, we may discover the situations of some of the Cabinets of the present one. We may become acquainted with the prime ministers stripped of their diplomatic decencies, and while we commiserate the difficulty of their situation, we may learn by what principles their political conduct is dictated.

The unveiling of the inner mechanism of diplomacy was an idea which appealed to him, though the book, of course, was pretty worthless. Naturally his name would not appear on the title page of so trivial an affair. But it was worth doing because it was a wedge to bigger things; it showed that Murray thought well of him, and did not hold Aylmer Papillon against him. And it might lead to something more.

The three partners had not told anyone of their Stock Market operations in the beginning and to confess now with the balance so heavily against them had become almost impossible. Powles had once found an eager disciple in Evans, and he next cast an acquisitive eye on young Disraeli. Powles was seeking some way to combat the insidious campaign of the Government against the mining companies. Rumours of fraud and official investigation still persisted. But the first reports of the commissioners dispatched to South America on behalf of the stockholders had come in, and Powles proposed to publish some of that material in pamphlet form, as an answer to the doubting Thomases at Westminster who were trying to undermine the whole boom structure of which he was one of the principal props. Mr. Maples mentioned that their Mr. Disraeli might be able to assist. . . .

During the conference that followed, the reports of the commission on the Anglo-Mexican Mining Association were spread before Ben's enraptured eyes—maps, estimates, tidy convincing marching figures—he was let in on the ground floor with no reservations. It was intoxicating.

First of all, the very names of the mines themselves caught at his fancy: Valenciana, Serena, San Cayetona, Tlalpuxahua, El Christo de Lagas—it was music! Could Santa Brigida be a fraud? Unthinkable! Could the Real del Monte betray its investors? Never! But at the same time his constitutionally hard-headed appreciation of facts as such was satisfied. His gaze followed the stubby forefinger of Powles down the pages, indicating the points to be made, such as: the Valenciana was being worked to a depth of 80 yards, surface of water 150 yards from shaft, 2,000 cargas of ore weekly, each carga weighing 300 lbs.; by improved Freiburg method of amalgamation more ore had been done in 24 hours than the Spanish had managed in 6 weeks; and here the report went into impressive and exhaustive details, written on the spot by a Cornish mining expert, one Captain Garby, of the colossal ignorance of the Spanish miners as to crushing and amalgamating ore—they seemed not even to be aware of the existence of a water-wheel—the introduction of the "improved Cornish system" would be extremely profitable, etc.; of the machinery, 9 *malacates* or *whims* remained (whims? in machinery? delicious!) outbuildings were in repair, assaying furnaces had been proved, etc., etc. A new vein had been discovered at the Concepcion, though its pumps were not working. The Serena had been drained to a depth of 500 yards, but was neglected since 1815. The question of fuel was admitted to be important, but coal was undoubtedly present, as even Humboldt had observed. The introduction of the steam engine would work untold wonders. Etc., etc.

Ben read on and on, as though it was a fairy tale. And yet it was all so practical, now that one had it down in black and white. Five ships had already gone out to Mexico with miners and machinery. The new Mexican government appeared to be solid, and was friendly to the enterprise.

His original scepticism receded. Investments in these amazing enterprises might be a gamble, but surely it was a gamble on a certainty! Surely it was only a question of time until these neglected, antiquated mines with the beguiling names began to yield their treasure to the enlightened manipulations of the estimable Captain Garby and his Cornish experts. He had been wrong—wrong! This was tremendous! This was empire-building! It could not fail!

He gathered up the maps and papers and the dozens of closely written sheets of the reports, and carried them home with him. He would write the pamphlet, and he would get Murray to publish it—on commission, of course, with Powles guaranteeing payment.

The *Enquiry into the Plans, Progress, and Policy of the American Mining Companies* appeared in March, anonymously. Step-child though it was, Ben handled the first copy of it tenderly—a beginning. Isaac thought it was rather full of commas, but it was very favourably reviewed by the *Gentleman's Magazine*. Government rumblings continued to be heard.

Evans and his friend were called into conference, these new facts and figures were laid before them in the strictest confidence, and the mounting toll of their incredible debt was faced. They looked at each other, appalled. Something had to be done. Ben read the answer in Evans' face. He had been wrong after all, and Evans was right—had always been right. Perhaps it was still not too late. They decided to shift to the "bull" side of the market at once.

But in the spring of 1825 the tide was imperceptibly turning, and with it the market. Without the least idea that they were deeply involved, Powles assured them it was only a temporary sag. And a second pamphlet entitled *Lawyers and Legislators, or Notes on the American Mining Companies* was published by the same anonymous authority, directed especially at the threatened restrictive legislative measures. In spite of it, there were no returns from the public's investments to throw into the scales—no gold and silver from the Andes, no pearls from the coast of Colombia. The public began to feel the need of ready cash. A thing called "temporary embarrassment" had begun.

VII

The acquaintance between Murray and Disraeli the younger was considerably furthered by the publication of the mining pamphlets under Murray's imprint; they were really impressive in their grave erudition and air of considered finality. Murray was struck anew by the good looks and enthusiasms and mature mentality of this lad who seemed to have emerged from childhood overnight. His own son was still at school. John III would have the business one day, of course. But Murray found himself talking of himself to Isaac's son, who listened with large, intelligent eyes and did not fidget or interrupt. Before that grave regard Murray somehow expanded and became rather a great man in his own eyes. Plainly Ben appreciated the achievement of the house of Murray, and the position it had come to hold in the publishing world. Plainly he was interested in how it had all come about.

Murray found himself telling the story of his life, in this odd new flattering intimacy. He spoke of the early connection with Constable, whose bad habits about accommodation bills and promissory notes finally led to a break in 1813. He lingered over the friendships with Scott and Byron in the gay days of the Regency. He went into details about the establishing of the *Quarterly Review,* his beloved periodical, originally backed by Scott and Canning in opposition to Constable's contentious *Edinburgh Review*—and dwelt lovingly on the endless, patient nursing it had required in its feeble infancy before it began to pay. He smiled ruefully over the pressure for ready money he had known in his first days in Albemarle Street, with Constable still drawing on him, and Byron's penniless sister counting on him for advances, which he always met. He glowed with justifiable pride over the growing tradition of his drawing-room and his dinners. He sighed over the inundation of unsolicited manuscripts by utterly unknown authors; and told again and again the ever humorous story of Jane Austen's belated rescue from anonymous obscurity with a cautious little bookseller at Bath. He chuckled over the astounding success of his first best-seller—*Mrs. Rundell's Domestic Cookery*—which still sold better than Byron. He even spoke wistfully of his desire for another periodical one day, to appear more frequently than the *Quarterly;* and reflected at length on the strange fascination of periodicals for those who have once fathered them. He had tried several since the *Quarterly*, with more or less disastrous results. A brief partnership in *Blackwood's* was ended because of the magazine's persistence in biting personalities in its articles—"too much firing at small birds," Ben's father had put it at the time—uncalled-for attacks on Hunt, Hazlitt, Keats, and what its spokesmen had dubbed "the Cockney school." Then there had been one or two other tempting little papers offered him—but nothing that had seemed just right. . . . And always he held forth on the necessity for personal supervision by the head of the house regarding the details of the publication of books; he himself left nothing to chance or his subordinates—the type, the binding, accuracy in printing, the very paper on which the books were printed, were matters of personal concern to him. That, he would point out, was where other publishers were careless —in the minutiae that made for a perfect whole. . . .

Ben would listen, absorbed, sometimes asking brief questions, following the workings of Murray's mind with scrupulous care. Here was what he wanted. This was how these things were done. This man had made a success of life. From him one could learn.

On the evening that the proof sheets of the second pamphlet had been approved by the author, they sat down alone together by the fire over a glass of port. Ben was tired and worried, and carried with him these days a dismal sense of impending disaster. They could not stave things off forever, he and Evans. His father would have to know. It would upset him. Anything rather than have to confess to his father that he owed several thousand pounds, on a hare-brained scheme to win a fortune overnight.

He gazed at the fire through the ruby-coloured glass, his eyes on a level with the brim. Should he tell Murray—ask for help from him so that the Governor need never know? No, that would be worse. Murray regarded him as a responsible person. He would forfeit all he had gained in this new intimacy with Murray if he confessed to such puerile folly as a gamble on the Stock Exchange. Besides—Powles assured them it was only temporary.

Murray poured himself another glass of port and settled his shoulder-blades more comfortably against the high back of his chair. This was very pleasant. The silent, companionable youth opposite, peering into the heart of the wine in his glass as though he read some mystery there, had grown very dear to Murray's diffident soul. No man is proof against being looked up to. Murray continued to think aloud.

With the *Quarterly Review* on its feet and prospering under Gifford's editorship, Murray was haunted anew by his dream of a periodical which would appear oftener, with a more immediate bearing on the topics of the day—not a newspaper, newspapers were hardly the thing, but something after all more or less along the lines of the *Times,* which was giving inadequate support to Canning these days—something conservative and yet up to date—something representative. . . . Murray paused in his vague ramblings— "What did you say?"

"I said, why not a daily paper to beat the *Times?*" The boy was leaning forward, his bright eyes on Murray's face.

It looked rather a large order to Murray. The *Times* led all the rest. Besides, daily papers were barely respectable. It would be difficult to find a sound man to undertake the editorship. Scott might know of someone, of course—Scott had been of great assistance in the early days of the *Quarterly*— if only Scott's son-in-law, Lockhart, had used a little more discretion in his writing, he was a good sound Tory—but the fellow was always trailing his coat in his *Blackwood's* days— there had even been some sort of nonsense about a duel— What?

"He's married now," Ben repeated patiently. "That always tones them down a bit, doesn't it?" His eyebrows were quizzical; one man of the world to another.

True, agreed Murray, Lockhart was married, and living in a cottage on Scott's estate—writing novels now—there was a small child, who was delicate—and a baby had died. . . .

"Very sobering," remarked Ben. "Obviously, Lockhart is our man. With Scott behind him, we can't go wrong."

Murray doubted if Lockhart could be persuaded to London now—especially to an editorship of a daily paper—the *Quarterly,* possibly, but a daily—? Ben said that a daily with Murray's name attached to it was good enough for anybody. They went on talking, supposing, conjecturing—and the doubts were all Murray's.

"Look here," said Ben suddenly, "suppose I go up to Edinburgh and see Lockhart about it?"

Murray blinked. He had only been thinking aloud. Once they brought Lockhart into it, he was committing himself. Yes, he would like to own a daily—he intended to have one some day—perhaps when John III was old enough to take some of the responsibility—but that would be years yet—

"But you'll be an old man then!" cried Ben in horror. "The time is *now,* while you're in your prime—*now,* while it's needed so badly! Call on me for the drudgery—I've nothing to do and I'll work myself to the bone for you! Look here, I'm leaving Frederick's Place anyway, you know—it leads to nothing. This is the sort of thing I've dreamed of! *I'll* take the responsibility for you—I'll do the odd jobs and the dull bits and the travelling and—anything else you haven't got time for—"

Murray murmured something about Ben's lack of experience.

"If a person has imagination, experience is of very little use!" cried Ben, and waved it aside. "What's more, I think I can bring you capital. This fellow Powles who got me to do the pamphlets—he's rolling in it! He'll come in on this like a shot, financially. Suppose I could get him to put up half the money—"

Murray never did know to his dying day quite how it happened, and neither, for that matter, did Powles, who had enough on his hands already in the City. But early in August the following astonishingly simple document was drawn up and signed at 50 Albemarle Street—with Powles actually involved for half the money, as he was the sole guarantor for young Mr. Disraeli's share of the enterprise.

The undersigned parties agree to establish a morning paper, the property in which is to be in the following proportions, viz.:

Mr. Murray . . . one half
Mr. Powles . . . one quarter
Mr. Disraeli . . . one quarter

Each party contributing to the expense, capital and risk in those proportions.

The paper to be published by and be under the management of Mr. Murray.

(Signed)
JOHN MURRAY
JOHN DISTON POWLES
B. DISRAELI

And the balance against Evans, Disraeli, & Co. was now £7,000, with the market still obstinately downward.

VIII

The first necessity for any paper is an editor; and so in September Ben set out for Scotland to bag Lockhart. He read Froissart on the way, and considered York Minster far superior to anything he had seen in the Netherlands or on the Rhine. The journey took four days.

He carried a letter of introduction from Murray, enviable alike for its brevity and its effect of complete *carte blanche*.

My dear Sir—

Do me the favour to receive with kindness my most particular and confidential young friend, Mr. Benjamin Disraeli, son of my oldest friend, his worthy father. Any communication which he may make, I beg of you to entertain as if it were given to you in person by myself.

Remaining always, my dear sir, most sincerely yours,
JOHN MURRAY

Lockhart, who had already been made aware that something was afoot, had at the same time got the mistaken idea
that it was Isaac himself who was on the way to Scotland to
see him. His surprise at sight of Ben, aged twenty, slim and
pale, with dark, pomaded curls and dandified dress, contained considerable disappointment, and his manner, always
reserved with strangers, turned icy. It was a bad beginning to
a series of errors which became anything but comic.

Ben was, however, invited to stay at Lockhart's cottage,
Chiefswood, near Abbotsford, and Scott came to breakfast—
a tall, white-haired, imposing figure in a white hat and green
coat, exuding a slightly impressive kindliness. Ben's native
charm and his irresistible enthusiasm had their usual magic
effect. Everyone dined at Abbotsford that night, and by then
he was friends with them all. Scott said it brought back the
days when Murray had come to Scotland as a young man
starting the *Quarterly,* and told fascinating stories of Canning, who liked *The Lady of the Lake*—stories of the long
enmity between Canning the actress' son, who was Foreign
Minister, and Castlereagh, the heir of a marquis, who was
Secretary-at-War, which culminated in a duel in which Canning was wounded; of the years of eclipse which followed,
and his dramatic return to power at the Foreign Office after
Castlereagh's suicide; of his wit and charm and unpopularity
in various high places. Ben listened enthralled. Here it was
again: Canning, obscure, adventurous, a genius, rising by
his own wits and will, to a position of international importance, and the friendships of men like Scott and Liverpool,
the Prime Minister. What if the King did hate him? That
meant he had the power to make the King uncomfortable.
But of course even Canning had been to Eton and Oxford,
and there he had known the Prime Minister and the Chancellor as schoolboys. . . .

Meanwhile the idea of his mission to Scotland was not lost
sight of—was, in fact, taking root. But Lockhart still hesitated.
His marriage with Sophia Scott was a real romance, which
meant a great deal to a man of his excessive reserve. Sophia
was her father's darling, lively, loving, and an adorable house-

wife, getting stout and prettier than ever. Lockhart's love of children was as passionate as any woman's, and his idolized son was a delicate child of three. They had lost a baby girl a few days old last January. He wanted a family, and he wanted to write novels in peace, and he enjoyed living in the reflected glory from Abbotsford. He liked to see Sophia driving out in her donkey-cart, or ordering the gardener about, or singing old Scotch ballads to her harp in the cottage drawing-room after dinner. His days were long and happy and without history. He objected to this strenuous young man's invasion of his uneventful life, bringing with him a cold draught from the world outside.

Scott, with his consuming kindly interest in everybody and everything, and his generous desire that everyone should have whatever they wanted of him, was much diverted by young Disraeli. In a house famous for its varied and boundless hospitality, the boy still stood out as an event. Scott, whose own magnificent health had begun to fail after years of overwork and abuse, enjoyed his guest's vitality and vocabulary. Scott was only in his fifties, but he had seen a son and daughter married, and in spite of—or perhaps because of—the hordes of devoted pilgrims to his shrine, he sometimes felt a little old, a little on the shelf.

He had achieved his great ambition—he had earned and built and was master of a great estate in his beloved Scotland; he had been given a title by his king; from that king to the least peasant on his lands he was known and revered; he lived in a luxury he had himself conceived and created. It had all come true. But with this ambitious boy came now a pleasant whiff of his own youth when it was all still to do—when he was a literary lion in London, before Byron had begun to eclipse him there—the glorious days of *Marmion* and *The Lady of the Lake,* when the Regent himself had linked arms with him. It occurred to him with a twinge that it would be very exciting to stand on the threshold of life again, with achievement all before him, like this long, handsome lad. He wished him well.

At the same time he knew that the loss of a daily companionship with the little family at Chiefswood and the adored grandson would leave him feeling older and lonelier still. But there was a thing to which none of them could close their eyes. The change of climate, to the milder air of London, might be good for the ailing child.

To Ben it was all very delicious. The somewhat ponderous ceremonial of Abbotsford, the long dinners, the toasts, the worshipping dogs which accompanied the master everywhere, the deferential peasantry, the sense of magnificent feudalism in the house itself, the baronial extravagance, and the sheer beauty of his surroundings—he found it intoxicating. To be received here on an equal footing, as a man of the world, marked his coming of age. It was his first important social venture from under the paternal wing of Isaac. He could stand alone. And he must show them all in London that he could succeed alone.

He was at Chiefswood for three weeks, while an intricate correspondence went on between there and London. It was as Murray had feared; they considered the editorship of a daily paper beneath Lockhart's dignity. Scott wrote Murray that doubtless this department of literature ought to be rendered more respectable than it was at present—but "I am neither young enough nor poor enough to be the man that takes the hazard," added Lockhart loftily. The title of "director-general" was hastily substituted for the despised word "editor." There was more correspondence.

Nobody knew quite how it happened, but at the end of three weeks Lockhart was borne off to see Murray himself in London. And there a compromise was reached. Gifford of the *Quarterly Review* was old and ill, and John Coleridge was filling in as editor, to the neglect of his own increasing Law practice. Lockhart was promised the editorship of the *Quarterly,* at a salary, to salve his dignity. And at another salary he was to act as advisor and (in fact) editor of Murray's new newspaper, to be called the *Representative,* and to write articles for publication therein. An agreement to this effect was signed in Ben's presence, and Lockhart returned to Scotland to collect his little family. Young Mr. Disraeli had won his case.

But at a cost. The old stagers on the *Quarterly* took offence at this summary replacement of a man they all knew and liked by a rank outsider like Lockhart, and moreover *the* Lockhart of those unfortunately outspoken articles in *Blackwood's*. A cabal was formed against him. Murray, who hated trouble in any form, took instant fright, and began to feel that he had acted hastily all along in this venture. He was in too deeply now to stop. Ben had thrown himself headlong into the organization of the paper. Offices were being taken, a printing establishment fitted up; reporters and sub-editors were being engaged, foreign correspondents enlisted; all on the model of the *Times*. In the midst of all this activity he was again dispatched to Abbotsford to implore Scott to use his enormous personal influence against the widespread criticism of his son-in-law's appointment to the *Quarterly*.

This he accomplished too. Scott liked him, and they got on together. Scott agreed to write certain letters. Lockhart's touchy pride flared up at the idea that he was not wanted in London and he had to be soothed and persuaded all over again. Even this was accomplished.

By the time Ben arrived back in London in November, a little exhausted, the City had caved in under an avalanche of commercial disaster, the inevitable result of the false inflation.

He had been so busy he had hardly noticed. But early in the autumn the failure of commercial houses had begun. The weakest ones went first, of course—firms generally known to be wobbly. Then some with supposedly unimpeachable resources stopped payment. The actual value of actual property was in doubt. Securities were so much paper. There was too much capital locked up in long bank loans and unproductive private investments. Little banks in the country districts began to close their doors. The Bank of England itself began to draw in.

People had come to look on bank notes with suspicion. The desire for gold and silver instead of paper spread from the country to London. Lombard Street began to collect in little knots of anxious men, and nobody could suggest anything to do. A few hopeful ones tried to say that it was only temporary. Most of the rest were of the opinion that now it had started there was no telling where it would stop. Rich people were driving up in their carriages and taking away bags of gold and silver quite shamelessly. It was panic.

On the fifth of December the banking-house of Sir Peter Pole closed its doors, and brought down forty-four country banks in its fall. Williams and Co. went the next day—and a landslide was on which crashed sixty or seventy banks within a few weeks.

It became a question not of how much business could be done, but how little. Two hundred and fifty joint stock companies went in a week without a shilling among them. It was difficult to get money just to go on from day to day. Even those who had property could not sell, for there was no one to buy. Pawnshops were swamped with things that had only a short time before been regarded as necessities, and finally even the pawnshops came to an end of their resources and refused to purchase. Respectable people who had always held their heads up stood out drearily against the charity loaf and soup, and were defeated by sheer starvation.

So the year that had begun so prosperously ended in unprecedented distress, though the Government was stable throughout. There is a scriptural text about the temptation and destruction of those that would be rich, and public credit received such a shock that all confidence was lost and ruin spread itself into the most unexpected places. There were some selfish people who had only wanted to get rich before the crash came, but most of the sufferers after all were the victims of seductive promises and their own imaginations.

You would not have known England as it had been a few months before. Its open-handed geniality was all gone. Country markets were no longer the sunny, chaffing, festive places they had been, now that every man owed his neighbour and was owed by the next man, and each doubted the other's intention or ability to pay. Carriages and footmen were dispensed with in Town, seaside holidays were foregone. Subscriptions to book-clubs and concerts were not renewed. Servants were asked to wait for reduced wages. Solitary women with incomes which had failed to arrive for months at a time could no longer face the butcher and his unpaid bill, and subsisted no one knew quite how. Young people with tragic faces postponed weddings, and girls of good family went out as governesses if they were lucky enough to find a post. Old governesses and old servants drifted into the workhouse.

Ben and Evans faced it with wry smiles; they had been right in the beginning, they had only been too soon. If they had held on—if they could have held on long enough, their wildest dreams of fortune would have come true. Instead, they owed several thousand pounds apiece, and for nothing. South American Mining Stocks were not worth tuppence, and Powles was declared bankrupt.

Even this was not the worst of it. For Powles' bankruptcy meant that his quarter of the *Representative* funds was not forthcoming, and naturally his guarantee of Ben's quarter was now worthless. Ben might conceal his debts, but he could not conceal the fact that he had not a penny to put into the venture. Murray was left with the *Representative* on his hands at such a time, and things had gone much too far for him to turn back. Lockhart was arriving in London with his family, the office premises were rented in Great George Street, a large staff was ready to begin work, the first issue was promised for January, 1826—Ben had been so thorough.

Humiliated to the core in his own ruthless young soul, he had gone through a lacerating scene in Albemarle Street, and left the house with Murray's helpless rage and wild accusations of undue pressure and childish bungling burning his cheeks. It was Murray who was being childish. Ben had gone to Scotland the first time with credentials beyond all reason lavish and unrestricted. He had acted on them, he had brought off exactly what he had set out to do—Lockhart was coming to London. The bribe of the *Quarterly Review* edi-

torship was nothing to do with him. The crash in the City
and Powles' defection was nothing to do with him. His own
lack of funds—well, yes, he had counted on Powles there,
and he should have known that Powles was a broken reed
from the beginning. That was where his defence broke down.
He had failed at just the point where Powles came into it,
and he was therefore, after all, blameworthy. Only one thing
was now clear. The fact of his own colossal indebtedness must
not come out. He and Evans must handle that part of it
somehow, alone, or he would die of shame.

In the midst of débâcle the house of Murray stood firm,
but nobody wanted the *Representative* now, and with Ben's
exit from Albemarle Street the heart and soul of the paper
went from it. It began life as an incubus, hated by its owner,
scorned by its editor, weighed down with financial panic on
all sides which was sending its older and better-established
competitors to the wall. Its first feeble number appeared in
January, a wretched mediocrity—four pages at sevenpence,
supporting the Liverpool Government, with a tame and colourless article by Lockhart, and no news. It dragged out a few
months' existence and then died of sheer inanition, at great
cost to its owner. Its mainspring was gone.

I X

He had failed. Failed in everything he had attempted.
And he was not yet twenty-one. He viewed the ruin of his
life in incredulous despair.

Where to turn for comfort, or for absolution from his own
accusing conscience, these days when he could not bear to be
alone with himself? Not to Isaac, pottering contentedly between his library and the British Museum; nor to his mother,
volubly vague about everything except her housekeeping,
which was competent in the extreme; nor to Sa, dear, loyal Sa
who thought him perfect, and denounced everyone who did
not instantly recognize the fact. Ralph and Jem were too
young. Besides, in the family circle he had contrived 'to save
his face, so far. What had Ben to do with a crash in the

City? So far, he had kept that from them. Powles had let him down. That was all they saw. It was because of Powles that his connection with the *Representative* had ended in disaster, and Murray was being unreasonably severe about matters entirely beyond Ben's control.

For Murray could not let it rest, but went on talking, to anyone who would listen, about how he had been rushed into this calamitous venture by Ben; whereas in August Murray had written to a friend that he had "never attempted anything with more considered circumspection, or with more satisfactory hopes of success." In September, while Ben was at Chiefswood, Murray wrote to Lockhart: "I have been acquainted with him from his birth, but it is only in the last 12 months that I have known him. I can pledge my honour therefore with the assurance that he is worthy of any degree of confidence that you may be induced to repose in him—discretion being another of his qualifications. If our great plan should succeed I am certain that you will find in him a most trustworthy friend, from whose energies you may derive the most valuable assistance." At the end of October he was blaming Ben's "unrelenting excitement and importunity" for the whole adventure.

Murray by this time was really a sick man, and took to his bed, so that even his publishing business began to suffer. The country house had been given up, and the famous parties in Albemarle Street were cut down, and the family was ordered to economize. But even from his pillow he continued to pour out accusations on Ben, alleging that he had bungled the Scottish business with youthful incompetence—failing to see that the lack of wisdom, if there was any, must come home to roost on his own choice of an apparently inadequate agent.

At last Maria Disraeli astonished everybody by going valiantly to her son's defence. She wrote Murray a letter. "I feel your disappointment," she wrote with fine dignity and sense, "and can forgive your irritability, yet I must resent your late attack on Benjamin." She went on to point out that the failure of the *Representative* must lie more with its owner and editor than it ever could with her son, whose connection with it had ceased before its publication. She reminded him that he had known Ben from his cradle and must have realized that though he was a clever boy he was no prodigy. And she demanded to know specifically wherein Ben had betrayed a confidence or exceeded his prerogatives. Maria had not listened to all those fluent Disraeli phrases for nothing during the past twenty years.

Mrs. Murray was drawn into it, and Isaac too; and finally some sort of peace was arrived at, among the elders. But Ben was not forgiven nor received back into the Albemarle Street fold.

He knew that if he wilfully forfeited the esteem of his family now by confessing the real proportions of the disaster, his own defeat would look at him forever out of their sympathetic eyes—follow him all his days. It was unthinkable. At any cost the family must not know how he really stood. Once they found out, there would be no sanctuary anywhere in the world.

But his expansive nature, driven in upon itself, suffered acutely, and his need of a confidante grew. He craved to talk to someone, because by talking he sorted out his ideas and thought more clearly. After a few weeks of brooding he decided to tell Mrs. Austen the whole story.

Miss Maples had married her captain while Ben was abroad; the Austens moved in the same circle, and Mr. Austen was also a solicitor. His wife was very nearly a great beauty, clever, talented and wise. She did many things well —music and sketching and entertaining, and she had a genius for friendship. Everyone who knew her counted on her for encouragement, advice, or applause. She was one of those blessed women born to make other people think well of themselves. She was older than Sa, and married, and she knew the world and would not condemn a man utterly no matter what sort of scrape he was in. Ben had a touching faith in the omniscience of married women. His pride would suffer least with Mrs. Austen, who could best understand how one got oneself into these things.

To her Ben turned instinctively now, blind with trouble,

groping for any helping hand in his smashed world. He could go no further alone. A few low words dropped into her ear during one of her informal afternoons, and she contrived that he should be the last to take his leave.

When the others had gone, he faced her in the dusky room, in that intimate time before the punctilios of the dinner hour begin. A maid looked in with a lighted taper in her hand and a wish to draw the curtains, but Mrs. Austen dismissed her and motioned him to a seat beside herself on the sofa. He was looking white and ill, and the meticulous care of his dress, the exquisite shirt frill and heavy gold chains, one for his watch and two hanging free, accentuated the stark misery in his eyes.

"Well," she said quietly, "so you are going to tell me the rest of it at last."

He looked up at her gratefully, his hands locked before him, the knuckles white with tension.

"You guessed there was more?" he said.

"Naturally. You've been looking like a ghost for weeks."

He was surprised and pleased that she had taken the trouble to notice how he looked.

"Why didn't you ask—" he began, wonderingly.

"My dear boy, I hoped you would come to me, of course— but you had to do it in your own way, and in your own good time. And so you have. What's gone wrong? Money—or a woman?"

He violently repudiated the idea that a woman could upset him to any such extent. She smiled and laid her hand on his clenched ones, and they relaxed under her touch.

"Tell me, then," she said gently.

He spread it all before her in a tumbling torrent of unfinished sentences, feeling young and helpless and humiliated, but somehow under her grave, kind eyes, not quite ridiculous. She neither laughed nor lectured him. She listened patiently, and without visible surprise or disgust, while he talked. And when he had finished—

"It's even worse than I thought," she said. "We must think what we can do."

We. That was comforting. She was his ally from the start. He no longer stood entirely alone. The gaze he lifted to her face was worshipful. He had had about all he was good for.

"I used to have schemes for making money," he said dully. "But now I—I just can't seem to think at all. Once I thought —you see, Scott has made a lot of money with his books, and—"

"Lots of people make money writing books," she agreed briskly. "Fashionable novels are the thing now—society, balls, gay living—a touch of scandal—a love story with a happy ending—couldn't you write something like that?"

"I'd begun one," he confessed. "Before all this happened. With lots of titles in it," he added humorously.

"That's the kind! *Crammed* with Dukes and ladyships! You must finish it at once."

"Well, you see—Murray has refused one of my manuscripts already—oh, a long time ago, this one is much better, of course. But as things are between us now, I could hardly ask him to look at another!"

"Murray isn't the only publisher in London!" she reminded him stoutly. "Let me have the manuscript, and I'll take it myself to Colburn. He thinks rather well of my judgment."

"But it isn't finished."

"Well, finish it. Let me see what you've done on it so far, at once. We might publish it anonymously, if it's scandalous enough. People love that sort of thing." The idea grew on her rapidly. "Yes, a mysterious author is always worth something to a publisher. So long as people aren't sure, they will imagine anything. What are you going to call the book?"

"The hero's name is Vivian Grey. But do you think Colburn will—"

"Colburn will read anything I ask him to," she said firmly, with the delicious air of authority he so admired.

"But if we published it anonymously and then it leaked out later that I wrote it—"

"It won't leak out. It can't. We'll make sure, by not letting even Colburn know, at least at first. Bring me the manuscript and I'll copy it out myself. Then they won't have even your handwriting to go by."

"If you're sure it wouldn't be too much trouble—" he began wistfully, much drawn to the scheme.

"It's worth trouble, my dear boy. It will be a beginning, out of your difficulties. Good heavens, we can't have you moping about like this! And you know I'll do anything I can for you, always." Her hand lay warm on his again. "It will be our secret—yours and mine. If anyone ever finds out, I swear it won't be from me."

He pressed his lips to her fingers wordlessly, and felt the first stirrings of life within him he had known for weeks. It had been untold relief just to talk to her; and to have her take it as she did, calmly, with her first thought not to commiserate or chide, but merely to find a way to get him out of it, was more than he had hoped for. The offer of practical assistance left him dumb with gratitude. She was a wonderful woman.

Whether she expected anything to come of the book about Vivian Grey or not, she had chosen with infallible instinct the surest way to save Ben's pride and re-establish his peace of mind. A creative nature like his, left idle, will fester. She set him to work again, gave him an outlet, and half the cure was accomplished. It was exciting, too, to share a secret with the most brilliant and beautiful woman he knew. His punished self-esteem revived under the stimulus of the innocent intrigue. And she, who loved to see people happy through her efforts, felt that she had never spent her energies on a more responsive and deserving protégé.

A few days later he brought her the first part of the manuscript of *Vivian Grey*. The old spirit of enterprise was burning again. He was writing feverishly, pouring himself out on paper. It was blessed relief, he had been bottled up too long.

His hero was oddly enough the son of a literary gentleman; a precocious lad, who at the age of twenty took as his motto a bit of Shakespeare—

Why, then, the world's mine oyster,
Which I with sword will open.

Realizing the need of a patron in order to succeed in fashionable society, Vivian Grey adopted the Marquis of Carabas, a
rich and rather stupid old nobleman, whose ambition to shine
in Parliament Vivian nourished successfully until an intrigu-
ing woman poisoned the Marquis' mind against him. There
was a duel, a scandal, general catastrophe, and Vivian retired
in disgrace and remorse to Germany and a lonely, self-im-
posed exile—leaving the way open for a second volume of his
adventures.

The neat manuscript was faithfully transcribed by Mrs.
Austen in her own hand, and she herself took it to Colburn's
office. Mysterious, assured, and very charming, she committed
it to his personal attention, with a reminder of her own gift
for detecting new talent; fenced dexterously with his attempt
to discover the author; and left him not at all sure she hadn't
written it herself.

Colburn saw its possibilities as an anonymous product. The
sheer impudence of the creation of such obvious characters as
a Duke of Waterloo was so broad that much speculation was
bound to result, and it would probably pass as the impertinent revelations of someone very much in the know.

It was a long chance, but Colburn took it, and within a
month of publication *Vivian Grey* was a great success. Everyone was talking about it; every paper reviewed it with a
puzzled respect for the possibly great unknown, fearful of
treading on noble corns; everyone was guessing at the identi-
ties hidden behind the manufactured names and titles. Finally a key was published, not by Colburn.

Ben and Mrs. Austen chortled with incredulous glee. They
had brought it off. The hoax had succeeded beyond their
expectations, to a degree which was almost frightening. Suppose it did come out now, who had written it? They had been
so careful. But Colburn, once he had committed himself to
publication, had had to be let into the secret, and was going
about with his tongue in his cheek. . . .

X

With his holiday comfortably out of the way, Isaac returned to his *Commentaries on Charles I,* and became immediately absorbed in the seventeenth century. He was only
dimly aware that something very unpleasant had been happening in the City. Besides the fact that his merchant father
had done very well for him, he had inherited a comfortable
fortune from his maternal grandmother, who was a Rossi of
Ferrara. One or two of his sources of income seemed to have
dried up, but there was still quite enough to go on with in
his quiet way. He really hadn't noticed.

He knew, of course, that Ben's venture with Murray's
newspaper had come to nothing, which was sad but not
altogether surprising. He had warned Ben more than once
against trying to become a great man overnight. He was
sorry to hear, also, that the failure of Constable in January
had ruined Scott, who had had a heavy financial interest in
the company which published his books. That was what came
of putting all one's eggs in one basket, said Isaac, who was
supposedly the least practical of men. It was what came, also,
of Constable's bad habits about accommodation bills, which
Murray had objected to more than ten years before.

All through that dreadful spring of 1826 Isaac kept happily on his way through the mid-1600's, preparing his defence
of the martyr king. Hazy about current details as he was and
remained throughout the depression, he was only dimly conscious likewise of the slow upturn later in the year. When
Parliament met in February, it had gone into the matter very
thoroughly, and drastic changes were made in the banking
system and commercial status. The Mint was speeded up on
coinage and a stream of gold and silver poured into the
country's empty pockets. Influential men adopted resolu-
tions showing confidence in commercial credit and enterprise. There were no longer daily crashes. Ships and forges
began to work again.

As always when she has touched bottom, England re-
bounded sturdily. But unemployment among the very poor

was still a serious problem, and rioting began in Lancashire, where the factory operatives smashed the machinery they held responsible for the glut on the market—destroying thousands of pounds worth of property and ruining the very source of their ultimate relief. Lancashire mobs shambled from town to town, wrecking as they went, snatching food from shops, facing the soldiery with improvised weapons, and sometimes, after the Riot Act had been duly read, being shot down. By summer the trouble had spread to Glasgow, and the starving weavers of Carlisle and Norwich and Dublin. The Isle of Man rose against the potato tithe. A hot summer was promised, with bad crops to follow.

But domestic discord, foreign wars, and political crises rarely penetrated the sacred silence of the British Museum Reading-Room, where Isaac spent his busy days. When they turned him out of the Museum each evening, he would hurry home across Bloomsbury Square and retire into his own library, his head full of interrupted arguments and new points to be made. And there he would stay until Sarah brought him his supper on a tray and persuaded him that it was time to go to bed.

He was waging a vigorous pen-and-ink feud with Lingard and Hallam over the question of Buckingham's impeachment, for instance. Lingard was of course prejudiced by his religion. But Hallam—there was really no excuse for Hallam's old-fashioned whiggery in his recently published *Constitutional History of England.* Hallam had begun the whole thing with a footnote, in which he referred to a chapter on the same subject which Isaac had published a while back in one of his *Curiosities of Literature* volumes: "Mr. Disraeli," remarked Hallam in small type at the bottom of the page, "has collected from the same copious reservoir, the manuscripts of the British Museum, several more illustrations, both of the arbitrary proceedings of the Council, and of the bold spirit in which they were resisted. This ingenious author," pursued Mr. Hallam, "is too much imbued with the 'monstrous faith of many made for one,' and sets the private feelings of Charles for an unworthy and dangerous minion above the liberties and interests of a nation."

In reply to which, Isaac had prepared a footnote of his own: "I regret that Mr. Hallam has too hastily assumed a sweeping conclusion on the articles of this impeachment. He tells us many of them were 'probably' well-founded. *Probably* is a term of nullity in historical evidence; it includes neither the labour of research nor the force of argument; it is the cypher of prejudice, which, placed beside a unit of fact, swells out into a mighty sum what in itself is of very small amount. A more accurate knowledge of the prevalent customs of the age, a very little candour, and a closer investigation of the articles themselves would have deterred the 'constitutional' historian from this unjust severity to the 'minion.' Rapacity and avarice were not the vices of Buckingham."

That would take care of that.

Isaac's library was a small, lived-in old room at the back of the house. Its bookshelves reached the ceiling, and there was a shaky little ladder with which Isaac was very nimble, though Ben swore that he himself had nearly broken his neck on it more than once. The furniture was worn to shabbiness and very comfortable. The sofa was drawn up in front of the hearth, so that one might have a nap in comfort with one of Sarah's knitted *couvre-pieds* across one's feet, and awake refreshed to deal with Hallam. There were dark red curtains to draw across the long window, where the writing-table stood, with its green-shaded student lamp.

It was an altogether cosy room, to harbour an absent-minded man in a velvet skull-cap, near-sighted behind his spectacles, with a cherubic fluff of greyish white hair around his ears and starting well back on his round, intelligent forehead. There he could wear his old brown velveteen coat, baggy and comfortable, and house slippers—but always a cheerful waistcoat. Isaac was very choice of his waistcoats, even in an age of dandies. He was sixty now, and a philosopher; the adored and cosseted head of his small family.

Tonight was no different from other nights, except that Hallam was being particularly trying about the Petition of

Right. With Clarendon on one side of him and Hallam on the other, and Lingard propped up against the lamp, Isaac was perfecting another footnote: "The most recent writer on this subject is Mr. Hallam, who, though not insensible to the injuries inflicted on the Monarch, has palliated the conduct of Parliament. I transcribe the passage for the benefit of the reader." And he did so, laboriously, with scornful flourishes, his very pen-point spurning the offensive words it was compelled to set down. "This sentence," continued Isaac, warming to it, "must have cost Mr. Hallam some trouble—not in the arrangement of so many monosyllables, but rather in the nice adjustment of that delicacy of decision which, while it discovers that the King was wronged, indicates how he might have been put more in the wrong! This is a sharp conflict between the truth the historian loves and the party which he loves more. What follows is much special pleading about the necessity that 'A foundation of confidence should be laid between the Crown and Parliament.' Heaven knows—"

He looked up, interrupted at a most crucial point, and peered across the dimly lighted room to where the door had opened—it was Sarah with his tray—already? A clock was striking somewhere. But surely it wasn't as late as that!

"Mmmmmm?" said Isaac, unhappily aware that he was being disturbed quite legitimately, and also, with some surprise and resentment, that he was hungry, and wishing for the thousandth time that there was some way of preventing one's stomach from intruding itself upon one's notice just as things were going well. "Oh—ah—yes—supper. Put it there, my dear, put it—ah—there." He swept up Hallam and a sheaf of notes to make room on the corner of the writing-desk, and peered critically at the tray as she set it down. It was an assortment designed to meet a gourmet's taste—sandwiches, a plain cake, a cheese, biscuits, a decanter of wine, and his nightly glass of hot milk. And on the edge, balanced against the biscuit barrel, was a magazine. "What's this?" he inquired suspiciously, poking at it, though he could see very well what it was.

"The new *Blackwood's,* father."

"Trash," said Isaac, mildly. "Anything in it?"

"Yes, there is." She ran a housewifely eye over the dim room, lighted by the single student lamp at his elbow. *"Must you always work in the dark? I keep telling you, your eyes wouldn't tire so badly if you didn't live like a mole!"* Her warm lips brushed his temple, her warm, sweet presence was all about him like a perfume, as she turned away to light another lamp which stood on the low-boy across the room.

He sat watching her contentedly, blinking behind his spectacles—she was quite right, his eyes were always tired by night, and it was pleasant to rest them by looking at his daughter. The light from the new lamp shone upward upon her face, illuminating the straight nose and lovely, humorous mouth. Her dark wavy hair was piled high on her head, and she wore a light summer silk dinner-at-home gown, with very short puffed sleeves which were continued to the wrist in white gauze, and bound there with her grandmother's twin cameo bracelets, which he remembered admiring as a child. It crossed his mind that she was fortunately not at all like her grandmother. Her likeness to Ben was apparent, and yet there was a depth of still waters about Sarah, an infinite repose beyond her years, a sort of—blinking, he groped after the right word—a sort of *receptiveness* which was missing in the more volatile boy. Isaac found himself wondering, not for the first time, how he and Maria had contrived to have such very attractive children.

"Is Ben home yet?" he asked. He knew the answer, but these little homely topics at the end of the day were a form of purring.

"No," she said quietly. "Not yet."

"Did he say where he was going tonight?" he queried, without any real curiosity. It was all a part of the supper-tray formula.

"No." She blew out the taper and came to sit on the sofa, facing the fire, and he noticed that she had still another magazine under her arm. Going to read in bed, no doubt. It was a habit she got from him. Her mother disapproved.

He selected a sandwich thoughtfully, and separated its

edges to peep and sniff at its contents before biting into it. Chicken.

"Mmmmmm," he nodded, munching. "Mustn't ask where he's been, I suppose. Young men hate their family keeping an eye on them. I dare say he's all right."

"I dare say," echoed Sarah, her eyes on the fire.

"Needs to enjoy himself," Isaac ruminated, relishing his supper and not yet conscious of her preoccupation. "Needs to have friends. A man's not twenty-one for long. And only once."

"Drink your milk while it's hot, dear," said Sarah. That too was part of the evening ritual.

Obediently sipping, he made a face.

"She's boiled it again!"

"I'm sorry, dear, I did tell her—let me get you another glass—"

"No, no—" He waved it aside, magnanimously. "It doesn't matter—much. She's a good cook. That soufflé tonight—marvellous. I suppose it's too much to ask of her, to take the milk off just as the bubbles begin to come at the edge—not before—not after. It's the only thing she can't make—hot milk. We must be reasonable." He went on sipping.

"I'll do it myself tomorrow night, and then it will be right. I meant to tonight, only—" She broke off, fingering the magazine under her arm.

"Only you got reading *Blackwood's*," he suggested without reproach. "What's in it?"

"Something about Ben's book."

"About Ben's book? Where? What's it say?" Isaac set down his glass with a bump and reached for the magazine. "Here —you read it out, Sa, my eyes are tired—you read it."

"Very well, I will. *Blackwood's* is bad enough, but the *Literary Magnet* is worse." She took it from under her arm as she spoke. ·

"That rag," said Isaac. "Where on earth did you get it?"

"It's not altogether a rag. Mr. Meredith warned me to get it. There's a long sort of article in it about Ben and *Vivian Grey*."

"Yes—well?" Isaac became conscious at last that she was not pleased. He did not see well enough to read people's faces at a glance. But Sarah's whole body drooped tonight, and the pose of her head against the firelight revealed a rare downward line—usually she carried herself so gallantly. "Let's hear it," said Isaac.

"You won't like it." She opened the *Magnet*.

"What's the matter? Don't they like the book?"

"The trouble is," she said slowly, "they've found out who the author is."

"They were bound to do that sooner or later. Mistake to publish it anonymously anyway—I always said so. Murray would have had more sense!"

"Murray!" cried Sarah resentfully. "Murray's still blaming Ben for the failure of that precious newspaper! It certainly wasn't Ben's fault there was a crash in the City just then, and—"

"Never mind Murray, my dear, he lost a lot of money, and that naturally clouded his outlook. When a man makes a bad investment he must blame somebody besides himself. Anyway, Colburn jumped at the book, didn't he—enterprising man! Well, what do they make of it?"

"They've found out Ben isn't—found out he's only a boy, and—"

"That's the rub, is it!" Isaac chuckled into his boiled milk. "Fooled 'em all, and barely come of age! Well, it *was* cheek. I always said so. Read it, Sa, read it."

"It's called 'Nuisances of the Press.' And then there's a subheading—'The New Unknown.'" She began to read in a low voice, hurriedly, so that Isaac must lean forward to hear. "'Young Mr. Disraeli is, as many of our readers are probably aware, the son of the very respected collector of the *Curiosities of Literature* and other useful and interesting compilations. That the young aspirant should have manifested his ambition to share the notoriety of his excellent father is by no means remarkable, but the course he has adopted may well surprise those who do not consider it worth their while to sacrifice their characters as gentlemen and their chances of future reputation as authors for the sake of a little factitious popularity; a popularity acquired by the meanest and most revolting artifices, and the total disregard of all honourable feeling, and sustained (until the cheat is exposed) by the eulogiums of an energetic publisher in elaborate and ingeniously worded news-panegyrics. With the assistance of such a coadjutor; a bold disregard of the decencies of life; an intimacy with footmen, ladies' maids, and butlers of persons of fashion, and five pounds worth of half crowns to slide into ready palms, the veriest dunce might in the space of three weeks concoct a novel calculated to make no inconsiderable noise in the world of fashion.—' "

"Very involved," remarked Isaac at this point, judicially. "Not at all well written."

" 'No matter how contemptible such a product might be,' " continued Sarah doggedly from the page before her, " 'the puffs preliminary would be certain of securing for it a large share of public attention. And if the hit were a decided one, the author would have the opportunity, by promising additional volumes, of extorting with little hope of detection considerable pecuniary compensation from some poor nervous scions of quality, for what he would modestly call the *suppressio veri.*' "

"Eh, what?" demanded Isaac, sitting up. "What's that?"

" 'He might, in other words, give his victim the option of buying himself out of the would-be satirical hotch-potch. Here, then, would be a source of profit open to the adventurer, independent of the forced sale of his lucubrations. The—' "

"But do you realize what that means?" interrupted Isaac incredulously. "Do you realize what they are implying?"

"Yes," said Sarah, her eyes on the page.

"Blackmail!" cried Isaac, as near to rage as his philosophy ever permitted. "That's what it comes to—they're accusing Ben of intention to blackmail!"

"Yes," said Sarah, looking down.

"Does it go on like that?"

"Yes."

"Read it."

" 'The entire gist of the book—for plot there is none—consists in the introduction of characters which we are told in the newspaper puffs are drawn from life.' " She looked up, her finger marking the place. "And then there's a list of the characters with their supposed counterparts—naming Wellington and Canning and Lady Blessington and so on. And it says he sneers at them. That's not true!"

"Go on," said Isaac grimly.

" 'The constant aim of the author of *Vivian Grey* is to appear to have mixed in what he calls fashionable society. Hence the most ludicrous affectations of good breeding, and all the slang and commonplace verbiage peculiar to those pretenders who derive their notions of good society from the housekeeper's room and the servants' hall. But we have neither space nor patience to pursue our notice of this catchpenny further. Mr. Disraeli promises a continuation, and in the meantime will, if he is industrious, turn a penny, though not an honest one, by giving persons the opportunity of buying themselves out of his book!' "

She threw the magazine from her on the sofa, and covered her face with her hands. There was a long silence.

"Poor boy," said Isaac then.

"But it's not fair, it's not true!" she cried passionately. "Ben does go into fashionable society! He was often at Murray's dinners with you—Moore liked him—Scott liked him—and the Austens know everybody—the whole thing is monstrous injustice!"

"Young Ben has been too clever," said Isaac ruefully. "He must expect to get their knives into his ribs. It always happens. The world adores—facsimile. Ben thinks he dares to be different. And all the little pattern-minds are alarmed, and want to take it out of him, quick. To be different is a sin."

"But, father—*you're* different."

"Mmmmmmm—maybe. But I'm quiet about it. All I want is to be let alone, here with my books. But our Ben takes it harder. He dresses in the fashionable way—and walks down Regent Street *looking* different. He writes a novel in the

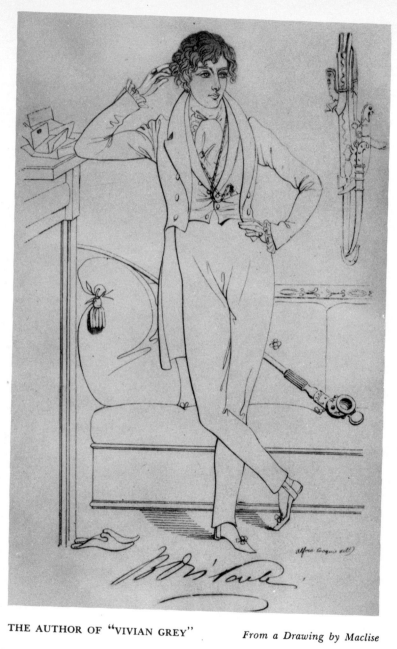

THE AUTHOR OF "VIVIAN GREY"   *From a Drawing by Maclise*

fashionable manner—and *it* is somehow different!" With a sigh, he reached for *Blackwood's,* opened it to her marker, and read, " '—a paltry catchpenny by an obscure person for whom nobody cares a straw.' It's too severe. Much too severe. Poor boy."

"I'll always think this is all that woman's fault," said Sarah sullenly, into the fire.

"What woman?"

"You know very well. Mrs. Austen."

"Mmmmmmmmmm," said Isaac, non-committally.

"Well, it was her idea to publish it anonymously. And it was she who took it to Colburn."

"Egeria," murmured Isaac. "Goddess of inspiration. It's a rôle few women can resist."

"Ben's goddess had better stick to her husband and mind her own business!" said Ben's sister vindictively.

"It's got to come, you know, Sa. All this. You can't keep Ben in cotton-wool forever. He's got to live, and make mistakes, and take his hard knocks like everybody else."

"And fall in love with married women? Does he have to do that too?"

"Oh, yes—that's one of the first steps, I believe," said Isaac philosophically. "If he is in love with her, which I somehow doubt. You must try not to be jealous and possessive, Sa. Sisters have their place in a man's world—"

"Ben's only a boy!"

"Ben's twenty-one. And though your place in his world is not the usual back seat, you're only a sister after all."

There was another silence, while Sarah stared into the fire and Isaac sat ruminating before the appetizing tray, his near-sighted eyes resting thoughtfully on the cover of *Blackwood's.*

"I'm not jealous." Sarah broke the pause at last, out of her own dark thoughts. "Not the way you mean. It's just that I can't bear to see Ben wasted on a woman who can never—who isn't free to—who has no *right* to encourage him!"

"Ben's got to try his wings," said his father. "There's a lot of trouble ahead for you, my dear, if you begin to take things like this Mrs. Austen to heart. Ben is adventurous—it's a favourite word of his. He's bound to come to grief now and then. But this won't down him." He tapped *Blackwood's* with a contemptuous forefinger. "He'll write another book. You'll see."

"It's his pride I'm thinking of," said Sarah, seeing, as she always did, to the depths of Ben's soul. "He'll feel as though he'd been flayed alive. And it's her fault, I swear it is! She might have foreseen something like this! She's old enough at the game, Heaven knows!"

"Do you know if he's seen the *Magnet* yet?"

"He hadn't when he left the house this afternoon, I'm sure. He was laughing—he was gay—" She made a little helpless, loving gesture of Ben being gay. "I can always tell when he's pretending there's nothing the matter with him!"

"Someone will have to break it to him," sighed Isaac. "That will be your job, I fancy."

"If he's at the Austens' tonight, it's *her* job! And I wish her joy of it!" Their eyes met apprehensively. "He's very late, isn't he. You don't think—you do think he's all right?"

"I think so," said Isaac with a small wise smile. "Has your mother gone to bed?"

"Yes. But, father—can you help him through this? Isn't there something *you* can say? Did you—did anything like this ever happen to you?"

"Not on such a grand scale, no," Isaac admitted. "Of course there was that time I wrote my first poem. I remember my father was very upset. He sent me off to Amsterdam with a tutor to get over it. But I caught a bad case of Rousseau instead, and when I got home I wrote a satire—in verse. The *Gentleman's Magazine* published it. And then he gave up all hope for me!"

"But they *liked* the satire, father?"

"Mmmmmmm?" Isaac came a long way back. "Oh, yes, everyone was most kind. But I wasn't really a poet. I had to give that up." He sighed cheerfully over a forfeit dream.

"But nothing like this ever happened to you?" she persisted. "That is, you weren't publicly bludgeoned out of writing poetry!"

"No, no—about that time I married your mother and settled down in the British Museum."

"And—people like Mrs. Austen? Did you ever—"

"I married a simple woman, my dear—and I have loved her very simply." He shook his head slowly, with his wise smile, chose another sandwich, peeped inside, sniffed it, and munched. "Ben will learn. He's too clever now, but he'll learn. You know, Sa—I think perhaps you exaggerate Mrs. Austen. She seems a very nice sort of woman."

"She's very pretty," said Sarah significantly.

"Is she?" Isaac was surprised and interested. "I hadn't noticed."

"Ben has!" said Sarah.

"She calls on your mother—isn't that the one?" Isaac was striving to sort them out in his memory, the troupe of women who passed dimly through his absent-minded, near-sighted ken. "With the nice voice," he decided, pleased with his own clarity. He nodded, to himself. He had her now. "Soothing, I always thought."

"She calls on mother, yes, and Ben runs downstairs looking picturesque with his jacket off and his boxing-gloves still tied on!" She met Isaac's bland, uncomprehending gaze with a look of bitter irony. It conveyed nothing to Isaac that Ben should be seen by this purring outsider with his dark curls damp and rumpled and his white silk shirt sticking to his fine young shoulders with healthy perspiration, breathless, apologetic, and dramatically different from the immaculate dandy of the drawing-rooms; just as it impressed the laughing woman who was obviously surprised (and pleased) that Ben was an athlete as well as an author. What business was it of hers, anyway? . . . "Ben says she understands him," muttered Sarah, turning back to the fire.

"No doubt she does," agreed Isaac placidly. "At Ben's age a man is fairly simple."

"Father—does anything really matter to you that isn't in a book?"

"I know—you think I belittle this business of Ben's. I don't. I think it's very serious—very sad—that his first book has received such harsh treatment. I agree with you that it is unjustified. I am afraid he will take it very hard. I know all that—" Isaac chose another sandwich with care. "But when all's said and done, Sa, it's growing pains. That's all. Growing pains."

"I think that's perfectly heartless," said Sarah, dissatisfied.

"I wish you'd tell them not to mix the white meat and the dark meat in the same sandwich," remarked Isaac, munching. "One likes to know what one's getting."

"I did tell them," she sighed.

"Tell them again."

Once more there was silence. A coal fell in the grate, and Isaac could be heard cutting himself a piece of cheese.

Sarah, who could always tell when Ben was pretending, sat and brooded. He had been gay this afternoon, yes—gay in a way. But while she accepted it for what it was worth, and laughed with him innocently, she knew that something was going on—something he would not tell her. They were very close together, these two, in that preoccupied household, where Isaac was always reading, Maria was always vague and busy, and the boys were so much younger. There were only two years between herself and Ben, and he had always been her particular charge, and had always turned to her, since their nursery days. She was that unique genus, the big sister, which partakes of mother, nurse, and sweetheart, and has advantages over them all. But now there was something he had not told her. . . . At last she spoke again, without moving.

"He confides in her too," she said darkly.

"You're just jealous, Sa."

"I don't know. Perhaps I am. But—"

"That time will come," Isaac told her gently. "But not yet. Mrs. Austen is only a phase."

"I'm sure it would do her good to hear you say so!"

Then a door closed somewhere, and Sarah was on her feet.

"It's Ben! Shall I—hadn't we better find out if—oh, do let's make sure he's all right!"

"Call him in," said Isaac, and with an unuttered sigh for Charles I he slid the large new Hallam volume over the *Blackwood's* on his desk.

X I

Ben had let himself into the house quietly, and paused just inside the door, listening. Light lay across the open threshold of his father's library. They were in there, then, waiting up for him. Or perhaps they did not know, yet. In any case he would have to face them. Might as well get it over with. Besides, he dreaded the thought of his own room, and bed. The silence of those four walls was already sufficiently haunted, and tonight would be worse than all the rest of it. He did not want to be alone.

He let the outer door swing shut behind him with a thud, and Sarah's quick shadow crossed the light in his father's doorway.

"I've just brought up supper, Ben. Do you want anything?"

"Supper?" He paused to lay down his hat and long ivory cane on the table in the hall, nerving himself to meet Sarah's observant gaze.

She watched him anxiously, trying to read his face, which could so readily become a mask these days, white and still, shutting her out from his thoughts. Her eyes ran over him worshipfully as he came toward her across the carpet, with his light, soundless tread—she thought him incredibly handsome, without realizing that his features were very like her own; the straight nose, the great tragic dark eyes and full, sweet mouth, the clear pallor. Sarah was tall and straight, for a woman, but she had to look up to her brother, and sheer pride of him shone in her lifted gaze. He was really splendid tonight, in his black velvet coat, lined with white satin—purple trousers with a scarlet band running down the outside seam, red velvet waistcoat, and long lace ruffles falling over his white hands. Beautifully but more conservatively dressed herself, she loved his exotic taste in clothes.

He lived up to them. Nothing was too grand for him. He wore more jewellery than she did, several gold chains at a time, and several good rings, but it all seemed so right for Ben. Dandyism set him off, because the body inside it was trained and fit and strong. He missed effeminacy by stature, and physique, and the smooth, cat-like sureness of his movements.

She fell back admiringly before him, and he entered the little library smiling, his head held high—entered it as though it was a drawing-room full of watching strangers, and thereby she knew that he had seen the *Magnet*. He was wearing the mask, and he didn't know that she knew. Perhaps it would be better to pretend, until he saw fit to tell them. . . .

"Good Lord, this family never goes to bed," he was saying, as though he spoke to an audience of several dozen. "I could do with a sandwich, I walked home from the Austens'." The telltale words lay there across the threshold in front of him. He had given himself away. With that admission, there was no longer any doubt that he had seen the magazines too. Isaac and Sarah looked at each other in covert despair, and away again, hastily. "Well, Governor, still at it? As one author to another—how does it go?"

"Slowly, Ben—very slowly. I shall be years at this job."

"Ah, but that's because you stick to facts." He chose a sandwich, and separated its edges to peep at its contents before biting into it. Chicken again. Sarah came to his side to pour out a glass of wine. "Anyway, why should you complain? In Heaven's name, sir, let there be a decent interval between my Vivian Grey and your Charles the First! It is shocking enough that they should both be born under the same roof-tree!"

"What do you mean, Ben?" murmured Sarah.

"I mean people should be allowed time to forget my book before his next one is published!" he cried, and Sarah silently handed him his glass. He took it with a lifted eyebrow. "Is that port?"

"Yes, dear, it's—"

"I know, good for me! Isn't there anything else?"

"Yes, dear, there's some very nice Madeira—"

He caught her up with an arm around her waist and kissed her cheek penitently.

"Bless you, Sa, don't spoil me—port will do." He raised the glass. "Here's fame to your next book, Governor—and a merciful oblivion to my first!" While he drained the glass Sarah and Isaac looked at each other helplessly again, and away. "What about a holiday, sir? Things are a bit on top of me, I don't mind telling you. I'd thought of going abroad again. Any objections?"

"So soon?" said Isaac.

"Well, after all," remarked Ben with careful nonchalance, "going abroad is supposed to be a cure for—almost any-thing, isn't it?"

"Yes," Isaac admitted drily. "What have you got?"

"*Ennui.*" He was moving restlessly about the room. "I say, would you two night-owls mind very much if this mere chicken goes to bed?"

Once again that quick glance passed between Sarah and Isaac, and Isaac spoke.

"Ben—are you serious about going abroad?"

"As serious as I ever hope to be about anything again, sir!"

"I'm afraid I'd find it rather hard to get away just now, but—" Isaac fumbled lovingly with his papers on the table—perhaps some of it could go along—or perhaps it would be all right if only Meredith went with Ben this time. . . .

"Well, as a matter of fact," Ben was saying with some diffidence, "the Austens are going to Italy, and they've asked me to join them." It was out.

"Italy!" repeated Sarah, rather blankly.

"Yes, darling, Italy—the one that's shaped like a boot!"

"But, Ben, you'll be howling with homesickness within a week! You did before! Your letters were full of wistful com-parisons—Bruges was like Winchester—Brussels had a Water-loo Place, just like London—"

"But the food, Sa—and the pictures!"

"Rubens!" said Sarah, and made a face with blown-out cheeks and thrust forward her shapely bosom in imitation of Rubens' blowsy females—a brief, hilarious pantomime, which vanished again, on the next tick of the clock, into her usual serene beauty.

"I admit," he went on, laughing at her, "that leaving England has always seemed to me like a cold plunge—horrible to contemplate, but beautiful when it's over. But at the moment I am a little out of sorts with England. No—let's be just. It's not England I'm sick of. It's the people in it. Have you ever considered, Sa, how much nicer trees are than men?"

"Misanthrope," she told him fondly. "That won't last."

"I hope not. I hope that I shall be homesick as the very devil. I discovered the first time I went abroad that with all its imperfections, England was worth all the world together. Do you know what heaven looks like, Sa? Buckinghamshire —without a soul in it! That's rather good! Nevertheless—" He broke off with an exaggerated shiver. "I—I'm cold. They tell me the sun shines in Italy."

She saw through all this—he was using talk as a screen, putting her off with aphorisms and platitudes, trying to make her laugh and forget what lay behind it. It was an old game, to make her laugh and so get his way; he had worked it before, but never since his crafty babyhood had he altogether fooled her with it.

"Why the Austens, Ben?" she inquired quietly, and could not catch his eyes.

"Why not?" He chose another sandwich. "They're by no means the dullest people I know, and—they think I'm devilish amusing!"

They had almost forgotten Isaac, sitting with an open book before him, but for once he had been listening.

"Going to run away, Ben?" suggested Isaac.

"Well, you ran away once yourself," said Ben defensively. "It used to be one of my favourite stories. And after you were found and brought back they gave you a pony. I'll let you off the pony this time—but I want to go to Italy with the Austens." He swung away from them, smiling, his head well up, looking young and undefeated—moved toward the sofa and for the first time saw the *Magnet* lying there where Sarah had left it. The sight of it jerked him to a standstill, with his back to them. He simply stood there, motionless, looking at it, while they watched him in an agony of sympathy and suspense. They had not meant him to learn like that that they had seen it. The silence seemed to them endless, and yet it was his to break. There was nothing either of them could say now. "You've seen it," he said at last, very low. "You were reading it—aloud, no doubt—before I came in. You might have told me!"

Sarah took one desperate step toward him, and somehow could get no nearer while he stood like that, frozen in his tracks, his back to them.

"Ben—don't take any notice of it—it's only a rag, after all—"

"I must say I consider it perfidious behaviour on your part not to tell me it was here!" he cried, near the breaking point, and turned on them wildly. "Cowards—*cowards,* to let me go on gabbling about holidays and Buckinghamshire—I might have known you would see the *Magnet*—I should have known it was in the house, the room reeks of it!" His wideflung gesture was hampered, very nearly made ridiculous, by the sandwich still in his fingers, and he regarded the thing with sudden loathing. "I *wish* they wouldn't put both dark meat and light meat in the same sandwich, one never knows *where* one is!" he exclaimed, and pitched it into the wastepaper basket, and crumpled up on the sofa, his head in his hands.

"Ben, darling—" She dared now to go and lay her arms around his shoulders. "Don't mind so much—don't— Father, can't you *say* something?"

"There's nothing he can say," muttered Ben into his hands. "He never thought much of the book himself—I knew that—"

"Oh, but he did!" she protested. "We all thought it was terribly clever, didn't we, father?"

"I do admire its cleverness—decidedly. I can't say as much for its judgment. It was bound to make you enemies." Isaac rose and stood looking down at his son with both pity and amusement shining behind his spectacles. "But if it hadn't been clever they could have ignored it. You'd have hated that far worse!"

Ben's head came up.

"I wouldn't mind so much if the fellow could write! But to have injustice and ridicule meted out to me in a vile piece of cheap rhetoric like that—!"

"Father noticed that too," said Sarah loyally. "He said before you came in that it was badly written."

Ben met his father's smile, and his own lips twisted.

"I'm sorry, sir, to have invaded your sacred precincts with my—juvenile indiscretions. You're working. *Your* first book wasn't a vulgar catchpenny. You get on with Charles the First, and I'll go to bed."

"No, no," said Isaac hastily. "I was just saying to Sa that my eyes had given out for tonight—I'm off. You build up the fire and finish supper—it's turned damn' chilly again—that's a nice piece of cheese—" He paused on his tactful way to the door. "You know," he said thoughtfully, "these things never look quite so bad by daylight. Good-night."

He closed the door softly behind him, and went upstairs to bed rather slowly, the smile, gone a little rueful, still on his lips. It was all most unfortunate, and Ben was of a nature to take these things much too hard.

His mind travelled back unwillingly to the time when he too had known and succumbed to the universal, inevitable urge to get away from the world which restricted him, and if possible even from himself. It seemed a very long time ago that he had been found lying exhausted and penitent on a tombstone in Hackney churchyard and brought home to a concerned but uncomprehending parent, who embraced him and begged him never to do such an inconsiderate thing again—and the next day the pony had arrived. Isaac's father was one of those well-meaning, blundering souls whose only idea of making people happier was to give them a costly present. His mother could not imagine how she had deserved the punishment of a dreamy, delicate, over-sensitive child who wrote poetry; and with some Spartan hope of curing him of juvenile foibles she had laughed at him, openly and systematically. There were no other children.

Tiptoeing conscientiously along the passage to the big bedroom he shared with his wife, Isaac found himself reflecting with some complacence that at least Ben was luckier than he himself had been in his choice of parents. Maria was asleep in the enormous four-posted bed, her shoulder turned to the bedside lamp which awaited him. He undressed with the soundlessness of long practice and no accidents, blew out the lamp, and slid carefully into his side of the bed.

The house was very still. He told himself firmly that he would not lie awake listening for those two in the library to come creeping upstairs. Sarah would see to this, better than he could. But his eyes would not close in the dark, and he lay on his back, thinking.

X I I

There was silence in the room when Isaac had left it. Then Ben rose restlessly from the sofa, avoiding his sister's eyes.

"Tactful man, the Governor," he said. "Sa, do you suppose we shall ever get like that—so that nothing really matters to us, I mean. Is it merely age—or is it a matter of temperament? He's sixty—where shall we all be when I am sixty?"

"Together, I hope," said Sarah simply.

"But you'll marry and go away," he objected, with a new and wholly dismaying idea.

"I don't see any signs of that," she smiled.

"One never does. It just happens. It might be anybody— at any time. Meredith, for instance."

He was astonished, now that he thought of it, that it hadn't happened before. Sa was nearly twenty-four, and entirely lovable. He was bound to lose her to some fellow before long. He was so taken up with the magnitude of the idea itself that he failed to notice the immediate effect of his

random shot about Meredith. Sarah went pink in the firelight, and her usually steady eyes fled to the flicker of her
rings as she locked her hands together. Her smile was just
a little self-conscious.

"Oh, nonsense, Ben—don't make bogies."

"Meredith's not a bogy, he's my friend." But in his own
distress he was unobservant, and swept on. "Sa, darling, I
hadn't realized—we're out of the nursery—we've grown up!
This bitterness—this frustration—this—beastliness I feel tonight—it's living! Is this what life is going to do to us? Does
this sort of thing go on and on—till one is sixty? And does
one finally cease to *care?*"

"But you're not like father, Ben. You're different. He
says so himself."

"Does he!"

"There's nobody quite like you in all the world," said
Sarah, her soft voice full of conviction. "That's why I'm so
proud of you."

"Proud, Sa! Tonight?"

She sat down with a rustle of crisp silk on the far end of
the sofa from where he stood, her face in its brooding calm
and the strength of its brow and chin oddly like his own in
the lamplight.

"I can't sweep you off to Italy for consolation," she admitted. "I can only sit here, with my heart aching to help
you—"

"Darling, don't cry over me!" he besought her, half impatiently.

"You've made your first flight from the nest, Ben—he said
a little while ago that time had to come."

"First flight!" he repeated bitterly. "And I *have* come down
to earth with a bump! No, this isn't the first. I have failed
more than once. There was that cursed newspaper of Murray's—"

"But surely he can't go on holding that against you!"

"Oh, can't he! He's convinced himself that I talked him
into it, and it's cost him roughly £30,000!"

"But surely you don't owe any of that money yourself?"

He did not answer. "Ben—?" she persisted incredulously.

"What's the matter with me, Sa?" he burst out, with a savage, restless movement away from her. "Why does everything I touch go smash? Why am I always wrong?"

"Oh, my dearest, lots of people make mistakes—seem to fail—"

"Certainly, the woods are full of them!" He caught her up ironically. "It gets to be a habit, have you noticed? They seem to fail, as you put it, and then they go on failing—on, and on, until finally they end in a debtors' prison or—blow their brains out!"

"Ben!" she cried, shocked.

"Well, why should it be *me?*" he demanded. "Why shouldn't I be one of the great ones? I mean really great, not just writing novels the family thinks are clever. I mean great as—as Byron was great!"

"It's too soon, Ben—you're too young—"

"Byron was recognized when he was barely twenty-four! Of course Byron was a genius!" He tried to laugh. "Perhaps I'm not!"

"Oh, Ben, my darling, you're going to do fine things—yes, *great* things, I'm sure of it—but you see, dear, Byron was a lord, and—"

"Yes, and he had a lame foot!" he agreed impatiently. "What's that got to do with it? A man is either great—or he isn't!" At the end of his fine gesture he passed a hand across his hair in a childish, weary gesture of fatigue. "My head aches. I'd better go to bed. Good-night, my precious Sa—" He stooped swiftly and kissed her. "Forgive hysterics—I never meant to worry you."

She accepted his kiss lovingly, and her fingers lingered on his sleeve as he turned away heavily toward the door. Two words had stuck in her mind. But while she sat there, wondering how to get back to them, he was gone.

With a sigh, she rose and after a last forlorn glance round at the small fire which was forever dying on Isaac's hearth on all but the hottest summer days, and at the almost untouched supper tray so eloquent of cataclysm in this house, she put out both lamps, took the last lighted bedroom-candle from the table in the hall, and slowly mounted the narrow stairs in Ben's wake. His door was already closed when she reached the upper passage, and the bright line of light beneath it indicated that he had all his lamps burning. Unlike Isaac, content absentmindedly to peer by a single candle, Ben insisted on a blaze of light in his own quarters. Doubtless he would lie awake tonight, reading.

Mindful of her parents' slumber, Sarah tiptoed into her own room and left the door ajar. Half an hour later she blew out her last candle and peeped through the crack in the door—Ben's lights were still on. She got into bed and lay quiet and tense, listening for any movement from him—but he moved so quietly. There had been a night during his unhappy early school days when she had heard him sobbing in his bed, and had crept in, half frightened of intruding on his boy's dignity—her throat tightened now at the memory of the convulsive clutch of his arms round her neck, his tears damp on the front of her nightdress. He had been grateful then that she came to him. But now he was grown up. Did she dare—?

Another half hour passed like that, while those two words knocked at her brain, and she yearned to lay her hands on him again, and feel the warm, confiding weight of the child he had been, against her shoulder. Would he mind—?

Softly she got out of bed and peeped through the door again, a white, Biblical figure in her long nightdress with a dark plait over each shoulder. The line of light was still there, beneath his door. A little breathlessly in the dark she found her slippers and dressing-gown. She would just ask if he was all right—or if he thought a glass of warm milk might help him to sleep—she was driven by her memory of a thin, shattered child sobbing into his pillow. . . .

Noiselessly she flitted along the passage and listened outside his door. He was walking—walking up and down his room. She tapped lightly and turned the door-knob.

"Ben—may I come in?"

He stood still in the middle of the floor, staring at her, startled.

"What is it?" he said quickly.

"N-nothing." She slipped inside and closed the door. "I couldn't sleep—and I got wondering about you. I looked out and saw your light. Can I do anything? Would you like some warm milk? Father thinks I'm the only person in this house who can make it properly."

They smiled at each other, wan in the bright light from his lamps. Even in his distress, he was picturesque. Most men would have been in a state of deshabille—showing braces, perhaps, with an open neck-band, clothes thrown down anywhere. But Ben's fastidious habits prevailed even in his solitary vigils. His coat was folded across a chair, his cravat was on the bureau, his boots lay beside the bed; he wore soft leather slippers and a silk dressing-gown corded in at his slender waist, and he looked to her unutterably beautiful and young.

"My dearest, I'm all right," he said gently, his chin well up. "I've been reading." He pointed to an open book which lay on the seat of an armchair to prove it.

"Ben—downstairs tonight you said—debtors' prison."

"Did I?" He glanced at her guardedly, and turned away to hang up his coat in the wardrobe.

"It isn't anything like that, is it—for you?"

"Not yet. I hoped the book would do well, and then I meant to write more. But now—it won't bring £200."

"And that's not all you need?"

"No," he said evenly, his back to her. "That won't be quite enough."

"You're worrying," she said, and came a step on into the room. "Don't think I don't know. Can't I do anything?"

"No, my darling, you can't."

"Wouldn't it be a good idea to tell me about it? Sometimes —if we talk things over—" She took a firmer tone as he did not instantly refuse. "Ben, do you owe a lot of money?"

"Yes. Quite a lot." He was brushing at an imaginary spot on the sleeve of the coat, his eyes avoiding hers.

"To whom?"

"To the moneylenders. Particularly to a fellow in Golden Square." He glanced at her quickly, over his shoulder. "You won't give me away?"

"Have I ever done that?"

"No. You've been an angel always."

"I didn't dream it was as bad as this," she said steadily, determined to be sane and straightforward and not panic like a sister. "Why didn't you tell me?"

"It wasn't that I didn't trust you. I was ashamed. I've made such a mess of things. I don't see any way out." He moved restlessly across the room, and returned the book to its place on the shelf.

"There are my rings and things," she said after a moment. "They must be worth a good deal. And grandmother's pearls were left to me, I can do as I like with them. You must take them—"

"My darling Sa—" He was infinitely touched.

"No one need know," she assured him quickly. "I never wear half my things."

"Dearest, you are humbling me in the dust, can't you see? And all to no purpose. It's so very much worse than that."

"You mean that wouldn't help?"

"A raindrop in the sea!"

She took it very quietly, staggered as she was.

"Ben, what on earth have you been doing? How did you get such debts?" He did not answer. "You can't go on like this, you'll be ill. Tell me. Perhaps we can think of something—together." She could not see his face. "Come and sit down."

"No, thanks, I'd rather walk about." He took another restless turn up and down the room, nerving himself to confession, while she crept to the armchair and sat on the edge of it, her eyes following him. It was better for Sa to know, he decided. She wasn't just the family. She was something of his own, rather special and infinitely dear. It would be comforting to have Sa beside him these days, it was lonely without her, lonely and frightening. He had never kept anything from her before. "You remember when the American Mining stocks crashed last year," he began slowly, wondering how to put it into words for her. "Well, Evans and I were in it. You see—we thought we were frightfully clever. We speculated for a fall, and it went on rising. We were in for £1,000 in no time. So then we shifted—became 'bulls'—just as the market began to drop. We were right in the beginning, you see—but we were too soon. And then the whole thing caved in."

"How much—" She swallowed. "How much did you lose?"

"Between us, over £7,000." Her eyes widened, but she made no sound. "Evans found a way to pay some of it," he added lamely.

"What are you going to do about the rest?"

"One goes on borrowing more at ruinous interest—from fellows in Golden Square."

"Does father know?"

"Of course not!"

"Aren't you going to tell him?"

"I'd die first! I got into this, and I'll get out of it some-how!"

"But father—"

"No," he said firmly. "Let him be. He's happy. Let's have one of us happy!" He ran a hand across his hair again, in that fretful gesture of pain and weariness. "My head never stops aching. You see, the book was a chance, and now that's gone. I don't suppose the *Magnet* can really make things any worse than they were, but somehow it was the last straw. And to have it come here, to father and you—! Darling, don't mind that I want to go to Italy, I can't stand it, I tell you, I must get away! *Byron* got away!" She was staring at him whitely from the armchair, her eyes wide and blurred with tears. He paused in his restless pacing to look down at her contritely. "Please don't cry, Sa—I shouldn't have told you—you know I always hate to see you cry. Besides—you'll get me started."

Silently she held out both her arms wide, and he flung himself down on his knees beside her and buried his face in her lap. His shoulders shook under her hands.

"Don't let's care, Ben—they want to hurt you and discourage you. But don't let's let them—don't let's *be* discouraged!"

"It isn't true, what the *Magnet* says!" he cried passionately, his face hidden. "I never meant to ridicule any person in particular—I wrote very fast—it was fun—the words came tumbling out—I wrote of what I had seen and felt—but it's not myself, I give you my word I never thought less of myself than when I drew that monster Vivian Grey—I thought he was just a character—somebody I'd made up—"

"Yes, darling, I know—I know—"

"There never was so much nonsense talked about anything!" He was calmer now, with great effort, and he raised his face, its white cheeks wet with tears. She wiped them away with her fingers, while her own dripped down unheeded. "But people in a hurry can mistake it for sense! People who read the book and were amused by it are beginning to think they were wrong and that it's full of hidden improprieties and scandal. Conceited asses who think they can see themselves in it are braying of violated confidences and faith broken where I had never pledged any. My own acquaintances look at me nervously and sheer off, as though they expect to be the next victims—"

"But, Ben, haven't you explained to them—"

"I hate explanations! I never want to explain anything! 'My dear fellow, I didn't mean—' It's awkward and undignified! Apologize, yes, if one has committed a fault—but explain or deny, *never!* Anyway, it's all too ludicrous!" Again he tried to laugh. "What does it signify? What do I care for their flimsy fame!"

"But you'll be writing other books, and—"

"I don't know. At first I thought not. And as I walked home tonight through the dark streets I tried to say good-bye to all the dazzling creatures still to be born of my pen—imaginary people, all of them—crowned monarchs and radiant heroes, and women brighter than the day. They seemed to crowd round me in the darkness with mournful faces, as if to entreat me not to desert them—"

"But of course you mustn't give up writing, just because—"

"And face that sort of thing again?" he interrupted savagely. "The insolence of it! Even if I can't write, surely I am not a fool! On the contrary, everybody has thought me rather an extraordinary person! What will they think now?"

"Just the same, Ben. Your real friends won't change."

"Friends!" he cried, and brushed them aside. "A handful out of all the world! But thousands of people who have never laid eyes on me and never will, will read that thing in the *Magnet* and think of me with contempt forever after! And there is no redress—none—from that original printed word. It is there for all time." He leaned against her wearily, crouched on the floor at her feet, grateful for the warmth of her mere presence, and the shelter of her loyalty; subtly wrought upon and comforted already by her blind belief in him. "It does hurt, Sa— I don't know why it should hurt so much, but it goes deep into the very soul—the horror, the blank despair of finding myself the subject of the most reckless, malignant derision! They have done for me—done for me, I tell you!—I am sacrificed—scalped—I am ridiculous—it is time to die!" He turned his face into her shoulder, and she bent, half smiling, half crooning, above him.

"Ben, my dearest—my darling—it's not as bad as that!"

The early English dawn was showing between the curtains, a blue slit against the lamplight.

XIII

The hot summer arrived as predicted in June, with an almost unprecedented drought. Green crops failed entirely, the grass burned up, the hay was practically nothing. Cattle had to be fed on dry fodder, and the price of fodder rose so high that only the wealthy could afford cattle at all. Ponds and reservoirs dried up, and people watched beside the remaining springs all night to get water for their families, or to peddle it round the countryside. A pitcher of water was a welcome gift from one neighbour to another. The deer in the noblemen's parks died of thirst. England wished for its fogs and rains back again.

But Ben lay on a sofa in his room and complained that he

was cold, all through that sweltering June, and it was obvious that he was actually ill. The doctors shook their heads and muttered of nerves and strain and inflammation, but Sarah suspected that they really did not know what was the matter with him. They advised rest, which he was getting, and change, which the Austens offered to provide abroad. When it was decided in July that he was to go to Italy with them if he was well enough he made up his mind to recover, and a flare of the old excitement in a new project brought him to his feet again, to begin his packing. His spirits soared—the tireless, adventurous spirits which flagged only with dulness and defeat, on which the prospect of more travel acted like wine. He even went out again in the evenings, and began to take an interest in his food. Sarah watched him sadly. He could get well to go away with Mrs. Austen to Italy, fast enough, and philosophize as she might, it rankled.

Mrs. Austen too was packing. She had as many new clothes for her Italian summer as a trousseau—whites and delicate colours, which as a rule seemed a little forlorn under pale English skies—parasols and broad-brimmed hats. She looked enchanting in that sort of thing, and she knew it. A smile hovered round her mouth these days, as she watched the lovely, fragile creations of her dressmaker into their travelling hampers. They made her feel young and frivolous and fatal, as no respectable married woman ought to feel, and for all her impertinent wit and advanced ideas, she was really *very* respectable, she told herself demurely, folding in the heliotrope ribbons of a large leghorn hat which tied beneath her chin and was crowned with pink marabout feathers. It would amuse Ben, that hat—she closed the lid rather guiltily on the thought. She did not buy hats to amuse Ben, but to look well for her husband.

They got off early in August from Dover to Boulogne; went to Paris by way of Beauvais and Abbéville, a four day journey, and settled in apartments in the Rue de Rivoli. By that time Ben was himself again, free of his harassments in England, with the childish sense of holiday that a journey always brought in him. He found Paris wholly delightful, and the ancient parts reminded him of the Old Town of Edinburgh. He went to the Louvre in the morning and the Opera in the evening, "lionized" the Quais, Notre Dame, and the Cité. Mrs. Austen wrote Sarah that he had improved beyond belief in looks and health in a week, and that he enjoyed everything, *"pour ou contre."*

From Paris they posted through Dijon to Geneva, and there he wrote a long letter home to Isaac, whose companionship he missed even in the stimulating society of the Austens. Besides, Byron had been a household god in Bloomsbury ever since Isaac's acquaintance with him in the old days at Murray's, and Ben could hardly bear that Isaac should miss Byron's boatman, Maurice.

> Geneva,
> August 11, 1826.

My dear Father,—

At the termination of the Jura ridge which bounds one side of the plain of Geneva, did I on Friday morning witness the most magnificent sight in the world—the whole range of the high Alps with Mont Blanc in the centre *without a cloud;* the effect was so miraculous that for a long time I did not perceive the lovely scene under me, the plain and city and lake of Geneva, the latter of ultramarine blue. Such a view of the Alps has been seen by few people in this country and was occasioned by the unparalleled dryness and heat of the season, which, as we are daily informed by travellers, much exceeds the heat now experienced on the other side of the Alps, in Italy. The heat does not, however, affect me in the least. I have not had a day's, nay, an hour's illness since I left England.

I take a row on the lake every night with Maurice, Lord Byron's celebrated boatman. Maurice is very handsome and very vain, but he has been made so by the English, of whom he is the regular pet. He talks of nothing but Lord Byron, particularly if you shew the least interest in the subject. He told me that in the night of the famous storm described in the third Canto of *Childe Harold,* had they been out five minutes more the boat must have been wrecked.

He told Lord Byron at first of the danger of such a night voyage, and the only answer which B. made was stripping quite naked and folding round him a great *robe de chambre,* so that in case of a wreck he was ready prepared to swim immediately. . . . One day Byron sent for him and sitting down in the boat he put a pistol on each side (which was his invariable practice) and then gave him 300 napoleons, ordering him to row to Chillon. He then had two torches lighted in the dungeon and wrote for two hours and a half.

I have been on the lake at all hours, and seen Mont Blanc by all lights, twice by sunset when the whole mighty mountain is quite rosy. The effect is beyond all description. The living at Secheron is most excellent; we much wanted it. Except at Dijon I have scarcely had anything to eat since I left Paris. In the Juras we were literally without a meal. The honey of the Alps, wild strawberries, butter, cheese, and eggs are all very well in romance, and certainly not to be despised as collaterals, but with us they were principals for successive days. Travellers require nourishing food. In the Juras we could not even get a bottle of common wine, and the bread was black, and not only sour but acid.

Mrs. Austen is very well, and speaks French with even greater rapidity than she does English. I hope to God my mother is better. Love to all. Tell Ralph and Jem I'd give anything for an election.

Your most affectionate son,

B. Disraeli.

Isaac read the letter many times in his late, quiet evenings, after the first ceremonious reading aloud in the drawing-room after dinner. Not an hour's illness—that was good. The boy was so tall and weedy—grown beyond his strength, living beyond his years—that was the trouble. Wanted time to catch up with himself. Liked the heat, did he—got that from his Venetian ancestors, no doubt. Ben was an atavism, way beyond the English Disraelis, to the more exotic generations of the Villa Reals and the Laras—there was a spot of genius from somewhere. Isaac sighed and smiled, and fingered the letter. Might go far. Had imagination, and courage, and perception. Got the most out of things. Enjoyed himself. So that storm in Canto Third was real, and might have wrecked the poet who immortalized it. Torches in the dungeon at Chillon —what a scene! Wild strawberries—he hadn't had any for years. . . .

What on earth did Ben want with an election? He'd get one soon enough, no doubt, but he surely didn't mean to go in for politics? He was too young, and besides—they didn't want Catholics in Parliament and they didn't want Jews—not even baptized ones, like Ben. The boy must not set his heart on another unattainable goal, he took failure too hard. It was a terrible thing, ambition, and Ben was cursed with it. Sighing, shaking his head, Isaac would fold up the letter and resume his pen: "Mr. Hallam, who sometimes alarms us with his eloquence . . ."

The next letter came from Milan and described the passage of the Simplon in a storm; the first lyric joy at the heat and colour of Italy after the snows; and the "idiotism" of various English encountered at Milan. Verona was "full of pictures which had never been painted." The first week of September brought them to Venice, which he never wanted to leave. They arrived on a fête day, and—

—the moon was so bright that a juggler was conjuring in a circle under our window, and an itinerant Italian opera performing by our bridge. Serenades were constant during the whole night; indeed, music is never silent in Venice. I wish I could give you an idea of the moonlights here, but that is impossible. Venice by moonlight is an enchanted city; the floods of silver light upon the moresco architecture, the perfect absence of all harsh sounds of carts and carriages, the never ceasing music on the waters produced an effect on the mind which cannot be experienced, I am sure, in any other city in the world.

They visited the tomb of Petrarch at Arqua, and found the door-posts of Tasso's cell in Ferraro covered with the names of its pilgrims—"here scratched with a great nail on the brick wall I saw sprawled BYRON." From Florence he wrote that he had seen enough in Italy "to know that we are not setting about the right way to form a National Gallery. At a recent sale in Florence the finest pictures were sold for a song. Why had not the National Gallery an agent on the spot? What is Lord Burghersh paid for?" Florence was also one of the cheapest cities in the world—

Here cheapness, *real* cheapness, is to be found, for here luxuries are cheap. An English family of the highest respectability may live in Florence with every convenience and keep a handsome carriage, horses, liveries, etc., for five hundred a year. I speak here of an average-sized family like ours. On this income you might enter into the best society, and the best society here is excellent. You may live in a palace built by Michael Angelo, keep a villa two miles from the city in a most beautiful situation, with vineyards, fruit, and pleasure-gardens, etc., keep *two* carriages, have your opera box, and live in every way as the first Florentine nobility, go to Court, have your own night for receiving company, etc., on less than a thousand a year, and this with no miserable managing, but with the enjoyment of every comfort and luxury.

Maria was much impressed by this letter. *Vineyards,* said Maria incredulously, at your very door, as it were! A palace— an opera box—and go to Court—on a thousand a year? It didn't seem possible. A Hapsburg grand-ducal court, Isaac reminded her dryly—probably pretty awful—all Tuscany had been restored to the Austrians—the present grand-duke was very unpopular, poor fellow. It was all this agitation about constitutions, Isaac would explain, after dinner, when they read Ben's letters aloud. Napoleon again, said Isaac. There was much unrest, all over the world, but particularly in Italy. Not a nice place to live, said Isaac. Maria said she had no desire to go and live in Italy. But—*two* carriages?

From Florence to Pisa, and from Pisa to Lucca, and thence to Genoa, "sated with scenery," but smitten most of all with the Mediterranean—

> On the third day we descended nearly to its shore, but what a shore! It required no stretch of the imagination to fancy ourselves in Asia and under an Oriental sky, for aloes, huge, everlasting aloes, here grow on the shingles, and groves of olive trees, dates and figs, and clusters of Eastern trees abound upon the green mountains, which descend into the sea, and whose only artificial ornaments are towns of coloured marble and amphitheatres of palaces. The shore, as I said before, is broken into innumerable bays, which vie with each other for superiority, until they all yield to their Queen—the gorgeous bay of Genoa, on whose mountain banks rises in a crescent Genoa la Superba, a crowd of palaces, villas, and convents. But I am writing of that which should be seen.

From Lyons, on the way home, he wrote to Sarah that the whole journey had been more than perfect, without a single *contretemps,* and his companions divinely agreeable. He had not been idle, and was bringing back a sheaf of papers—diaries, notes, and so forth. And he had, as a gift to his father, a miniature of Charles I copied from a noble likeness by Van Dyke in the Pitti Palace, especially to his order.

> Everything that I wished has been realized, and more than I wished granted. I have got all the kind of knowledge that I desired, and much more, but that much more, I am convinced, was equally necessary. To discover new wants and find them instantly gratified, or rather to discover unexpected necessities anticipated, is the most pleasant of all things.

Sarah read that last bit again, with a little frown. She knew him so well. But on paper one could not be so sure of him. They were simple enough words, at first glance—simple and complete on their face value. He had had an enthralling journey, he was well again, and had plans for more work to do. A very healthy summing up of four happy months. And yet—it was almost too explicit. It closed the door so very firmly on questions. It was as though he answered her, with anxious emphasis, questions which she had not dreamed of asking. Or was it, on the other hand, an unconscious revelation, an unguarded outpouring of too innocent truth?

"To discover new wants and find them instantly gratified—" And Sarah, frowning at the page, was wondering exactly what he had wanted of Mrs. Austen.

XIV

She did not realize quite how complicated a question that was.

When they left England in August, not even Ben knew the answer to it. To him, Mrs. Austen was the guardian angel who had already once restored his self-respect, and was now rescuing him again from illness and defeat. He did not blame her in the least that the result of their venture with *Vivian Grey* had humiliated him far more than the original disaster with Murray. They had been as careful as they knew how to be. It was Colburn who had given the game away, somehow.

She was a gloriously excitable companion for one's first days in Paris, and she remained cheerful on the uncomfortable journey to Geneva, and through the Alpine snows to Italy. So far his mind was all objective, delighting in what he saw, stretched to catch the last high note of ecstasy in the novelty and beauty of his surroundings. They travelled slowly, usually without fatigue.

In Italy they became still more leisurely, driving through beautiful country "where the vine is married to the mulberry," under deep blue skies and dark olive trees. The days were long and hot and golden, the nights were soft and moonlit. Mrs. Austen was a joy to the sun-dazzled eye in her pale organdies and printed muslins, a big hat tied under her round chin. At dinner time she would change into misty white, looking cool and fresh in the candlelight which flickered on the marble walls of old palaces turned into hotels. He began to watch her as well as the scenery, and to appreciate the picture she made in these bizarre, magnificent surroundings, so unlike her little drawing-room in Guildford Street. It was a new frame, and she filled it exquisitely.

They were in Venice for nearly a week, living in apartments in the one-time palace of the Bernadinis, with marble floors, satin hangings and upholstery, ceilings by Tintoretto, and gilt work which shone as bright as new after two hundred years. There was a balcony over the canal, with growing plants and long cane chairs—a small, secluded heaven of indolence, with the placid water below and amorous music always in the air. They would sit out there in the evenings, forgetting to talk, drugged with the peace and the beauty and the melodious stillness.

They were all three enchanted with Venice, in their separate ways. Mr. Austen fancied himself as a scholar of architecture, and pottered endlessly about the Palace of the Doges, with its doors from St. Sophia's, pillars from a Morean temple, and granite columns from Jerusalem—all testifying to the glory and triumphs of the Venetian Republic days; he spent hours among the marbles and porphyry and mosaics of St. Mark's; and pointed out that the bronze horses *ambled*, not pranced, as the guide-book said. Mrs. Austen wrangled happily with Ben over the respective merits of the Venetian school, professing to prefer Veronese to Tintoretto for the sake of argument, and complained prettily of a crick in her neck from so much gazing up at ceilings. To Ben it was another milestone in his coming of age—for while they were in Venice he acknowledged the need of a woman's hand to respond to the pressure of his own fingers. It was here, in the city of his ancient fathers, that he faced the stupendous fact that he was in love.

Their small party was seldom separated, and surreptitious contacts, shoulder brushing shoulder, the locking of little fingers in the dark, did not occur to him and would have revolted his soul. Scrupulously he kept his distance from his goddess, but his eyes would rest on her profile with wistful worship now, while her face was lifted to the view.

On their last night in Venice they sat as usual on the balcony after dinner, the smoke of Mr. Austen's new Viennese porcelain pipe fragrant on the quiet air. Mrs. Austen pretended not to like it, but her protests were largely funny ones, meant only to emphasize the fact that her husband habitually did exactly as he pleased, with her full consent. At last he rose with a sigh and a stretch, and went into the drawing-room through the long windows to deal reluctantly with the week's accounts and pay off the servants.

Neither of the two left on the balcony spoke or moved for minutes when he had gone. Mrs. Austen lay back in her long cane chair, her white lace flounces foaming about her small white satin shoes, pointed starwards. Her bright cachemire shawl had slipped back, and the moonlight modelled her face and neck and shoulders with pearly highlights. Her hair was a pile of gleaming curls, apparently held only by a large tortoiseshell comb, and uncovered like a girl's. She was relaxed, content, and wholly without guile.

Ben's eyes rested on her freely, his face in shadow. At last he rose with a creak of cane in the stillness and went to the balustrade over the canal, impatient of a sudden tightness in his chest. This took him farther from her, which was unbearable. He wanted her beside him at the railing.

"Look," he said, and pointed downwards.

She could not see the water from where she sat.

"Must I get up?" she objected lazily, without moving.

"Yes, you must."

Sighing, she rose and came to his side, and her eyes followed the direction of his finger to the perfect reflection of the full moon in the canal. A gondolier was singing down by the bridge, a tenor love song—a girl's voice joined in, young and clear.

"Two moons," said Mrs. Austen thoughtfully. "How very generous of someone."

"It's typical of the whole trip, I think," he answered. "Always two moons—always a superabundance of perfection."

"You are enjoying it, aren't you," she murmured with satisfaction. It had been her idea in the beginning.

"It has been unbelievably—exquisite. And I have you to thank for it all."

"I wonder just how you mean that!" She smiled up at him under tilted brows.

"Oh, *that!*" he said, referring to the misery which had driven him from London. "I am grateful now for the row about the book. Without it, I might never have had this. I am grateful to you—for everything."

"I'm glad," she said simply, for she liked people to be happy through her, and her eyes went back to the black water, silver-stencilled, beneath them. "I've loved it too."

He was not quite sure how it happened. But the next thing he knew he had kissed Mrs. Austen, there by the balustrade of the Palace of the Bernadinis. He kissed her, and for a moment it was just as he had dreamed it. Then she stirred in his arms and drew back, but gently, without doing violence to the perfect moment which was gone.

"You must never do that again," she said quietly, and returned to her chair.

He stood still where she left him, waiting for a suddenly giddy world to steady itself. His hands were shaking and he could not trust his voice. Astonishingly the scene with Miss Maples in the conservatory shot across his mind. Why should he think of Miss Maples now? He had felt that night like a man in a novel. But this was different, this was real, this was in his pulses, this was not in the least funny. And yet he felt —what was it?—unoriginal. Did all one's personal crises come out like something someone else had written? Was life as hackneyed as that? He desired another man's wife—the knowledge ran through him like flame—well, yes, it had been done before! A moment more he waited, making sure of his voice. Then he followed her, and when he spoke the words sounded to him oddly familiar.

"You aren't angry with me?" he pleaded, looking down at her.

"No," she said, and her voice was low and drowsy. "No woman could be angry at being kissed on a night like this— and so nicely too—by a handsome young man."

He searched her face in the silver light for mockery and there was none. Her eyes were half closed, and the moon was so bright that he could see the shadow of her lashes on her cheeks. He sat down on the foot-rest of her chair, brushing aside her white flounces to make room, and then locked his hands between his knees.

"I couldn't stop myself," he confessed. "It—just happened."

"But it mustn't happen again," she reminded him softly.

"I don't promise," he muttered, looking down at his hands. She sighed, and made that ancient plea.

"Don't let's spoil things," she said.

"I know." There was a silence, while he steadied his voice again. "But I love you so very much—"

"You mustn't say that. We mustn't think about it after tonight. We must pretend it never happened at all."

"I'll try. If only I can be near you—often," he said, and this was innocence.

"We must just go on as we were—good friends," said she, for she was inexperienced too.

"The very best of friends." He meant it as a vow.

The next morning when they met at breakfast she seemed to watch him expectantly, her lips a little parted, her eyes very bright. She looked young and candid and unworldly in the morning light, dressed in fawn-coloured muslin and that most enchanting garment known as a spencer of embroidered white, with green ribbons. Ben, who had not slept well, and had a headache, thought what a babe she was, and began with strong black coffee. Mr. Austen, who had read a guide-book in bed, lectured them learnedly on Petrarch throughout the meal and bundled them off early to visit the tomb on the way to Bologna.

The headache wore off in the carriage, and they were very gay at luncheon. But from that day forward, Ben was dogged by a restless passion to have her to himself for even five minutes—with no hope of touching her again, with not even an indiscreet sentence to whisper, he longed wretchedly to feel however briefly that they were alone together—a reckless stretching of his self-command from which he derived a sombre satisfaction, while she never betrayed by a look or a word that she remembered the balcony at Venice. But an unprejudiced fourth might have observed an added sheen to her prettiness, a sort of inner glow, which could, of course, be put down to her daily pleasure in the beauties of Italy, and her always excellent health.

Thus they traversed the Apennines to Florence, where they remained a full fortnight, conversed with Bertolini, and made the acquaintance of a man who had been intimate with the late Emperor Alexander of Russia. From him they learned the astonishing details of the succession of Alexander's youngest brother Nicholas on the Czar's death last December, when everyone had expected Constantine to inherit. Constantine, who was the elder brother, had made a morganatic marriage and was said to be willing to renounce his claim to the throne. Nicholas, who was unpopular, had shot his way in, and was a true Muscovite, without Alexander's mysticism or Western veneer. Constantine was meanwhile behaving with unbelievable brutality in his own province of Poland. Nicholas was expected to intervene in the interminable war between Greece and Turkey, not so much because he loved the Greeks as that he hated the Turks. Canning, of course, would not approve of this—for Russia might thus reap all the benefits of the Greek uprising.

It all sounded very far away and improbable, in the luxurious surroundings of a Florentine villa. To sit there and say that the Greek cause had become desperate, and that gallant Missolonghi had blown itself up with its own powder magazine rather than surrender, was nightmarish. Famine, violent death, and women sold into slavery were merely incomprehensible words in this golden world of sunshine and old masters. They left Florence reluctantly for Pisa and Genoa, and then turned homeward across France.

During that next month Mrs. Austen found Ben's behaviour so circumspect as to be positively touching. The situation could so easily have become awkward, especially for a woman who was honestly devoted to her husband, as she was. But it was impossible to find the smallest flaw in

Ben's manner toward his host, or the slightest hint of presumption toward herself. He was being incredibly good. As a reward, she used to link her arm more often in his as they climbed a flight of stairs, or let her hand linger just an instant on his shoulder when he helped her from the carriage. And she noted with satisfaction that he took no advantage of these indulgences.

Ben, who was genuinely fond of Mr. Austen and admired him as a successful and cultivated man, had been making himself promises. He had no intention, of course, of wronging his friend. Such an idea was beneath contempt. It was only that he was pitiably cold and hungry and desired to feed on crumbs and warm himself a little at the fire. Surely there was no harm in that. He asked nothing but to be allowed to worship her too. Beyond this self-dedication to a sort of abstract devotion he refused to think.

They crossed from Turin into Savoy over the Mont Cenis pass, which they found vast and dreary compared to the sublime Simplon. They stopped for a meal at an inn beyond Susa, in the heart of the mountain range, where they fell into talk with the inn-keeper who spoke of the beauties of a small lake, a half mile beyond the road—a small blue lake, he told them with pride, in the midst of eternal snows, fringed with fir trees. Ben became enamoured of it at once, and desired to see the place. The inn-keeper pointed a path which wound away up the slope. Only a step, he said—there was also a small cascade. It would be possible to visit the lake while the trout were cooking.

Mrs. Austen said it sounded enchanting and stood up, ready to start. Ben was already on his feet. Mr. Austen looked at them plaintively, and said that he was hungry enough already and meant to sit where he was with his feet to the fire till he was served. So much energy on an empty stomach, he said, was indecent, and he would not be a party to it. Mrs. Austen found Ben's eyes beseeching her, and took his arm with a laugh. Mr. Austen said he would try not to eat it all in their absence, advised them to be quick, and settled

himself more comfortably to exercise his Italian on the inn-
keeper.

They took the little winding path in silence, single file,
their senses excited by the tang of the high, fir-scented air,
their feet crunching on slippery dead needles. Before they had
gone far the chuckle of the cascade came to them through
the mighty stillness. The path ended suddenly on the bank
of the lake, whose glacial blueness was ringed about with
snow-tipped peaks. They stood side by side and gazed. There
were no words big enough for that small sapphire gem in its
eternal setting.

They turned to each other simultaneously, their eyes wide
and grave with beauty, and each met self again with a shock.
She recovered first.

"We must go back," she said rather breathlessly, and added
—"It is the divinest memory of the whole trip for me."

"And it's ours," he said, looking down at her. She wore a
little fur cap and jacket, against the crisp mountain air,
and her cheeks were pink from the climb. She was very different from the languorous moon-clad lady of the Venetian balcony—but equally disturbing. "Our own private memory,"
he added. "We have two of them now." He laid his hand on
her sleeve.

She turned away from him, looking down the path they
had come.

"The trout will be ready to eat," she said, but lingered.

"My darling—I've done the best I could—"

"You've done very well," she murmured.

"But have you any idea how hard it's been? And now the
gods have given us this blessed spot." His arms slid round her
carefully. "Don't let's waste it—utterly."

"Oh, Ben, we mustn't go on like this— Well, just one
more—" Her lips came up to his. After all, he had been so
very good. . . .

A minute later they began the descent in silence again, arm
in arm and very close together, because of the narrowness
of the path, past the babble of the little cascade. Not until
they reached the last turning above the inn did she draw

ahead, and preceded him the rest of the way. They had not spoken. The last words between them were still in his ears as he followed her up the steps of the inn: "Just one more—" Their appetites for trout quite logically surpassed even Mr. Austen's.

It was only a few days later, in mid-October, that he wrote that letter to Sa, from Lyons, in which his unexpected necessities had been anticipated. He had not seen Mrs. Austen alone again since the little blue lake in the Cenis. His behaviour as they crossed France was as exemplary as it had been in Italy. But they were returning home swiftly now, and he had begun to look forward to reaching London. He carried with him always the feel of her fur jacket under his hands—and three soft, yielding words: "Just one more—"

X V

England was convalescent during the winter, making a fair recovery. The famine did not materialize, wheat and potatoes did better than anyone had hoped, and signs of universal suffering abated. Wages stayed low, but there was less unemployment, and it began to look as though the European peace might hold.

But in January, 1827, the whole aspect of things in England was altered by the death of the Duke of York, who had become the heir apparent when George IV's only legitimate child, the Princess Charlotte, died in childbirth ten years before. York's health had been declining for some time, but still no one had expected the King to outlive him. For all his vices, which were said to be not unprincely, he had a certain popularity and a royal presence. He had been his father's favourite son. He was ill-educated, and a terrible martinet, and there had been scandalous episodes. But he was kind-hearted and easy of access, and in most quarters he was sincerely mourned.

When Princess Charlotte bore a dead child to Leopold of Saxe-Coburg at Claremont and died the same night, the House of Hanover was left without a single legitimate heir in its succeeding generation. Charlotte had six uncles, and at the time of her death only two of them were living in respectable wedlock; York's wife, childless through their twenty-odd years of marriage, had long since retired into an eccentric existence at Oatlands, and seldom saw her husband at all; and Cumberland, the fourth and best-hated of George's brothers, had recently married a thirty-seven-year-old German princess, a widow, and their first child had died at birth. The Duke of Clarence, who came next after York, had been involved for many years in an irregular but enduring connection with Mrs. Jordan, the actress, but was by 1817 recently at liberty. The Duke of Kent, who came third, was still living blamelessly with the elderly French Canadian lady who had been his companion since 1792. They had gone to Brussels to escape his debts, but were very comfortable there. The Duke of Sussex, fifth in the succession, had long ago been entangled in a morganatic marriage with Lady Augusta Murray, which he still regarded as binding, though they had separated. Cambridge, the youngest duke, aged forty-three, lived in Hanover as Governor-General, and was a bachelor.

When it came to providing heirs to take the place of Charlotte and her unborn children, York had to be written off. Clarence had done pretty well, with ten children by Mrs. Jordan in twenty years of cheerful domesticity at Bushey Park; since his break with her and her death he had been making valiant attempts to find a wife; it was even said that his desire for eligible offspring had caused the break. Doubtless it was his new eminence after Charlotte died which made him so suddenly successful, with Adelaide of Saxe-Meiningen. She was twenty-six, plain, religious, and had been well brought up. They were married in the summer of 1818, within a year of Charlotte's death. The Duke of Kent was almost literally torn from the arms of his devoted Mme. St. Laurent by his responsibilities to the succession, and he married Victoria, widow of the Prince of Leiningen; she was thirty-two, and the sister of dead Charlotte's husband Leopold, and had two children by her first husband. And about the same time the Duke of Cambridge married the young and attractive Princess Augusta of Hesse-Cassel.

In 1819 four babies were born. The Duchess of Cambridge was first, with a boy. The Duchess of Clarence's daughter, born during the same week, lived only a few hours. On May 24 the Duchess of Kent's daughter came into the world at Kensington Palace, and three days later the Duchess of Cumberland had a son. But Kent came before Cumberland and Cambridge in the succession, and Kent had won, with a girl.

Now in 1827 England was counting up its heirs again. The new heir apparent was the Duke of Clarence, the sailor prince, who had been with Nelson in the West Indies. He lived soberly with his dull Duchess at Bushey Park; where he had formerly enjoyed a perhaps jollier existence with Mrs. Jordan (who was famous for her heart-warming laughter) and their tribe of hearty offspring surnamed, conveniently, Fitzclarence. Some of these had married well and were raising liberal families of their own; Army, Navy, and the Church had all received Fitzclarence sons. Half a dozen Fitzclarences still regarded Bushey Park as home, absorbing their somewhat bewildered German step-mother into the family circle with scarcely a ripple.

William, Duke of Clarence, was very democratic in his habits, and had not his brother York's regal bearing. Another baby had died in 1821, and people's thoughts glanced past him down the line. The Duke of Kent should have come next, but he had died of a chill in 1820—his one child, the Princess Alexandrina Victoria, was not yet eight years old. After her there was the Duke of Cumberland, but he and his son were reserved for the throne of Hanover by the Salic Law, and owing to his unpopularity England would never have accepted him in any capacity. He spent most of his time abroad. Sussex and Cambridge were still alive, Sussex very popular with the Whigs, Cambridge living entirely in Hanover. From all that long, lusty family of George III and good Queen Charlotte, fifteen sons and daughters, there was only the Duke of Kent's small girl Drina to inherit England.

The country had not long to speculate on the future of the Crown before another blow fell. Lord Liverpool, who had been Prime Minister since 1812, was stricken with apoplexy early in February, and Canning, who had so many enemies, was due to succeed him.

George was at Brighton, and Peel went down with the news. The King was in one of his most exclusive moods, when he isolated himself in his stuffy apartments from the sight of everyone but his harassed servants and Lady Conyngham, who was said to be slowly dying of boredom and confinement, hating the King, and almost never even troubling to speak to him. He minded this latter less than might be expected, however, as he talked incessantly himself; reminiscences, mostly, which took an ever wilder turn and grew ever more highly improbable, and were punctuated frequently by "God damn me, ma'am, *you* remember!"—endless, pointless stories which revealed embarrassing delusions and indicated that he might soon be as mad as his father had been. He was nearly blind now, and could no longer walk up or down stairs, and lived largely on pastries and cherry brandy.

Into this stagnant, overheated atmosphere of unbalanced invalidism came Robert Peel as Home Secretary—tall, fair, long-faced, and stiff of manner. At thirty-eight he found himself in a position of considerable importance and responsibility, and he was a singularly unambitious man, happily married, with a desire for travel and leisure—a politician largely by force of circumstance and his father's wishes. Good fortune dogged him. It was his fate to acquire an early eminence which men like Canning had to sweat blood for. He was born a Tory, and went to Oxford. At twenty-two he was Under-Secretary for War in the Liverpool Government. At twenty-four he had been appointed Chief Secretary for Ireland and spent six years there, involved unhappily in the eternal struggle for Catholic Emancipation. During that time he quite naturally made an enemy of the tireless Irish agitator, O'Connell, who had gradually achieved the union and leadership of the whole of Catholic Ireland. O'Connell, who was thirteen years older, spoke of him contemptuously as a gentleman dandy. Peel, who was young and arrogant, was heard to refer to O'Connell as an itinerant demagogue, and to hint that his motives in the religious war were not entirely disinterested. O'Connell dared him to repeat it in his presence—and so on, until matters reached the duelling point. The challenge came from Peel. O'Connell had already killed one man who challenged him, with a shot in the hip— to his own honest horror. His wife prevented him from meeting Peel by informing the authorities, which made everybody look a little ridiculous. But the feud went on.

Peel did not solve Ireland, during those six years' residence, but he contrived to rule it. In 1818 he had returned to England weary of official life; married, and spent three comparatively quiet years in the House of Commons. In 1821 he became Home Secretary and was from then on in direct conflict with Canning, who was his senior by eighteen years, and his active opponent on the Emancipation question. Peel did not want to antagonize Canning in the House, but the lines of demarcation were drawn for him. He represented Oxford, the stronghold of the English Church. Automatically, he was Wellington's ally and Canning's rival, with a growing Protestant following.

When Liverpool collapsed in 1827 the road rose again under Peel's unwilling feet. If Liverpool died the choice of a leader would lie between Canning and Peel, and Canning was ambitious. Canning cared. After years of effort and humiliation and endurance, Canning had outlived and outworked the men who had stood between him and his goal. He was not popular with the King, and many of the old-school Tories had turned against him, but he had earned the premiership. And Canning was in Brighton too, in bed with a cold caught at the Duke of York's funeral. He had advised old Chancellor Eldon to stand on his hat that day in the damp stone chapel at Windsor, but he had not taken the same precaution himself.

The King frankly did not know what to do, and allowed several weeks to go by, hoping against hope that Liverpool would rally. At last it was only too clear that Liverpool's active days were over, and that a successor must be appointed.

George made a tentative gesture toward the Duke of Wellington, who had been the leader of the High Tory party since
Castlereagh's suicide in 1822, supported by that section of the
old Cabinet which was most hostile to Canning. Wellington
replied that as a military man he would be worse than mad
to think of taking the premiership. There seemed to be no
way out but Canning, who was determined to have it. But
still the King hesitated. He knew that if he appointed Canning the Duke would resign, Peel would go with him, and
others would follow them. If Canning became Prime Minister it seemed likely to wreck his party, and yet he was their
ablest and most experienced man. He was known to regard
Catholic Emancipation as inevitable, and there the split
would come.

Liverpool had never been a brilliant statesman, but for
years he had held a contentious Cabinet together by tact
and hard work. It was difficult to quarrel with Liverpool, and
he had managed to prevent his colleagues from quarrelling
overmuch with each other. Canning was his close friend,
and lately the Government had been largely Canning's under
Liverpool's wing. But to men like Wellington, Canning as
Liverpool's right-hand man was a very different matter from
Canning as Prime Minister in his own right. They could only
just bear to work with him. But *under* him? Oh, no.

Political enmity flared higher that spring than it had done
for years. Canning could see that if he came in, the main-
stays of the former ministry were sure to go out, taking their
following with them. Wellington was saying openly that
nothing would induce him to connect himself with *"that
man."* A great deal of the hard feeling was due to the
jealousy of rank and birth for sheer genius; the rest could be
laid to Canning's own sarcastic tongue and irritable temperament as much as to his political views. Canning had fought
for every inch, and had hardened on the way. Even so, the
abuse he was receiving on all sides cut him to the heart and
embittered his achievement. Peel alone behaved decently to
him, and Peel was not cordial.

Not until April was the appointment unwillingly con-

firmed by the King, and when that was done all the Liverpool Ministry were invited to remain in office. Wellington
promptly resigned and stamped off into retirement, nursing
his grievance. Peel withdrew into his cold dignity, and the
friends of the old ministry fell away one after the other until
it looked as though Canning could not possibly form a Government. To do so at all he was forced into an alliance
with the Whigs, for which he was mercilessly censured—but
he gave no concessions to them, and made the condition that
they were not to raise the question of Reform, which was
the eternal threat of the Opposition. This in its turn brought
a split in the Whig party and Earl Grey launched a slashing
attack on him in the Lords. Grey, the personification of the
old Whig aristocracy, was the champion of Reform. And even
while Canning was in the act of coalescing with his former
antagonists he had declared that he would oppose Reform
to the end of his life under whatever shape it might appear—
thus alienating a large portion of the party on which he was
now dependent. Grey led the Opposition in the Upper
House, and everybody descended to personalities. Rancour
rose. The fellow had retained his place. Power was slipping
away from the hereditary influences.

A Coalition Cabinet was inevitable, since those Tories who
had been willing to work with Canning for years under Liverpool could not bring themselves now to be his subordinates.
He was deserted by his own former colleagues, and men he
had thought his friends became his most bitter enemies and
sank so low as petty spite to thwart him. His Coalition Cabinet was the first break in the Tory grip since 1784, but they
had brought it upon themselves.

Canning had never properly recovered from his January
chill, and was still in very poor health, but there was no time
to take a holiday. He held patiently on his way and by May
had completed his Cabinet. Lyndhurst, a moderate Tory, was
Chancellor in old Eldon's place; and the Duke of Clarence,
an ardent and garrulous Whig, was Lord High Admiral. It
was a ministry of considerable ability, when he had finished,
and it had a working majority in the House. If it had been

destined to endure, Canning, who was Pitt's pupil, might have revived and strengthened the Tory party as Pitt had done years before. By sheer personal talent and zeal, a commoner had become the leader of the Government. But he stood isolated at the top, estranged from his own party and his old friends, and in a difficult situation to form new connections. "Fame is a squeezed orange," he wrote in a bitter disillusionment. He had reached the heights. But it was a solitary grandeur.

And it did not last long. Canning died in August, worn out but not defeated, and the country found itself back where it had started the year, rudderless, more than ever without guidance. Even his enemies felt lost. The gloom cast by his death was international, for while to the conservative element in England he had appeared to be a friend to revolution he had only understood a little sooner than most men that the old order was gone. He had tried to hold the balance between two extremes and in the attempt had lost the allegiance of both, but he stood for enlightenment and liberal principles all over the world.

Because the King was vexed with the other ministers who had made things uncomfortable and difficult for a man he himself disliked, he would not consider any of the deserters for the vacant post. Probably with some idea of a compromise between the old Tories and the Canningites, he chose Goderich for Prime Minister, and a new Coalition Government was formed which was doomed from the start. In fact it was no Government at all, it was merely a loose collection of too many great names and strong personalities without a dominating factor.

Goderich, unofficially known as "Snip" or "Goody," was a minister *pour rire*—he could carry out instructions unimaginatively at the Colonial Office, but he could not give them himself from the Treasury. He tried to resign in November, but was persuaded to remain. In January, overwhelmed by the magnitude of his task and his own incapacities, he tearfully threw up his hands and departed. Grey's name was whispered, but the King sent for Wellington. "Arthur, the

Government is defunct," he announced with visible satisfaction.

A soldier's sense of duty to his King and country was all that induced Wellington to undertake the premiership. But he did accept this time, and the Tories were happy again. The Duke was busy, good-humoured, and efficient. His Cabinet would be the same well-disciplined machine that his army had been. Now order would emerge from chaos. Now common sense would rule. But it did not work out quite that way.

In the construction of his Cabinet Wellington avoided the proverbial weakness of a Coalition Government by gathering about himself a ministry wholly Tory again, with Lyndhurst continuing as Chancellor, and Peel back in the Home Office. But a Whig majority in the House made things difficult. And the Catholics, who had been quiet under Canning with some confidence in his intentions, became rampant now, for Wellington was a known enemy to their cause. In Ireland the hostilities between Catholics and Orangemen became more violent, the war against tithes and rents was unremitting, O'Connell was an indefatigable trouble-maker, and the Irish election riots were not far from civil war. The Irish question had been the cross of every session since the end of the Napoleonic war, and now, with the election of O'Connell, a Catholic, for County Clare, it had got out of hand, for O'Connell claimed his seat in the House, but refused to take the Oath.

Peel, born and reared in Toryism, and its appointed guardian, still was less a Tory than Wellington. He was able to see as Canning had done that concessions to Ireland were obligatory, and his influence with the Duke was great. Under his manipulation Wellington gave way on Emancipation at last. "It is a bad business," he sighed, "but we are aground." As a good general he always knew when to retreat. If it was to be O'Connell in the House or civil war in Ireland, he chose O'Connell, as the lesser evil.

Peel himself introduced the Bill, proposing a change in the Oath, and spoke for four hours amid alternate cheers and tense silence. Many of his colleagues blamed him heartily for what seemed to them a shameless *volte face,* and even his opponents were surprised. "Peel is a very pretty hand at hauling down his colours," remarked one of these, sardonically. Wellington suffered too in the estimation of his High Tory followers, and was bitterly attacked by men who only a short time before had admired him and hoped much from his régime—the "military and aide-de-campish" Government the Opposition so detested. Among these disappointed adherents was Lord Winchelsea, the ninth and least important earl. He wrote a letter to the Press in which he accused the Duke of insidious designs for the infringement of British liberties. Winchelsea was notorious for abusive garrulity, but he was the last straw. The Duke, first and last a soldier and a man of action, not words, sent the Secretary at War—a former staff officer—to demand an apology. Winchelsea presumed to make conditions. The Duke's seconds then claimed for him that satisfaction "which a gentleman has the right to require and which a gentleman never refuses to give."

The arrangements were speedily and secretly made. They met on a chilly March morning in Battersea Fields. The doctor provided by the seconds nearly dropped dead himself when he recognized the principals in the duel. The Duke was first on the ground, and in a hurry. When Winchelsea arrived the distance was paced off, they took their places, the order to fire was given. The Duke put his ball neatly through his opponent's coat, Winchelsea fired in the air. An apology— alterations dictated on the spot by the Duke—was read by Winchelsea's second, the Duke jerked two fingers to his hat, and rode away to breakfast with friends.

The King, when he heard that the Prime Minister had called out Winchelsea, was charmed, and vowed he would have done the same himself.

The Whigs, who had hoped to create strife in the Tory ranks by those twin Opposition measures, Emancipation and Reform, found themselves unexpectedly on the side of the Government. The Repeal of the Catholic Disabilities was carried in April, 1829. But George had fretted himself ill over the matter, and would see nobody if he could avoid it, except Wellington, who bullied his Cabinet and treated his sovereign as an equal. George complained bitterly that even Canning had promised him he would not be troubled with the Catholic question. But Canning was dead. George was a little afraid of the Duke; he was sulky as a bear, they said in the clubs, but he obeyed his Prime Minister. This somehow did not increase Wellington's popularity. He was discovering in his turn that the premiership made for loneliness. He remarked with rare self-pity and his usual humour that there never was a man who suffered so much—and to so little purpose.

The Duke's best abilities were not political ones. He had alienated the Canningite element in choosing the rigidly Tory personnel of his Cabinet; and he had now split his party by the Catholic concessions. Meanwhile the Canningites had drifted toward the Whigs, and bereft of their uncompromising leader had even taken up Reform. Party landmarks wavered and shifted so far that there was even talk of a coalition between Wellington and Grey, whom the King loathed. But Grey knew that a mutual hatred of the dead Canning and the belated passing of a Bill he considered long overdue were not sufficient basis for union with such an opponent as Wellington, who compelled respect even in his reactionary wrong-headedness. Besides—the Whigs had promised Canning not to push Reform, but Canning was no longer among them. And the Whigs, having gained one measure long useful as an Opposition gadfly, could now concentrate their augmented forces on the other. From now on, the issue and the battle-cry was solely Reform.

XVI

All this activity at Westminster found Ben very quiet in Bloomsbury meanwhile. *Vivian Grey* had done well after all —well enough for Colburn to offer £500 for a sequel, continuing the young man's adventures abroad. This was published in March, 1827, and out of that payment Ben sent £150 to

Murray, to make good Powles' debt on the mining pamphlets. It was a gesture, for he had many more pressing creditors; particularly the money-lenders, to whom he and Evans had had recourse to a ruinous extent to handle the Stock Exchange debt, and these now began to dog his footsteps in London. He affected a large, impractical innocence which impressed them and staved them off—but he meant to pay them somehow.

The second part of *Vivian Grey* was not so good as the first. The author had lost the original naïve pleasure in his own work which had made it at least vivid and human and alive, and the new volume made no great stir. The springiness was gone out of him, as it had gone out of his hero in his remorse and exile. Vivian's life at the little German court where he found refuge was amusing and imaginative. But the effects were not sustained. It was the work of a tired, driven brain, with only an occasional flash of the wit and epigram which had so enlivened the first volume.

Produced at the time of great political excitement in England, it served to exercise its author's growing interest in government and statesmen. It contained a Prime Minister of plebeian origin who, like Canning, had raised himself to the pinnacle. "Fate, Destiny, Chance, particular and special Providence—idle words! A man's Fate is his own temper!" said Beckendorff, in *Vivian Grey*. It was what Ben himself was striving desperately to believe. And again—"No conjecture can possibly occur, however fearful, however tremendous it may appear, from which a man by his own energies may not extricate himself." A large creed, but there were times when he could really believe in it. There were other times, black, hideous hours, when it was all empty words, infantile optimism—and he wondered why he went on striving, and what he was hoping for, when his life was already wrecked and wasted.

The renewed health and ambition which he brought back from Italy were seen mysteriously to fade away again during the following year. He was tormented with headaches, and much of the time he felt languid and aimless and unsatisfied.

There were intervals of comparative peace—but if a few days went by without a glimpse, however formal, of Mrs. Austen, the world was drained of interest and he accomplished nothing. He rarely saw her alone, but sometimes there was a chance to kiss her hand, or speak to her for a few moments with all barriers down—and sometimes he was allowed to hold her for a few moments in his arms. Then he would go away and work feverishly again, until the fit of achievement passed in a headache, and an idle haze of vague longing and restlessness.

His loyalty to Mr. Austen troubled him acutely, and he often considered confessing to the older man that he had fallen in love with his friend's wife. Once he mentioned this desire to Mrs. Austen, and her horror was so genuine and her panic so pitiful that he realized more clearly than ever before just where he stood with her; realized with a dull thud of his self-esteem that she did not love him. Obviously she was fond of him, flattered by his devotion—fond even to the point of liking the desperate clasp of his arms around her, and she suffered his rare snatched kisses with an odd, guilty thrill. He was very young and his ardour was clean and honest and disarming. She meant to be kind to him, and told herself that provided it went no further than those scant, intimate moments in her drawing-room there was no harm done to anybody.

She was not a flirt or a wanton. She was an essentially virtuous woman, and a very innocent one in many ways, unaware of the damage she did where she intended only a tender-hearted lenience with a small romance, so long as no hurt came to her husband's domestic security. She would never have left Austen for Ben, nor carried on an intrigue under his roof. She had married him when she was very young, and her knowledge and experience of men was limited to the shelter of that relationship. She was still in love with him in the comfortable, confident way of a well-settled marriage which has been a very pleasant success. At the same time she had grown fonder of Ben than she had altogether intended. His graceful homage, his well-turned speeches, and the sheer animal magnetism of him as he stood before her, disciplined and devout, were demoralizing. Her eyes would linger on his lips, even while she held him from her with small desperate hands pressed hard against his breast—perhaps—just one more. . . . She could not bear to banish him, she was too much drawn to control him, and she very nearly wrecked him on her own integrity.

She wrung from him a promise never to let her husband suspect that he felt for her anything more than the warm surface friendship for an older woman which was visible to everyone. The difference in their ages, though she was still young and very lovely, naturally protected them from comment or suspicion. And Ben, contemplating the abyss which would open at their feet if Austen found out and chose to be difficult, pledged himself unwillingly. God knew he did not want to further muddle his life with an unsavoury scandal over a married woman. He was not so mad, even now, as to want to run away with her, and he too sickened at the thought of deceiving Austen. He did not know what he wanted or where he was heading. He forced himself not to avoid Austen, and in the older man's frank, open-hearted company he found a solace which at the same time added to the strain of his suppressed infatuation.

There were also days when he thought of ending the whole thing, breaking off completely, and never seeing her again. But that in itself presented difficulties so long as they both moved in the same social orbit. Then he would swear to see less of her—to taper off gradually as a man reduces a drug. But this would always make her miss him, wonder if he was ill or sulking; and the briefest note in her handwriting or a friendly word from Austen would set the hunger gnawing again and he would return to Guildford Street, despising himself for a weakling, deriving a sort of fatalistic satisfaction from the proof of her hold on him, resigned to his own cowardice.

His moods and tempers and alternating defiant high spirits and depths of despair bewildered or exasperated her, who only meant to be kind. Why could he not accept what she could give, and be content? It was not as though she flouted him, or led him on. And surely she had never allowed him to hope for more? No, he would agree bitterly with a grunt of sardonic laughter, he had never aspired to more. And troubled at his misery, she would give him her lips again, and coax him back into good humour. And so his slavery dragged on.

Somehow he got another book written, working doggedly against his debts. It was called *The Voyage of Captain Popanilla,* and was directly descended from *Aylmer Papillon.* Colburn published it in the spring of 1828, "by the author of *Vivian Grey."* It caused very little comment, though Plumer Ward, to whom it was dedicated, likened it enthusiastically to Voltaire.

In the summer the family went to Lyme Regis for their holiday, and the headaches stopped, though he was listless and inclined to be irritable even with Sarah, who watched him these days with a mixture of apprehension and sorrow, and was the only one who dared intrude on his moody solitudes. At first he kept up his guard with her too, but by patience and tact and the lifelong affection which knit them together she gradually won him back to something of their old intimacy before Mrs. Austen had taught him to keep a secret.

They walked hand in hand like children along the Parade in the evenings, and talked of homely, trivial things—the precious, sane small talk of small families, as close and comforting a contact of minds as the warmth of palm to palm. And Sarah, her fingers clasped in his, noted how he avoided pauses and subjects which came too near to what was in both their minds, and she thought how like he was, even now, to a little boy who was nervous of the dark, and so kept up a cheerful babble on his way down the black passage to bed.

For Ben this enforced absence from London which had at first seemed merely a thing to be lived through somehow till it was over, like a fever, had now become a sort of nirvana where he rested between worlds, only half alive, but at peace. It was good to have Sa to himself again, for these long, sunny days. Her undemanding devotion, her ready laughter, her delicious ability to keep the conversational ball atoss, her magnificent lack of curiosity—Sa never pried—were balm to his tormented spirit. He basked in Sa, and in the Dorset heat, and thanked heaven for a breathing spell in the midst of life's complications in London.

Gradually as the time drew near for returning to Town, he felt a growing disinclination to resume his troubled existence there. He had an idea for a new book. He could have written it in the country, without worry or distraction, with only Sa to listen and to praise. . . . He viewed these tendencies, once he had discovered them and dragged them forward in his mind, with dismay. Already? Was he so little able to stand up to life that now at twenty-three he could contemplate becoming a country recluse with only a sister as his companion? He looked down at Sa gratefully, at her clear, straight profile, strong and sweet under the spreading brim of her bonnet, and her straight shoulder brushing his as they strolled in the late twilight above the quiet sea. There was an ache in his throat.

"Sa, I shall hate leaving here. I've enjoyed this."

"Have you, dear? So have I. It's good to be—really together again."

"I should like to stay in the country, I think. It agrees with me."

She glanced up at him, astonished, and away again before he saw. He was gazing out to sea, and there were little lines of strain around his mouth again, at the thought of going back to London.

"It's been good for us all, I think," she said only. "I'm sure father is the better for not being able to spend all day in that stuffy Museum Reading-Room. As a matter of fact, they were talking about it last night, before you came down to dinner—about going to live in the country, I mean." It was a long shot, made on the spur of the moment. She waited in considerable suspense for his answer.

"To *live?*" he repeated incredulously, and checked in his stride, and then went on again more slowly, turning it over in his mind. "Well, yes, why not?" he said eventually. "Why not? A lovely house with trees—high ceilings—room to move and breathe—gardens—a place to keep a dog—more than one dog—"

"We can't afford another Abbotsford, you know," she reminded him gently.

"A garden," he went on without heeding her, his fingers gripping her arm in a new excitement. "An old-fashioned garden, Sa, with old-fashioned flowers in it that smell deliciously as the sun goes down! I should love to see you in our own rose garden in a big hat, snipping blooms into a basket! And we could have picnics on the lawn—"

"You mean you'd *like* it?" she cried, trying not to sound too surprised and too hopeful.

"Like it? Why wouldn't I like it?" he demanded.

"Well—they were saying last night—asking me if I thought you'd miss Town, and all that. Father would hanker a bit for the Museum, of course, now and then, but he feels that it would be so good for mother, and— You see, they were afraid you'd be bored and unhappy away from—all your friends."

She waited, careful not to press it, while they walked on, perhaps a score of paces, and he did not answer, and she did not dare to look at him. Then—

"I wonder if it's happening—so soon," he murmured with a humorous twist to the words.

"If what's happening?" she encouraged him softly.

"Old age."

She laughed, and squeezed his arm.

"Ben, *darling!*"

"I mean it. You remember what I said that night we talked about the *Magnet*. I was wondering then if one ever ceased to care, as time went on—and then it didn't seem possible. But apparently one does. A year or two ago I should have hated the idea of being buried in the country for the rest of my life. I'd have said Yes, it was time perhaps for father to retire and be a country gentleman if he wished. But I would have said that I myself had things to accomplish first, a life to live, work to do. And now—well, it all seems

too much trouble! Perhaps he feels that way too. Perhaps he's
felt that way for roughly forty years! So he's just gone into
the Museum and stayed there, where nothing could get at
him. I'm not at all sure he wasn't right, you know."

"You're tired," she said finally. "You'll want to get on
with things again one day. You wouldn't be content as he has
been. But there will always be times, I suppose, when you'll
feel like this, and want some sort of refuge."

"Yes, that's it!" he agreed eagerly. "A refuge. Somewhere
to go to earth, when things get too much for me." He drew
a long breath. "Things *are* too much for me at the moment,
Sa."

"My dear—I know—"

"Yes, there's not much you don't know about me, is there!
One can't talk about it—at least, one shouldn't. But talking
to you is rather like confessional, for me." He paused, striving for words, and she waited, afraid to frighten him off with
too much sympathy or understanding. "Sa—I don't know
quite what to do, I—all this isn't getting me anywhere, is it.
I mean—things have got into a rut, I just—go on. And I was
going to do such splendid things!" His laughter was scornful. "Sa, I'm wasting my time!"

"So long as you know that," she said gravely.

"I do know it now. I can see that I am. But I'm weak, Sa.
I sit here, with a new book in my head, and because I'm in a
muddle about other things I let the days stream past me—"

"Weak!" she cried. "You!" And then, biting back a dozen
phrases he had given her an opening for at last—"New
book, Ben? Tell me."

"Did you ever hear of Alroy?"

"Yes—'way back in the Middle Ages, wasn't he?"

"Twelfth century. What an educated woman you are, Sa!
Well, I want to do a book about him. It's the loveliest background—Caliphs and the Tombs of Kings—Jerusalem itself—
and the Sultan too! He had a sister. That's where *you* come
in." He caught her hand and drew it through his arm, and
his step quickened, she matching hers to it again. "This will
be *our* book, Sa—yours, in fact. A son of the house of David,
avenging his sister. How do you like the idea?"

"Need you ask? And you'll let me see it as you go—page by page?"

"Yes, I will," he promised, realizing belatedly what it must have cost her to see another woman sharing his enterprises while she was left out for the first time. And with that a sense of the futility of any endeavour while his life held on its present course overtook him. "Sa—that house in the country—did they mean it, do you think?"

"It would be nice for mother," she said carefully, anxious not to press it yet. "Bloomsbury Square is small, and old-fashioned, and makes housekeeping difficult. She wants another maid, and more kitchen and scullery room. With the boys growing up, there are complications. They haven't really made up their minds about it yet, of course—I think more than anything they were hesitating on your account."

"Can you convey to them—somehow—that I should welcome the change?" he suggested, smiling down at her.

"I think so."

"You might put it that I realize the distractions of Town are preventing me from settling down to anything worth while."

"Yes, Ben."

"And that this holiday has proved that my health is better in the country."

"Yes, Ben."

"And that I mean to do a really serious novel next time—something that will endure, like the Governor's things—not just a fashionable nine days' wonder."

"I shan't give you away, if that's what you mean," she murmured, and laughed.

"Oh, bless you, Sa, such tact! You mean you'll never admit to them that I know I've made a fool of myself over a woman!"

"Never!" she said emphatically, and laughed again from sheer relief.

They swung on down the Parade, in step, and looking very much alike, their arms locked tight together, and her eyes were very bright. Ben was himself again.

II. BRADENHAM

THE uprooting was not altogether easy. The family had
lived in that house in Bloomsbury for twelve years, and for all
of them it had associations. At first the search for a country
home went but spasmodically, and Maria, after the manner
of a tooth which stops aching at sight of the dentist, became
suddenly philosophical about the inconveniences in Bloomsbury Square. They looked at one or two houses which were
not suitable, and during the winter the enterprise lagged.
But Sarah kept it alive. Sarah had least cause to cling to the
old home, for her life was rooted in Ben himself and went
with him wherever he was, and she saw only that he was
unhappy in London and would benefit by a change. Loyalty
to his confidence in her on the Parade at Lyme Regis for-
bade her to cry to them—"You must do this to save Ben—you
must help me to get him away from that woman—you must
give him a chance to find himself again!" It had all to be
done sidewise, without giving Ben away. And this took time.

He had made no open break with the Austens, but he went
less often to Guildford Street now, and when he did go it
was Mr. Austen's society he seemed to seek. It was a friendship he had counted on and cherished for years, and he knew
how near he had been to losing it entirely. Mrs. Austen was
still disturbing in her beauty and her warm welcome after
his absence. He was not out of love with her, but the madness had passed into a weary and almost derisive acceptance
of the misery she wrought in him. She still moved him, but
now he had got perspective, he saw it must end in nothing,
and even as he kissed her he could smile. This made him feel
very old and world-worn and jaded—a bystander to his own
youthful emotions. He remembered to remind himself that
life was going to be very funny.

He retired into a growing dandyism as behind a mask.
His waistcoats were sublime, his tailoring a miracle of per-

fection, his colour schemes transcendent. It made more bills, but where there were so many that didn't matter much. He shrugged them off, or charmed his creditors into waiting while he wrote another book. And as his clothes spoke for him of innate exoticism and a love of luxury and a passionate individuality, his tongue became less talkative. He listened now, while the conversation swirled around him; developed a sort of courteous aloofness which was at once a challenge and an enigma. He was quick to see the effect of this, and took pains to increase it. What had begun as a natural reaction he cleverly exaggerated into a pose. His pale, unusual face with its brilliant eyes and expressive mouth was made for mystery. He schooled it to an impassive, slightly ironical mask and behind it was delighted with the result.

Even Mrs. Austen complained that he had changed, which pleased him. It was the impression he had meant to convey. He discovered that people were very gullible. They believed what they saw; or rather, could be sure of nothing they did not see. He perceived how very useful this might be. It amused him to learn how a little silence, a question turned aside, an air of smiling detachment from the human coil, baffled and attracted them. Enigma. It became his watch word.

To Sarah's observant eyes he was moping—low-spirited— perhaps ill again. Sarah was used to his loquacious days. She began to harp, when he was not there, on the house in the country. Isaac sighed patiently, and took up the search anew. No doubt a change of air would be good for them all. Maria was not well. But it must not be too far from London, he insisted, not too far from the British Museum. . . .

In June, 1829, they left London for good, and settled in an old manor house in the Chiltern Hills, near High Wycombe. Isaac was pleased to find that Bradenham House was mentioned by Camden, and had been in Royalist hands during the Civil War, with some rebuilding after the Restoration of Charles II. Ben was entirely captivated by it, the embodiment of the vague ideal he had had in mind that evening at Lyme Regis. It had yew terraces, and great iron gates open-

ing on to the village green, with parish cottages and a vicar-
age, and there were fine old beech trees and junipers on the
land roundabout.

Together he and Sarah inspected every foot of the house
and grounds, finding new virtues round every corner, imagining painstaking improvements. They stood on the cobbled
carriage sweep hand in hand, the morning they arrived,
laughing like children at the absurd bloodhounds, *couchant,*
which guarded either side of the steps leading up to the front
door, and which Isaac informed them were left over from
the prosperous Lovelace days. The door opened straight into
a noble hall with two fireplaces, and long sash windows
looked back through the iron gates and down the sloping
green to the village. Turning to the right, you came to a little
parlour with dainty old wallpaper and a blue and white tiled
mantelpiece; and then to a magnificent corner room which
looked down the stretch of green lawn and away to the common land and the hills. This, said Sarah, would be the library
—wall space for all the books, and a view to stretch their
father's eyes between pages as he wrote. The dining-room lay
beyond, at the end of a stone-floored passage connecting with
the kitchens, which Maria said were too far away, but practical enough once you got there. Here the ancient timbered
Tudor walls were visible, and you could lay your hand on fat
black beams which had been there in Queen Elizabeth's time.
And from this passage a big square white door with a Gothic
fanlight opened into the garden, though it was possible to
raise the sash window in any ground floor room and by stooping just walk out of it, over the sill; which seemed to Sarah,
who loved gardens, even more practical than the kitchens.

The gun-room opened off the other end of the great hall;
an impressive room, though Ben remarked on a certain
scarcity of guns in the family. And from one corner of the
hall rose the great oak staircase with a painted ceiling. The
rooms above were endlessly discussed and re-allotted. There
were so many of them to choose from. A whole row of them
faced down the slope across the village toward the wooded
ridges beyond and the sunset. A square sitting-room at the top

of the stairs with doors opening off it in all directions caught their fancy. Sarah turned to the right—a room for Ben to write in, and another, just across the passage, for him to sleep in— "See the sun it gets!" she said. And he, turning to the left— "And this one, with the dressing room—what's that, a powdering closet?—for you, so I can shout at you across the sitting-room! It looks the same way as mine—so that we see the same thing when we wake up in the morning. I like that," he added thoughtfully, and she gazed at him with adoration, as grateful for the gracious thought as for a lover's compliment. "We shall adopt this room between us, I think, for our very own," he was saying. "No boys or dogs allowed—" meaning the excitable Jem's expansive ideas about allegedly dumb companions. "I can work here," he murmured, gazing out at the Chilterns. "God knows I can work here!" And this was what she wanted. Her scheme had come off. He was safe. He was hers again.

Their parents' room, the largest, had a magnificent white mantelpiece. The best guest-room was of superb proportions. The boys were left to choose their own. There were top floor rooms as well, up another great oak staircase—where little, deep-set windows framed miniatures of the view, and the great old beams cropped out in unexpected places, along the floor and overhead. They talked of a billiard room up there, and a gymnasium. "But what space!" Ben would cry again and again, flinging wide his arms to embrace it. "What height! What freedom! What air! I shall be well! I shall do wonders here!"

It was a new game, and they played it wholeheartedly. This was a home, it had roots, and permanence. It was good to feel oneself a part of it. It had the magic healing peace of the English countryside in summer. France was on the verge of revolution again—Belgium was restive under the tactless Dutch rule—there was massacre in Poland. This was England, smiling, green-clad, small, and secure.

For nearly a year he remained at Bradenham, sometimes ill and despondent, sometimes working hard at the new book. An appearance in London was always a risk now because of his creditors. He went there rarely and then incognito. Mrs. Austen wrote to him, kind, friendly letters, hoping he was well, urging him to come to dinner when he was in Town and tell them his plans. He wished she wouldn't. Obviously she missed her bondsman, as a child misses a caged bird. He was so nearly free of her now that her innocent attempts to get him back again were unreasonably infuriating. In March he turned on her:

My dear Madame,

Your repeated kind messages require my personal acknowledgment, and deserve something better. With regard to myself, in a word, I cannot be worse. With regard to London, it is of all places the one, in my present situation, least suited to me. Solitude and silence do not make my existence easy, but they make it endurable.

My plans about leaving England are more unsettled than ever. I anticipate no benefit from it, nor from anything else, but I am desirous of quitting England that I may lead even a more recluse life than I do at present, and emancipate myself from perpetual commiserations. . . .

It was ungracious, no doubt, but she was behaving stupidly, and for that he did not forgive her. He had suddenly outgrown her, in so far as she was able to torment him in the old way. But a dead fire is always a dismal sight. He was forming new enterprises. He had found it impossible to create the heat and colour of Alroy's Oriental background in the cool green light of Bradenham. Once again the itch for travel was on him. He must go to the East—to Constantinople —to Jerusalem. Until then, *Alroy* could not be completed.

He had consulted Mr. Austen about it. Not Mrs. Austen, any more. It was a man's head he wanted now, not a woman's sympathy; an older head, and a practical way out of his difficulties. He could not stir without money, of course. His father still had no idea of how involved he was, and was not intended to know. Ben held to his decision to solve it himself, but consulted Mr. Austen as a solicitor for a way to deal with his debts, and received much valuable advice and no lectures.

The book, the great book which would make his fortune, could not be finished without the additional investment of a tour of the East. The answer was to write another of the fashionable potboilers which his pen spun off so easily. He would hack for it. Most of his creditors would have to wait, but with another advance from Colburn on a new book he could get to Jerusalem and back. In the spring of 1830 he wrote *The Young Duke,* and Colburn gave him £500 for it in post-dated bills.

During the early summer he spent some time in Town, staying with Will Meredith who was going along again as travelling companion; making arrangements, seeing a few people. As always, his health improved with the prospect of change and exertion, and his spirits rose. Adventures. New clothes, new hopes, new friends again—above all, new friends, and above all of these, Edward Bulwer.

They had exchanged some correspondence months before while Ben was in retirement at Bradenham, when Bulwer's *Pelham* had been the novel of the year, to be followed by *Devereux,* another fashionable success. Bulwer, less than two years older, seemed to Ben to have achieved already an enviable career. He kept a splendid house in Hertford Street, gave brilliant dinners to literary and political celebrities. He had all the advantages of birth, looks, talent, and a beautiful Irish wife. Bulwer, with his English fairness, his light brown curls and exquisite dress, his famous friends, his background of ancestry and wealth, was the ideal hero of one of Ben's own novels. He had arrived.

What Ben did not know, among other things, was that while *Devereux* was worth £1,500 to Colburn in advance, the extravagant Hertford Street establishment cost £3,000 a year to run; that Bulwer had married against his mother's wishes, so that though she was wealthy he received almost nothing in the way of financial aid from her, and was sacrificing health and leisure to the driving need of money, always more money; that the lovely Rosina had no comprehension

of or interest in his work or his home, and wept because life
was not a perpetual courtship composed entirely of compliments and raptures, and quite without responsibilities. He
did not know, for Bulwer could not tell him, how Bulwer
envied him his freedom, his gaiety, his air of don't-give-a-
damn self-possession—Bulwer, the slave of his own stretched
nerves, hypersensitive, overworked, possessed by a still stormy
passion for his beautiful encumbrance, Rosina.

At Bulwer's dinners Ben heard a great deal about politics,
and the growing necessity for Reform. The Wellington Government, which had actually removed the Catholic disabilities, was nevertheless regarded as hopelessly reactionary in its
general policy. The results of Emancipation were not as
happy as had been expected. It had been received with the
most flagrant ingratitude by the Irish, who merely took advantage of their new privileges to launch further attacks on
the Protestants, and a wilder agitation for Repeal of the
Union, which was their ultimate goal. O'Connell's personal
influence had increased alarmingly, for he wielded a dangerous power—the gift of swaying a mass of people with picturesque words. An inheritance from an uncle had relieved
him of private financial pressure, so that he could devote
all his time to the cause he so violently espoused. He had
taken his seat at Westminster and was now using his cus-
tomary shocking language in support of Reform, which he
regarded as a necessary step to Repeal, uniting his dangerous
influence to that of the Whigs in Opposition.

Wellington was at war with the Press—always a mistake,
and a dreadful sign of weakness in a man who for years
had been regarded and had regarded himself as beyond the
reach of censure. The King's health had failed during the
past hard winter, and he was invisible in the dreary Lodge
at Windsor. His usual birthday festivities had been counter-
manded in April, which was frightening, but nobody seemed
to know anything really about him these days. Wellington
could deal with his caprices better than anyone, and the
Government had become virtually a regency ruled by the
Prime Minister. He was dubbed King Arthur, but not in a

friendly way. His main support, it was said, was in the draw-ing-rooms, and he had become the fashion with the ladies. He habitually snubbed the Duke of Clarence, who might reasonably expect to inherit the throne almost any day, and who displayed a natural interest in his brother's health and the Prime Minister's intentions.

Ben listened to all rumours and theories attentively, in Bulwer's drawing-room, absorbing the talk, almost regretting that he would not be in England during the coming sum-mer, which was bound to be exciting. Bulwer had announced his intention of standing for Parliament at the next elec-tion, and to Ben's amused astonishment insisted that his sympathies were with the Radicals and for Reform.

I I

Meanwhile the preparations for the journey were made, and they expected to be off late in May. Meredith, who was never in a hurry, was pensive. He found the prospect of losing sight of Sarah for so long a time more and more de-pressing as their departure drew nearer. She had become very necessary to his enjoyment of life. Laconic himself, he liked to hear Sarah's outspoken views. Unspectacular in his quiet University way, he admired her dark beauty and abounding spirits. He found her warm and intelligent and very alive and unself-consciously friendly—not like the prim chaperoned English misses whom he met in his mother's drawing-room. One could argue with her, taking the opposite side to urge her on. One could laugh with her, in some sur-prise, over non-drawing-room humour. It was a great pity that she was not going with them to Constantinople, they would miss her laughter on the journey. . . .

Meredith had stumbled into love.

Sarah at first was much amused, then touched. She saw what was happening, of course, long before he did; read his simple mind like a book, and found her own name on every page. She was not surprised when he proposed to her that spring. She knew the answer, and it was Yes. But she was not prepared for the complete capitulation their new intimacy wrought. She had been fond of him so long; not as fond as she was of Ben, of course, but—always so glad to see him. Before he asked her to marry him she knew that no other man would do, for her. But by the time the date of the departure for the East was set, she was a woman gloriously in love.

Something had happened to them, in those few weeks. Some deep racial reverence for her plighted troth awoke in her, and a blind joy in the mere presence of her master. She did not let him know. Not yet. She still made fun of him in the old way, disputed with him, mothered and sistered him. But there was something more; till Meredith, dazed with delight and always a little bewildered at her, perceived that he held in his arms a woman flamingly aware of him, and caught fire like tow.

The belatedness of their actual discovery of each other added to its miraculousness, and they faced the separation with a growing dread. Meredith wanted to chuck it. Sarah shook her head. He had promised Ben, who was counting on him, and he must go.

"But Ben can find someone else just as good!" he cried impatiently.

Sarah smiled at him.

"There is no one else just as good as you," she said. "I know that. So does Ben."

And after an interval—

"But he'd never want me to go on with it if he knew how I felt about it now!" he said.

"Then he mustn't know."

"Well, he ought to know! He knows we're engaged. Doesn't it occur to him that that might make a difference?"

"We told him it wouldn't, in the beginning."

"But surely—"

"We thought it wouldn't, ourselves," she reminded him. "We can't blame Ben. He's never felt like this himself."

"Perhaps—" Meredith reddened a little. "Perhaps somebody ought to explain it to him." He met her eyes and they both laughed, without embarrassment, and the clasp of his fingers tightened on hers.

"We can wait," she said. "We must. He'll get well out there in the heat, with you. Bring him back well. I'll still be here."

He was inclined to argue, but he saw it at last. To desert Ben now might be to thrust him back into that state of mind where he lay on a sofa with a headache and read impossible books, and would not eat, and could not sleep; uncomplaining (which was not like him), inert, without ambition, *flat*. They could not do that to him. He must have this tour he had set his heart on, and it must be Meredith who went with him, because Meredith could look after him best.

"You mustn't be jealous of Ben," said Sarah gravely to his protests. "He was here first. I should feel—traitorous and mean if I stole his holiday."

"It will be months," he warned her.

"A year, he says."

"No—Sarah, darling, I can't face it!"

"Do you think I want to lose either one of you for so long?" she cried. "But promise me not to drag him back too soon. Promise to give him time to find himself again. Besides—you always meant to make the Grand Tour before you settled down, and this will take only a little longer. You'll enjoy yourself," said Sarah bravely, "once you're across the Channel. It's only saying good-bye that looks so hard."

"And you?"

"Oh, I shall manage. I'm going to do big things with the garden this year; it's been neglected. And father needs help with the eternal Charles—it saves his eyes if I read aloud to him. And I shall have lots of letters from my travellers—I hope."

"By every boat!" He kissed her hands. "He'll know, some day, what this costs us."

"I hope not," she murmured. "Let him be happy. A year of my life is not too much to give—to make Ben happy."

And so Ben and his brother-in-law-to-be left London on the last day of May on a steamer bound for Falmouth, and after a week's delay there, sailed by mail packet to Gibraltar.

Ben was not the ignorant babe nor the selfish invalid he might seem. He was genuinely pleased that if Sa had to marry somebody it should be only old Meredith, and not some embarrassing stranger to the family circle. Now that Meredith was indeed one of the family it was more than ever natural that he should be the one to make the Eastern tour. Ralph and Jem were both still at school, and his father had not the strength nor the leisure for such extended travel. And though Ben himself never left Sa behind without almost a lover's pang, it hardly occurred to him to stay at home on that account, or to encourage Meredith to do so.

A few months away—long enough to escape the winter— and when they returned, bringing her gifts and stories doubly amusing for the two of them, there would be a large, exciting wedding at Bradenham, with the villagers bobbing and smiling round the church door, and Sa looking very beautiful and happy on old Meredith's arm. . . .

I I I

Gibraltar,
July 1, 1830.

My dear Father,

I write to you from a country where the hedges consist of aloes all in blossom; fourteen, sixteen feet high. Conceive the contrast to our beloved and beechy Bucks. I say nothing of geraniums and myrtles, bowers of oranges and woods of olives, though the occasional palm should not be forgotten for its great novelty and uncommon grace.

This Rock is a wonderful place, with a population infinitely diversified. Moors with costumes radiant as a rainbow or an Eastern melodrama; Jews with gaberdines and skullcaps; Genoese, Highlanders, and Spaniards, whose dress is as picturesque as that of the sons of Ivor. There are two public libraries—the Garrison library, with more than 12,000 volumes; and the Merchants', with upwards of half that number. In the Garrison are all your works, even the

last edition of the *Literary Character;* in the Merchants'
the greater part. Each possesses a copy of another book,
supposed to be written by a member of our family, and
which is looked upon at Gibraltar as one of the master-
pieces of the nineteenth century. You may feel their intel-
lectual pulse from this. At first I apologized and talked of
youthful blunders and all that, really being ashamed; but
finding them, to my astonishment, sincere, and fearing they
were stupid enough to adopt my last opinion, I shifted my
position just in time, looked very grand, and passed myself
off as a child of the Sun, like the Spaniard of Peru.

Tell my mother that as it is the fashion among the dandies of this place—that is, the officers, for there are no
others—not to wear waistcoats in the morning, her new
studs come into fine play, and maintain my reputation of
being a great judge of costume, to the admiration and envy
of many subalterns. I have also the fame of being the first
who ever passed the Straits with two canes, a morning and
an evening one. I change my canes as the gun fires, and owe
to them even more attention than to being the supposed
author of—what is it?—I forget! . . .

Granada,
August 1, 1830.

My dear Mother,

Although you doubtless assist, as the French phrase it,
at the reading of my despatches, you will, I am sure, be
pleased to receive one direct from your absent son. It has
just occurred to me that I have never yet mentioned the
Spanish ladies, and I do not think that I can address anything I have to say upon this agreeable subject to anyone
more suitable than yourself.

What we associate with the idea of female beauty is not
common in this country. There are none of those seraphic
countenances, which strike you dumb or blind, but faces
in abundance which will never pass without commanding
a pleasing glance. Their charm consists in their sensibility;
each incident, every person, every word touches the far eye
of the Spanish lady, and her features are constantly con-

futing the creed of Mahomet, and proving that she has a soul; but there is nothing quick, harsh, or forced about her. She is extremely unaffected, and not at all French. Her eyes gleam rather than sparkle, she speaks with vivacity but in sweet tones, and there is in all her carriage, particularly when she walks, a certain dignified grace which never leaves her, and which is very remarkable.

I sat next to a lady of high distinction at a bullfight at Seville. She was the daughter-in-law of the Captain-General, and the most beautiful Spaniard I have met yet. Her comb was white, and she wore a mantilla of blonde, I have no doubt extremely valuable, for it was very dirty. The effect, however, was charming. Her hair was glossy black, her eyes like an antelope's, but all her other features deliciously soft; and she was further adorned, which is rare in Spain, with a rosy cheek, for here our heroines are rather sallow. But they counteract this defect by never appearing until twilight, which calls them from their bowers fresh, though languid, from the late siesta. To conclude, the only fault of the Spanish beauty is that she too soon indulges in the magnificence of embonpoint. There are, however, exceptions to this. At seventeen, a Spanish beauty is poetical, tall, lithe, and clear, though sallow. As she advances, she resembles Juno rather than Venus. Majestic she ever is; and if her feet are less twinkling than in her first career, look on her hand and you'll forgive her all.

There is a calm voluptuousness about the life here that wonderfully accords with my disposition, so that if I were resident, and had my intellect at my command, I do not know any place where I could make it more productive. The imagination is ever at work, and beauty and grace are not scared away by those sounds and sights, those constant cares and changing feelings, which are the proud possession of our free land of eastern winds.

You rise at eight, and should breakfast lightly, although a table covered with all fruits renders that rather difficult to one who inherits, with other qualities good and bad, that passion for the most delightful productions of nature with which my beloved sire can sympathize. I only wish I had him here over a medley of grape and melon, gourd and prickly pear. In the morning you never quit the house, and these are hours which might be profitably employed under the inspiration of a climate which is itself poetry, for it sheds over everything a golden hue which does not exist in the objects themselves illuminated. At present I indulge only in a calm reverie, for I find the least exertion of mind instantly aggravates all my symptoms; and even this letter is an exertion, which you would hardly credit. My general health never was better. I have constantly ridden eight hours a day on horseback. I travelled through three successive nights and saw the sun set and rise, without quitting my saddle, which few men can say, yet I have never known fatigue. A feverish feeling, of which all travellers complain, I have not known for an instant, so extraordinary and so beneficial is the influence of this climate upon me, and so entirely does my frame sympathize with this expanding sun.

The Spanish cuisine is not much to my taste, for garlic and bad oil preponderate; but it has its points: the soups are good, and *the most agreeable dish* in the world is an olio. I will explain it to you, for my father would delight in it. There are two large dishes, one at each end of the table. The one at the top contains bouilli beef, boiled pork sausage, black-pudding; all these not mixed together but in their separate portions. The other dish is a medley of vegetables and fruits, generally French beans, caravanseras, slices of melons, and whole pears. Help each person to a portion of the meats, and then to the medley. Mix them in your plate together, and drown them in tomato sauce. There is no garlic or grease of any kind. I have eaten this every day, and it is truly delightful. The tomato sauce here is very light, piquant and pleasant. It is thin. We have it with us too thick and rich. The Spaniards eat the tomato in all possible ways. I obtained the recipe for one dish, which infinitely pleased me, and with which I think my father would be charmed. It is very simple. Take four pounds of tomatoes, fry them very small, add four eggs, yolk and all. Mix them well. They should be served up very dry, and indeed on the whole like a dry soup, but of a very pretty colour, I need not tell the mistress of so experienced a cuisine as you, to add a small quantity of onion in frying the tomatoes. . . .

Gibraltar,
August 9, 1830.

My dear Sa,

Did I dream six months ago of Andalusia, where I have spent some of the most agreeable hours of my existence? Such a trip! Such universal novelty and such unrivalled luck in all things!

This is the country for a national novelist. The al fresco life of the inhabitants induces a variety of the most picturesque manners; their semi-savageness makes each district retain with barbarous jealousy its own customs and its own costumes. A weak government resolves society into its original elements, and robbery becomes more honourable than war, inasmuch as the robber is paid, and the soldier is in arrear. Then a wonderful ecclesiastical establishment covers the land with a privileged class, who are perpetually producing some effect on society. I say nothing while writing these lines—which afterwards may be expanded into a picture—of their costume.

Oh, wonderful Spain! Think of this romantic land covered with Moorish ruins and full of Murillo! Ah, that I could describe to you the wonders of the painted temples of Seville! Ah, that I could wander with you amid the fantastic and imaginative halls of delicate Alhambra! Why, why cannot I convey to you more perfectly all that I see and feel? I thought that enthusiasm was dead within me and nothing could be new. I have hit perhaps on the only country which could have upset my theory—a country of which I have read little and thought nothing—a country of which indeed nothing has been of late written, and which few visit. I dare to say I am better. This last fortnight I have made regular progress, or rather felt the progress which I had already made. It is all the sun.

Write to me whenever you can, always to Malta, from whence I shall be sure to receive my letters sooner or later. If I receive twenty at a time, it does not signify; but write; do not let the chain of my domestic knowledge be broken for an instant. Write to me about Bradenham, about the dogs and horses, orchards, gardens, who calls, where you go, who my father sees in London, what is said. This is what I want. Never mind public news, except it be private in its knowledge, or about private friends. I see all the newspapers sooner or later. Keep on writing, but don't *bore* yourself. Mind this. A thousand thousand loves to all. Adieu, my beloved. We shall soon meet. There is no place like Bradenham, and each moment I feel better I want to come back. . . .

Malta,
August, 1830.

My dear Ralph,

Mashallah! Here I am sitting in an easy chair, with a Turkish pipe six feet long, with an amber mouthpiece and a porcelain bowl. What a revolution! But what if I tell you that I have not only become a smoker, but the greatest smoker in Malta. The fact is, I find it relieves my head. Barrow, who is a most knowing young lieutenant, has given me a meerschaum, and Anstruther a most splendid Dresden green china, set in silver—an extremely valuable pipe, but there is nothing like a meerschaum.

I forgot to say that we had a very rough and disagreeable voyage here, the wind—a devil of a levanter, and sometimes sirocco—full in our teeth half the time, and not going, even with the steam, more than four knots an hour. I maintained my character as a sailor, but was otherwise very unwell in my head. The sky was covered with clouds nearly the whole time. This is the only disagreeable weather we have had.

To our surprise we find James Clay here, and quite a hero. He has been here a month, and has beaten the whole garrison at rackets and billiards and other wicked games. Really he has turned out a most agreeable personage, and has led a life which for splendid adventure would beat any young gentleman's yet published in three vols. post 8vo.

On Wednesday morning I quit this place, in a yacht which Clay has hired, and in which he intends to turn pirate. The original plan was to have taken it together, but Meredith was averse to this and so we have become Clay's passengers at a fair rate, and he drops us whenever and wherever we like. You should see me in the costume of a Greek pirate. A blood-red shirt, with silver studs as big as shillings, an immense scarf for a girdle, full of pistols and daggers, red cap, red slippers, broad blue-striped jacket and trousers. We shall touch at Corfu on purpose to get the letters which will come out by this packet. All letters must be sent on to Corfu; I will enclose a direction. This is the last regular letter you will receive, perhaps the very last in direct answer; but do not on any account cease to write every packet, in order that the chain may never be broken, and that I may not return with the feelings of a stranger.

Our yacht is of fifty-five tons, an excellent size for these seas, with a crew of seven men. She is a very strong sea-boat and bears the unpoetical title of "Susan," which is a bore; but as we can't alter it, we have painted it out. And now, my dear boy, adieu. I enclose a letter to Sa. . . .

Corfu,
October 10, 1830.

My dear Father,

We had a stormy but not disagreeable passage here. I like a sailor's life much, though it destroys the toilette and one never feels, or is indeed, clean. This, though a poor village, is a most lovely island, offering all that you can expect from Grecian scenery, gleaming waters, woody isles, cypress, olive, vine, a clear sky, and a warm sun.

I am disappointed in entering Albania, for the whole country is in a state of insurrection. One of the rebel beys, of Velona, arrived here a fugitive the day before us, with many rich pipes and pistols, but without his women, he fled in such haste.

I continue much the same, still infirm, but no longer destitute of hope. I wander in pursuit of health, like the immortal exile in pursuit of that lost shore, which is now almost glittering in my sight. Five years of my life have been wasted, and sometimes I think my pilgrimage may be as long as that of Ulysses. . . .

Athens,
November 30, 1830.

My dearest Father,

I sit down before we sail from the harbour of the Piraeus to let you know that I am still in existence. We sailed from Prevesa through the remaining Ionian Islands among which was Zante, pre-eminent in beauty; indeed, they say none of the Cyclades is to be compared with it, with its olive trees touching the waves, and its shores undulating in every possible variety. For about a fortnight we were forever sailing on a summer sea, always within two or three miles of the coast, and touching at every island or harbour that invited. A cloudless sky, a summer atmosphere, and sunsets like the neck of a dove, completed all the enjoyment which I anticipated from roving on a Grecian sea. We were, however, obliged to keep a sharp look-out for pirates, who are all about again. We exercised the crew every day with muskets, and their increasing prowess and our pistol practice kept up our courage.

We sailed round the coast of the Morea, visiting Navarino (which has become quite a little French town with cafés and billiard-tables), Modon, and Napoli. From Napoli we had a very quiet passage to this place. November here has been warmer than our best English summers, but this is unusual. Never was such a season, all agree. On the afternoon of our arrival in Piraeus, which is about five miles from the city, I climbed a small hill, forming the side of the harbour. From it I looked upon an immense plain, covered with olive woods and skirted by mountains. Some isolated hills rise at a distance from the bounding range. On one of these I gazed upon a magnificent temple, bathed in the sunset; at the foot of the hill was a walled city of considerable dimensions, in front of which a Doric temple, apparently quite perfect. The violet sunset—and today the tint was particularly vivid—threw over this scene a colouring becoming in its beauty, and if possible increasing its delicate character. The city was Athens; but independent of all reminiscences, I never witnessed anything so truly beautiful, and I have seen a good deal.

We have just returned from an excursion into the country to Marathon, and I can give you no idea of the severe hardship and privation of present Grecian travel. Happy are we to get a shed for nightly shelter, and never have been fortunate enough to find one not swarming with vermin. My sufferings in this way are great, and so are poor Clay's, but Meredith escapes. Our food must not be quarrelled with, for we lived for a week on the wild boar of Pentelicus and the honey of Hymettus, both very good; but I do not care for privation in this respect, as I have always got my pipe; but the want of sleep—and literally I did not sleep a wink the whole time I was out—is very bad, as it unfits you for daily exertion. We found a wild boar just killed at a little village, and purchased half of it, but it was not as good as Bradenham pork.

It is near sunset, and Constantinople is in full sight; it baffles all description, though so often described. An immense mass of buildings, cupolas, cypress groves, and minarets. I feel an excitement which I thought was dead. . . .

Constantinople,
January 11, 1831.

My dearest Father,

I have been silent because it is possible to write too frequently, which prevents you giving any results, or occasions you giving the wrong ones. In the first place, I can give a favourable bulletin of my health, which continues improving; in fact, I hope that the early spring will return me to Bradenham in a very different plight to that in which I left it. I can assure you that I sigh to return, though in very agreeable company; but I have seen and done enough in this way, and a mingled picture of domestic enjoyment and fresh butter, from both of which I have been so long estranged, daily flits across my fancy. Meredith quitted us, to our great regret, a fortnight ago, as he had always intended, and is now wandering among the Bithynian mountains, which are remarkable for being more devoid of interest than any hills in existence. We anticipate meeting him at Smyrna, and if so may probably find him not disinclined to renounce his ambitious intentions of being a discoverer.

Since Meredith's departure, in consequence of an unfavourable change in the weather, we have left our ship and taken comfortable lodgings in Pera. H. E. has given us a general dinner invitation, so that if we wish to dine with him, we only send to the Palace in the morning. He has introduced us to all the other ambassadors, and invites us to every picnic, here a favourite expedition. We visited in his suite the other day the Seven Towers, which are never shown, probably because there is nothing to see. A more amusing affair was the departure of the Mecca caravan from Scutari, the Asiatic suburb. We were entertained here by one of the ministers very sumptuously, smoked out of pipes with diamond mouthpieces, and sipped coffee perfumed with roses in cups studded with precious stones. . . .

We have seen the Sultan several times. He affects the affable activity of a European prince, mixes with his subjects, interferes in all their pursuits, and taxes them most unmercifully. He dresses like a European, and all the young men have adopted the fashion. You see young Turks in uniforms which would not disgrace one of our crack cavalry regiments, and lounging with all the bitterness of royal illegitimates. It is on the rising generation that the Sultan depends, and if one may form an opinion, not in vain.

I must return, if only to save you from reading these

stupid letters. I expect in ten days' time to be in Egypt, as the wind is most favourable. From that country I shall return to Malta and then to Naples; at least these are my plans, which may probably not be executed. I wish to get back for Bradenham sports, but very much fear I shall not, unless I can somehow or other shuffle quarantine, which is a month or six weeks from these awful parts. *Esperons!* Kiss my mother and Sa—tell my dearest Sa I shall soon have her letters. . . .

Alexandria,
March 20, 1831.

My dearest Sa,

Here I am at last in the ancient land of priestcraft and of Pyramids, about which I must at present say little. It is so long since I have written, although I miss no reasonable opportunity of so doing, that I almost forget what I was about when I wrote to you last—I think on the eve of my departure from Constantinople, Meredith having already departed for his exploration of Asia Minor, respecting which he was very mad, although I believe it to be a country equally satisfactory to the topographer, the antiquarian, and the man of taste.

From Jaffa, a party of six, well mounted and armed, we departed for Jerusalem, and commenced our journey over the delightful plain, bounded in the distance by the severe and savage mountains of Judea. In the wild stony ravines of these shaggy rocks we were wandering the whole day; at length after crossing a vast hill, we saw the Holy City. I will describe it to you from the Mount of Olives. This is a very high hill, still partially covered with the tree which gives it a name. Jerusalem is situate upon an opposite height, which descends as a steep ravine, and forms, with the assistance of the Mount of Olives, the narrow valley of Jehoshaphat. Jerusalem is entirely surrounded by an old feudal wall, with towers and gates of the time of the Crusaders, and in perfect preservation; as the town is built upon a hill, you can from the opposite height discern the roof of almost every house. In the front is the magnificent mosque built upon the site of the Temple, with its beautiful gardens and fantastic gates; a variety of domes and towers rise in all directions; the houses are of a bright stone. I was thunderstruck. I saw before me apparently a gorgeous city. Nothing can be conceived more wild, and terrible, and barren, than the surrounding scenery, dark, stony, and severe; but the ground is thrown about in such picturesque undulations that, the mind full of the sublime, not the beautiful, rich and waving woods and sparkling cultivation would be misplaced. The city on the other side is in the plain, the ravine not being all round. It is, as it were, in a bowl of mountains. I have dotted down materials for description; I have not space to describe. I leave it to your lively imagination to fill up the rest. Except Athens, I never saw anything more essentially striking; no city, except that, whose site was so pre-eminently impressive.

God bless you all! I am afraid you will never get this as I am out of the bounds of regular posts, ambassadors, and public offices. . . .

Cairo,
May 28, 1831.

My dear Sa,

I have received all your delightful letters, March packet inclusive, and one from Ralph, for which give him my warmest thanks. I am waiting here for a ship to convey me to Malta, and in all probability will come home straight, but at any rate if I arrive overland it shall delay me very little. Meredith is now at Thebes, and I have no means of communicating with him. If he kept to his plans he will return in a few days to this place, but I fear he may be tempted to advance higher. I cannot convey in writing all the considerations which occur to me, but my impression is that three or four weeks may elapse before I sail from Alexandria, and that therefore it is pretty certain that he will have returned to Cairo and will depart with me.

This is a very inelegant epistle, but I am writing it at night with at least fifty mosquitoes buzzing about and

biting me in all directions, which destroys sentences. Clay
has got an intermittent fever, which in itself is bad enough,
and as he has never been ill before in his life he is exceedingly frightened. Luckily here is a very good French phy-
sician. I rather imagine he will go off in a day or two to
Rosetta for a change of air. I am very well indeed, and find
the climate of Egypt delicious, very hot, but always a most
refreshing breeze.

I am very sorry about my companion, as he has been to
me a highly agreeable one. I owe much to his constant
attentions. You know that, though I like to be at my ease,
I want energy in those little affairs of which life largely
consists. Here I found Clay always ready; in short, he saved
me from much bore. I am sorry to say that his faithful
servant Giovanni, better known by the name of Tita (he
was Byron's chasseur of renown), who is a Belzoni in appearance and constitution, is also very ill, which is a great
affliction. Thus you see the strong men have all fallen, while
I, who am the habitual invalid, am firm on my legs; but
the reason is this, that I, being somewhat indolent and
feeble, live *à la Turque,* while Clay and Tita are always in
action, have done nothing but shoot and swim from morning till night.

As I am on the subject of domestic troubles, you will
hear with regret that my favourite servant, a Greek of
Cyprus, gave me warning yesterday, his father being very
ill at Alexandria. He leaves me directly, which is a great
bore at this moment, especially as I am about to be alone,
and would annoy me at all times because he wore a Mame-
luke dress of crimson and gold, with a white turban thirty
yards long, and a sabre glittering like a rainbow. I must
now content myself with an Arab attendant in a blue shirt
and slipperless. How are the mighty fallen!

I cannot sufficiently commend your letters; they are in
every respect charming, lively, and witty, and full exactly
of the stuff I want. Tell Ralph to write as often and as
much as he likes, and that I have become a most accomplished smoker, carrying that luxurious art to a pitch of

refinement of which he has no idea. My pipe is cooled in a wet silken bag, my coffee is boiled with spices, and I finish my last chibouque with a sherbet of pomegranate. Oh, the delicious fruits that we have here and in Syria! Orange gardens miles in extent, citron, limes, pomegranates; but the most delicious thing in the world is a banana, which is richer than a pineapple.

This Cairo, in spite of its dinginess, is a luxurious and pleasant place. The more I see of Oriental life the more I like it. . . .

Cairo,

July 20, 1831.

My dearest Father,

If you were not a great philosopher as well as a good man, I do not think that I could summon courage to communicate to you the terrible intelligence which is now to be communicated by this trembling pen; but I have such confidence in your wisdom that it is your assistance to which I look in the saddest office that has ever yet developed upon me.

You have already guessed the fatal truth—Meredith is lost to us. It is too terrible to believe. I would willingly have given my life for his. The anguish of my soul is great. Our innocent lamb, our angel is stricken. Save her, comfort her. I will come home directly. I wish to live only for my sister. I think of her day and night. It is some satisfaction that I was with him to the last. Oh, my father, I trust a great deal to you and my dear mother. I do not know what to write, what to think. I have not said anything that I wanted, yet I have said too much. . . .

My own Sa,

Ere you open this page, our beloved father will have imparted to you with all the tenderness of parental love the terrible news which I have scarcely found strength to communicate to him. It is true. Our friend of many years, our hope, our joy, and consolation is lost to us forever. Oh, my sister, in this hour of overwhelming affliction my

thoughts are only for you. I have no wife, I have no be-
trothed; nor since I have been better acquainted with my
own mind and temper have I sought them. Live, then, my
heart's treasure, for one who has ever loved you with a
surpassing love, and who would cheerfully have yielded
his own existence to save you the bitterness of this letter. . . .

Meredith had died of small-pox at Cairo on the eve of
sailing for England.

IV

Autumn had come early to Buckinghamshire, and the
leaves of the Bradenham beeches were falling. Isaac sat at his
desk in the library in the dull afternoon light, his pen travelling steadily across the page. From his chair, which faced the
long windows with the desk between, he could look down
the sweep of lawn which lay between the yew-clad hillside
and the lower terrace with its last draggled dahlias and bare
rose bushes. The fine turf was wet and green under a grey
sky. There was the drowsy afterdrip of rain from the eaves.

A comfortable fire glowed in the white marble and tiled
fireplace of Isaac's sanctum. The chintzes were gay and new,
and there was a large new sofa drawn up to the hearth. But
it was the same desk and ancient armchair, the same books
and many more, the same rickety little ladder, and thumbed
dictionary on its iron stand. So far as he could, Isaac had
brought Bloomsbury with him into the country, and he felt
cosy and at home in the midst of all his old possessions, and
not at all uprooted as Sarah and her mother had feared he
might. The volumes which surrounded him made his world.
Where they were, he was content. So long as the same chair
with the same flat cushion fitted into the same knee-hole
desk he was comfortable, and his thoughts flowed undis-
turbed off the tip of his pen.

The last volume of *Charles I* had been published earlier
in the year, and he had begun a commentary on the history
of the Jewish race. ". . . The Jewish people are not a na-

tion, for they consist of many nations: they are Spanish, or Portuguese, German, and Polish, they are Italian, English, and French; and like the chameleon, they reflect the colour of the spot they rest on. The people of Israel are like water running through vast countries, tinged in their course with all the varieties of the soil where they deposit themselves. After a few generations, the Hebrews assimilate with the character and are absorbed by the feelings of the nation where they become natives. . . ."

It lay very near his heart, it was a thing he was tremendously anxious to get into words, this one-ness of himself and his children with the land of his father's adoption, his own birthplace, where his home had always been, and where the roots of his children's lives were as firmly fixed as though Disraelis had always been English and never Italian. His own father had been born at Cento, barely a hundred years ago. But now Italy was a foreign country, and there remained in the third generation no faintest nostalgia for Ferrara—except perhaps in Ben's passionate craving for heat, his lizard-like languor and baskings in hot sunlight. Odd, that single, vestigial trait in a person otherwise so Anglophile. ". . . It is evident that the Jews, for every protecting government, become the most zealous patriots. I do not know that their patriotism springs from the most elevated source—it lies more level with common feelings, but it will never dry. The Hebrew identifies his interests with those of the country; its wealth is his wealth; its victories secure his prosperity. Every native Jew, as a political being, becomes distinct from the Jew of any other nation. The Hebrew adopts the hostilities and alliances of the land where he was born—he calls himself by the name of his country. . . ."

"Isaac—isn't Sarah here with you?"

He turned guiltily, with a glance at the sofa, which was empty, and then at Maria in the doorway.

"She was here a minute ago—"

"Oh, Isaac, I'm used to your ways, God knows, but you might have spared a thought for your poor girl at a time like this!"

"But I did," protested Isaac, unable to protect himself
from appearances. "We were talking—saying it was almost
time for the carriage—only a few minutes ago." He looked at
his watch. "It's after four. No doubt she'll come back soon."

"More likely she's gone to her room and locked herself in,
the way she does now." Maria came on into the library,
closing the door behind her, and sat down on the sofa. Ordi-
narily Isaac's privacy was never so invaded, but Ben was due
back today, and no household rules could hold out against
that. "I sent off the carriage hours ago, to meet the mail-
coach," she said, and her voice broke a little on the commonplace words, "and the luggage cart as well. Ben always
has as many trunks as a prima donna. Heaven knows what
it will be like this time." She was fumbling helplessly now
for her handkerchief. "Oh, if only he hadn't gone to Cairo
perhaps poor Mr. Meredith needn't have died! It was a crazy
place to go to—I always said so—" She was crying again.

"Now, now, Maria, you'll only make things worse like
that—"

"Where is the sense of so much travelling?" wept Maria.
"Three times abroad before he is thirty! It is wanderlust!
You should have said No, Isaac. But you never could say No
to Ben—"

"Now, now—" Isaac laid down his pen and went to pat her
shoulder. They had been over it all again and again.

"It was against nature," said Maria, and blew her nose,
"for a young man to get engaged to a fine girl like our Sarah
and then go jaunting off to heathen places for a whole year
with Ben! I wonder Sarah stood for it in the first place—"

"You were the first to say that Ben was too ill to travel
alone," he reminded her. "It was very generous of Sarah to
lend her young man for such a long time, I agree—but she'd
cut off her right hand for Ben any day."

"Oh, Isaac, don't say such things! I suppose he will know
how to manage her—I'm sure I'm at my wits' end what to
do—"

Upstairs, in the room Ben had chosen for her, which faced
down the drive and across the village green, Sarah sat alone,

knitting, absorbed in the silent counting of her stitches, her black poplin skirts rebuking the frivolous chintz of the sofa beneath them. Above the unrelieved mourning her face bent white and calm over her busy needles; the click of those needles was as steady and passionless as the ticking of the clock on the mantel. Knit two, purl one, knit two, thread over—knit two, purl one, knit two, thread over. . . .

This was the day she had dreaded so, when Ben would come home—alone. Each hour of it stretched before her, a perilous desert of dull pain to be passed through stoically, wrapped in this blessed numbness, the precious, beleaguered state of stony calm in which she had contrived to exist for weeks, since the news came. Ben's arrival today threatened to wrench her out of it into awareness. Ben always brought one sharply into focus. The sight of him, so dear, so vital, so— *alive*—and now full of understanding and pity, would sharpen the precarious absence of sensation into agony, and for weeks she had felt nothing but a sort of emptiness.

It was unthinkable, not to want Ben back. But when he came she was going to realize for the first time exactly what had happened in Cairo, and she couldn't face that—not yet. Knit two, purl one, knit two, thread over. . . .

There was the sound of horses' feet—a carriage was turning in at the gate. She rose, holding her breath, to look out of the window. Yes, that was Ben, even though she could not see him beneath the hood of the carriage, and behind him, his retinue of luggage, corded boxes piled high in the cart, odd parcels and queer, tied-up bundles—enough luggage for two men. . . . She sank back against the cushions, clutching her knitting in fingers gone cold and damp. No, no, she must not do this, this was giving way, in a moment she would break down. Desperately she fought for the control she had kept so long. Methodically, she set the points of the needles together again and slipped a loop from one to the other—go on knitting—just a few moments—just to steady herself—just till he was out of the carriage—there was plenty of time—just a few minutes more, of peace—of numbness—knit two, purl one, knit two, thread over—knit two, purl one. . . .

V

Anyone less travel-stained than the young man in the
Bradenham carriage would be difficult to imagine. His clothes
appeared to have come out of a band-box rather than a trunk,
and his clear, tanned pallor was healthy and becoming. He
was, in fact, a symphony in brown; a wide brown cloak with
a fawn-coloured lining, and a high brown hat; a brown tail
coat with a lining of the same shade, and very dark brown
trousers, strapped under the instep of a slender, polished
boot; a gold brocade waistcoat, the heavy gold chain round
his neck following his watch into the waistcoat pocket on the
left side; linen white as driven snow, with a low, Byronic
collar and black ribbon tie; fawn-coloured gloves. A dandy
of dandies, clean, immaculate, and bright-eyed, untouched by
fatigue and uncrumpled by thirty miles of jolting travel over
November roads from London. It was a secret of his own,
compounded of luck, bodily relaxation, money and time
freely spent, and the anxious devotion of a tireless valet.

Beside him sat an apparition. Its dress had elements of the
Venetian gondolier, only slightly modified by service in the
Albanian army, a position as *chasseur* throughout the Eastern tour, and by an English autumn, which had added a large
woollen scarf tied round his neck under one ear. His black
beard and enormous mustachios were unimpaired by all these
vicissitudes. He was believed to have stabbed two or three
people in his time, and was the most good-natured-looking
man Shelley ever saw. Byron's Tita had adopted the picturesque young Mr. Disraeli like a large benevolent dog
when Clay had no further need of him—and like a dog he
shook and shivered now in the November chill.

They had traversed the last two miles from High Wycombe
to Bradenham almost in silence—Tita to keep his teeth from
chattering, and Ben because his thoughts had flown on ahead
to Sa. Whichever way you looked at it, this afternoon was
going to be a dreadful business. Sa would cry, and he always
found that hard to bear; he usually wanted to cry too, if she

began. Probably they would both break down. It was really not to be contemplated.

England was not at its best today, but he beheld its sombre green and grey with affection. It was good to be home. He had been pushing the boat all the way. The delay in quarantine had nearly sent him mad. He longed for the stillness and peace of Bradenham after those hot horrible days in Cairo, with Meredith's life slipping through his fingers—and then the awful desolation of the long journey homeward, where every hour stood empty with the loss of his friend. The first meeting with Sa was a thing to be got over as quickly as possible, and then life could settle into its dear, accustomed ways. Sa must not be allowed to grieve. He had come back with work to do, and she must be coaxed into working with him, he needed her loyal support and understanding more than ever now. Through Bulwer's letters, and through periodic batches of newspapers from Paris during his tour he had kept in touch with the increasing political tension at home, and watched the march of this disturbance called Reform with a growing excitement and apprehension. He was arriving home with a new ambition, and a new grip on England.

The carriage turned into the lane which linked Bradenham village to the West Wycombe-Princes Risborough Road, and now the village itself lay under his affectionate eyes, with its blunt grey church tower, the dark yews growing in terraces behind the green, which was fringed with cottages. Beyond the manor house lay the Chilterns in their gentle wooded ridges. It was like a scene on canvas, almost too precisely painted—the essence, the distilled spirit of England. His throat closed as he beheld it.

And now the wheels were on the cobbled way which led from the green to the house—the lovely iron-work gates stood open to receive him—the rosy bricks of the house itself he saw through a blur. He was home.

Tita's uncontrollable excitement invaded his private emotion. Yes, this was it. Yes, it was indeed a lovely house. Yes, of course they were expected. He leaped out as the carriage stopped, calling to Tita to follow with the luggage, and swept into the hall in a swirl of brown cloak. Where was every-body? Instinctively he made for the library, and met Isaac and Maria on the threshold, on their way to him.

"Not a soul at the foot of the staircase to greet me!" he reproached them, and received his mother on his bosom with a fervid embrace.

"My boy—my eldest son—my tall one—safe home again—" Maria was babbling.

"Quite safe, darling, so don't cry, for heaven's sake!" His other hand found Isaac's behind Maria's back while she still clutched him convulsively. "Where's Sa?"

There was a silence. He looked from Isaac's grave face to his mother, and back again. Isaac seemed to have no words. Maria gulped and raised her head from his bosom, tears of joy shining on her cheeks.

"Oh, Ben, it's been terrible since the news came. I know I am a foolish woman and cry too much—but Sarah never cries at all!"

"Poor old girl, I must see her at once—"

"It will be a shock," said Isaac. "She is greatly changed."

"As bad as that?" Their voices had sunk, as though some-one in the house was dangerously ill.

"She will be ill," moaned Maria. "She is like someone dead herself. She must get relief somehow—she must break down—"

"Very well," he said a little grimly. "I shall tell her how he died."

"Was it so horrible?" quavered Maria.

"No. It was beautiful."

"We've been afraid to speak of him—" Maria's hands beat helplessly on his sleeve. "And the poor man's name has not passed her lips since—"

"Then that's the trouble," said Ben firmly. "We must speak of him—yes, as though he might return any day. I pre-fer to think of him that way. I shall mention him at every opportunity, exactly as though nothing had happened. I'll go up to her at once."

Isaac and Maria looked at each other across him. They had known all along that Ben would tell them what to do. This was unexpected, and it seemed very drastic, but he must be right. They accepted it without further question, and while they looked at him gratefully, so sure that he would be right where they had failed, he turned with a reassuring smile for each of them, his brown cloak sweeping from his shoulders—tall, handsome, fashionable, graceful—their splendid son. They followed him anxiously through the little parlour toward the hall and the stairway.

"Now, just you leave this to me, I'll have her down for dinner, somehow," he was saying over his shoulder, and broke off with an exclamation. "Oh, heaven, I forgot! Tita, I'm frightfully sorry, I forgot all about you!"

The little procession of three had reached the hall where a fire burned in one of the two big fireplaces. In front of it, bent as close as he could get, his hands outstretched to the blaze, was the Venetian. As they approached he straightened his superb bulk, smiling and hopeful of his welcome. He had followed this insouciant young man half across the world, and his simple soul knew no mistrust of the two who had begot him. Mr. Disraeli had said there would be a place for him at Bradenham. He stood forward to claim it, humbly, but without misgiving. No Disraeli, he was sure, could be anything but gracious to him, who had known Lord Byron.

"Mother, this is Giovanni Falcieri—better known as Tita. Lord Byron died in his arms. We found him at Malta at a loose end, and since then he has been everywhere with us—done everything for us."

Isaac and Maria were staring, stunned. Then Tita spoke, with diffidence, two bows, and his radiant smile.

"Meester Disraeli does not tell quite all," he said, his eyes on Isaac's face. "When they find me at Malta I am—" He spread empty hands. "—starving. Nobody hires my memories, till them."

"That's very well put," said Isaac, much touched. "Very well put indeed. I assure you that memories of Byron will always have a home in this house."

Ben slid an arm around his mother, who was still gazing, paralyzed, at this flamboyant addition to her household.

"Mother, it was a long cold way from London, and Tita is not accustomed to this foul English climate. All the way down in the coach he was shivering—positively shaking! If you could find something hot for him to eat—and perhaps a nice glass of wine—and then he will help with the luggage."

"Ah, yes, the poor man!" Maria was all sympathy, and sure of her ground now, her awe lost in her solicitude. "No doubt he is not dressed for this cold—*underneath*. Just you come along with me, my good man, we'll go down to the kitchen and see what there is—"

There was a pleasant bustle of hospitality. He left his mother fussing happily over one more chick to cosset while his father looked on with questions about Byron bubbling up inside him, and turned again toward the staircase, his smile fading as he went. It was not going to be easy—to speak of Meredith as though nothing had happened.

V I

Up the broad, worn, slippery stairs two at a time he went lightly, his cloak swinging wide behind him. His eyes swept the sitting-room lovingly—their two opposite doors had always stood open across it. To get to her you crossed a little dressing-room where she kept her own books and her sewing and her writing-desk. It was empty now, and the door which led out of it to her bedroom was closed. Of course. The fire was in there. But he was breathing rather quickly as he tapped, opened the further door, and looked in.

The room itself had not changed. Its wallpaper was still cheerful with a small garlanded pattern, the chintzes with their bright scattered bouquets were still gay. There were still fresh flowers from somewhere in a vase on her dressing-table, and a coal fire was burning cosily. The dear, familiar look of it enveloped him with a sense of homecoming his own four walls would not bring more strongly. Here was where his heart was.

She rose to meet him, and then stood, the knitting still in her hands—calm, and somehow smiling, but utterly remote. It had not occurred to him that she would wear mourning for a man she had not yet married. . . .

"Hello, Ben," she said.

"Sa, my darling—!" He reached for her in a sort of blind compassion, and the folds of his brown cloak fell about her. "My dearest girl—!"

She gave back nothing to his kiss, but stood rigid in his arms, withdrew as soon as she could, and seated herself again on the sofa, motioning him to a place beside her. He watched her silently a moment, his face drawn with pity. This was serious. This was worse than he could have believed. This was not Sa at all, it was some woman in a trance. His mother was right, one must break through somehow.

"It's good to see you at last, Ben," she was saying. "Did you have an easy voyage home?"

"The voyage wasn't bad, but I nearly lost my mind in quarantine," he answered, taking his matter-of-fact tone from her, and pausing to lay aside his cloak before he joined her on the sofa. "To be so near—and powerless to come another step. Tita saved my reason, I think. He taught me to play cards the way they do in the army—*his* army."

"You're looking very grand," she murmured, and dropped her eyes at once to her knitting, and the points of the needles began to move methodically. "Who is Tita?"

"But I wrote you about him. He was with Byron for years at Ravenna—Shelley was there too, can you imagine it? He valeted them both, and he has the most wonderful stories, all true. He was a gondolier before that, and after Byron's death he fought for the Greeks with the Albanian army. Clay found him at Malta, hungry and without a job, so we adopted him. Then Clay got that fever and decided to come home—so Tita adopted *me*."

"And you've brought him back with you?"

"Yes, he's downstairs. The Governor took to him like anything. I hoped for that, because Tita is capable of the most fanatical devotion. Meredith always swore that he had stabbed several people, but I've never been able to find any proof of that!" He rounded the end of the sofa with one of his quick, cat-sure movements, and sat beside her, his eyes on her face, wondering what was before him, to what lengths he would have to go, and how to come at her at all. Talk about Meredith—wear her down—make her think—reach her vivid imagination and turn the screw—yes, conjure up Meredith before her, relentlessly, alive and well and very much his University self, which had never ceased to amuse her. Bring home to her what she had lost of laughter and devotion. Don't let her shirk it, she must *feel* again. Make her think of Meredith, make her speak of him, and always, always turn the screw, until the tears came. Watching her narrowly, seeming to humour her wish for impersonal conversation, he went on talking. "Clay had already been at Malta a month when we arrived, and had beaten the whole garrison at billiards, and hence was a local favourite. To govern men you must either excel them in their accomplishments or despise them. Clay did one and I did the other, and we were equally popular! You see, from Malta to Smyrna there were three of us."

"On Clay's yacht," she nodded, above her busy needles. "You wrote us that."

"Then Meredith deserted us for a time. He said Clay and I were idle and frivolous—you know how Oxford used to come out on Meredith every now and then! Well, this was one of those times. He went off to some unheard-of cock-and-bull city in Asia Minor, while Clay and I went on to Jeru-salem. Meredith joined me again in Cairo, just before he was taken ill." He waited a moment, and then turned the screw. "It's a queer thing—small-pox was raging at Malta, and quarantine kept us out of Sicily entirely. But none of us caught it there. It was nearly a year later when poor old Meredith did come down with it, and there wasn't even an epidemic at Cairo."

"Ben, you're not—not showing your usual tact, are you." The click of the needles had not faltered, but her words came breathlessly, as though she was in pain. "I'd rather not talk about—that."

"I think that's rather heartless of you," he said, watching

her with a surgeon's eye, using words like a scalpel, probing, torturing, deliberately pressing on the wound, to bring her the relief of tears. "He wanted to talk about you, right up to the end. I don't think he knew he was going to die. He kept talking about seeing you again soon—he was homesick in the Egyptian heat for English woods and flowers. You remember how he loved the yew terrace here at Bradenham—"

"The garden didn't do well this year, it was too dry," she remarked quietly, above her busy needles. "You would have broken your heart over the roses."

"Sa, I want you to know." He leaned toward her, striving to penetrate the wall of icy commonplaceness she placed between them. "It wasn't an ugly death. He was quite himself. He would not have been—disfigured, if he had lived." He waited, watching her. She went on knitting as though she had not heard. His lips tightened, and he went at it again, flaying himself at the same time. "There was no last message, or—gasping for breath. He knew me, we smiled, and spoke of coming home before long—he seemed to doze—and was gone." He stopped again on the word, not quite trusting his voice. Sarah went on knitting. "Sa, my darling, in pity's name, if you are beyond comfort I am not! I have lost my dearest friend—I have had a desolate journey home—I would have died myself to spare you this loss! Forgive me for living when he is dead, and help me to bear my own grief by sharing yours with me!"

There was silence in the still, brightly furnished room. Another shower had come on outside, and a gust of wind blew fine rain against the window-pane, and Sarah thought of the first shovelful of dirt on the lid of a coffin. . . . Knit two, purl one. . . . Rain hissed on the red coals in the grate, the mantel clock whirred and struck the half hour. She could hear Ben breathing beside her, irregularly, with his own emotion . . . purl one, thread over, knit two. . . . The light was going, one would have to ring for lamps soon if no one brought them. The fire needed mending, Ben would feel the cold after so much sun in Egypt. . . . She had had a fire burning in his room all day, to take the empty feeling out of it. Ben was trying to get at her, about what had happened at Cairo. He was being very deep, poor Ben, no doubt very clever, but it was all wasted. When would they learn to let her alone . . . thread over, knit two, purl one. . . .

"I have nothing to share," she said, replying automatically to his last words. "My life is finished—just as completely as his is. I am twenty-nine, and love will not come again. I no longer feel gladness or pain. I eat and sleep and breathe —as is God's will. But there is nothing to go on with."

"Only me," he said.

"You will marry some day."

"I doubt it. I find women amusing, but not for long. You have always been my genius, my solace, my companion, my joy. Without you I am lost."

"I can do nothing for you now."

"But you can, Sa—you must! Listen to me—" He drew a long breath, and sat back against the cushions. No good so far. A new tack now, with the same end in view. "I'm going into politics, what do you think of that? The times are damnable. I want to *do* something. I have dilettanted long enough. I must get rooms in Town, and meet the right people—like Edward Bulwer. I must conquer London first, and then—"

"How are the debts, Ben?" she inquired without looking up.

"Still with me, I'm afraid!" he confessed. "I should be lonesome without them now! But I have begun two new books, and *The Young Duke* is selling well. I shall get into Parliament as soon as I can. You see, I've had letters from Edward Bulwer while I was away. He was elected last spring, and he says we are due for the most stirring times since 1688. This Reform question is likely to drive Wellington out of office any day."

"Why is Reform such a dreadful prospect?" she queried with an idle interest very unlike her usual intelligent grasp of things.

"Why, it will bring in tradesmen and manufacturers, against the landowners and the gentry!" he cried impatiently.

"We shall be governed by butchers and ironmongers! Your grocer may be your next representative in the House! It's unthinkable! It's revolution! I must *do* something."

"Singlehanded?" she murmured above the knitting.

"No." He seized his opportunity. "Always with you to help me, Sa. I must bring people here—you must come up to Town and charm them all. Because if there is an election soon, and Bulwer thinks there will be, I shall offer myself here at Wycombe. And I shall want friends."

"This is all very sudden, Ben." She was not at all swept away, and she had used to enter so eagerly into all his enterprises. "Are you a Whig or a Tory?"

"Neither." He brushed them both aside grandly. "My politics are described by one word, and that word is—England."

"But I thought you had to be one or the other. Of course there are Radicals."

"Yes, who knows, perhaps I shall have to start as a Radical, like Bulwer! I don't say I can stomach their ideas on Reform, for one thing—but Toryism is worn out and I cannot condescend to be a Whig!"

"How like you that sounds," she said, her head bent above the knitting. "Still the same Ben."

"I wish I could say the same of you."

She shook her head, never looking him in the face. For a few minutes she had thought he was forgetting her, she had breathed again, more easily. But now he was at her again, his eyes probing, raking her face—she could feel them through her own down-dropped lids; his voice caressing her, his arm along the back of the sofa inviting her to lean against his strength.

"It's no use, Ben. The fountain of life has dried up in me. I watch myself going through my days, and wonder who it is."

"Help me, Sa." It was a desperate appeal through her love for him. "*I* still need you, even if Meredith doesn't. *I* am still here, with my way to make in a stony world. Don't desert me!"

"You must find some good, pretty woman and marry her."

"God in heaven, Sa, I loathe good, pretty women, as no one knows better than you do! What in the name of common-sense would I do with a wife? It's you I want to back me up, as you always have done. Do you remember when the *Magnet* attacked *Vivian Grey* and I wanted to die? Do you remember how you sat with me that night, until the fire was out and dawn was showing between the curtains, patching up my shattered soul, and giving me the courage to face a world that had rolled me in the dust? You swore then never to desert me. You promised never, never to leave me to trudge on alone." Diffidently, against her preoccupation, feeling for words to reach her, he forced himself to lay bare his new and most secret ambition to be and to do. "Sa, I want to do splendid things—I want to be great—not almost great, but really the greatest! I want to be—" He groped for unscalable heights. "—Prime Minister! But not alone! Not without you!"

"Edward Bulwer will help you," she said, unmoved, taking refuge behind the first name that came to her. "He knows everybody. They say that marriage of his will never be a success. There are two children—or will be soon. What do you think of his wife, Ben? What's she like?"

"Very pretty. Very spoilt. I think a trifle mad."

"What a pity."

"Yes. Especially as he is still in love with her." Once more, with the most intimate appeal of all, his own future, he had failed to reach her. He felt drained, devitalized, before her dreadful self-possession. It was like beating against cold marble walls. He was exasperated, wrung with sympathy—and terrified. This could not go on. She might go mad—or die.

He rose, with careful nonchalance, and crossed the room to the window, staring out across the peaceful village. The children were all inside, on account of the weather, and lights were beginning to come on in the cottage windows. The fine rain was unceasing now, blurring the window-pane—or was it his own sight that blurred? He set his teeth, and after a moment spoke calmly, apparently at random.

"Tita is not resigned to the lack of flowers here in England. I tried to explain that they had gone earlier than usual this year and that they would come back. He is a great gardener. Even at Malta—" He saw his way again. He went on slowly, with his back to her, planting his sentences neatly like banderillas in her heart. "Even at Malta, Tita made a garden. You know, Sa, I'll never cease to be thankful that if poor old Meredith had to get small-pox he survived that Malta epidemic. It gave him one more year of glorious life. He did enjoy himself out there—you got that from his letters, I suppose."

"Yes." Only a thread of sound, but it set every nerve of his tingling. For once she had not parried. He dared not move, but his voice flowed on smoothly for fear she would notice that he had gained an inch in this ghastly tug-of-war between her will and his.

"Poor old Meredith was terrified that I would lose myself to a Spanish lady! In vain I assured him that I was an admirer of the blonde, and pointed out that Spanish ladies always lose their shape. No, he would regard them as a menace to my sacred British bachelorhood!"

"But you escaped them all, and came safe home to us." Off her guard with his lounging attitude against the window, released from the steady scrutiny of his eyes, she glanced up at him—met his gaze, so guileless and serene, across the room, and smiled at him.

Wondering, he smiled back, and drew a long slow breath of triumph. He had her now. It was only a matter of time. He saw his way clearly now. She had shown him the way, herself, unwittingly. Don't rush her—go on talking—Meredith alive, and amusing, and wrong-headed—Clay and the yacht named *Susan*—pirates—sunsets—stories, for a child—stories, with jokes to them—tales of his own prowess and dilemmas—give her nothing to resist, nothing to beat against, let her have it all her own way, and then take her unawares with one swift merciless turn of the screw. . . .

"Yes," he smiled, and perched on the arm of a chair near the window, his face in shadow while hers looked toward the fading light, "I've come back to you, my darling—but not for want of their trying!"

"And you even went to Granada," she continued gently, pleased to have turned him aside again, hoping that he saw at last that it was no use going on like that or expecting her to show a sorrow she could not even feel. "It must have been very beautiful there."

"It was. We went everywhere, and most of it was beautiful. We had the most wonderful adventures! Spain was full of bandits!"

"Heavens!" she murmured indulgently, and smiled again above her knitting.

"We rode armed to the teeth, in Spain. Very uncomfortable, that was! And Albania was full of wars!"

"More than one war?"

"Dozens! There was a time when I thought of joining the Turkish army, so we went to Corfu. That was sheer *Arabian Nights!* By the time we got there the Grand Vizier had decapitated half the province, and the so-called war had dwindled till it was known as an insurrection. The Governor at Arta gave us a letter, and we went into the interior. Did Meredith write you about the half-way house at Yanina?" He rocked on the arm of the chair with reminiscent laughter, and hurried on, weaving his relentless magic of words. "My God, what a night that was! The place was really a sort of military post, in charge of a young bey who was perfectly charming and spoke no known language. Even Tita's Greek was no good to us there, the bey knew just enough to misunderstand everything Tita said. We'd had a horrible ride through the mountains, and we were dying of hunger. Our host talked all the time, with the most graceful pantomime, mostly about his pistols and ours. We sat in an amiable row and smoked, for what seemed like *hours*—and finally Clay thought that if we gave the bey some of the brandy we carried with us it might act as a hint for a meal to follow. We drank it out of coffee cups. On empty stomachs, mind you! The bey asked for more. We all became extremely gay. Meredith began to hiccough, and we all got a little hysterical. And then, just when we had given up hope, supper arrived, and to our horror it was accompanied by—*wine!*"

For the first time her knitting had dropped to her lap, and she was watching him as she used to do, smiling a little, her eyes adoring his brilliance and his good looks. He was able to pity her more than ever now, for he knew that he had her, and he flung himself into the story, calling on all his wit and all his charm for her undoing and her salvation.

"We ate, we drank wine—we ate with our fingers, we drank in a manner I never recollect! The wine wasn't bad, but if it had been poison we must drink it. We quaffed it in rivers. Then the bey asked for more brandy. He drank most of it. We emptied the bottle. The room turned round. The attendants seemed to be dancing. The bey shook hands with me again and again—he shouted what he thought was English—I invented wonderful Greek. 'Very good,' he would say, having caught it from Tita. 'Kalo, kalo,' I would reply. He roared—I smacked him on the back—we were terribly witty! Meredith upset his wine and giggled at it like a girl, and that's the last I remember until in the middle of the night I awoke and found myself on the divan rolled up in the sacred carpet. I had a thirst like nothing on earth—and found a flagon of water and drank about a gallon. Then I sat and stared round that never-to-be-forgotten room in the light of a dying fire. Meredith had reeled to the hearth before falling flat on his face. Clay was snoring in two-four time with his head *under* a cushion. The bey was—indescribable. I thought of you all here at Bradenham with amazement—and then I went to sleep again in the sacred carpet, and woke up in the morning without a headache! We parted from the bey with deep emotion on both sides, and—"

His words ran out at last to a full stop and he waited, watching her. She was laughing, helplessly, on a rising note of hysteria, a hand at her temple. And then suddenly she was crying. With one of his lightning movements he crossed the room to her in time—and with a wild burst of sobbing she flung herself down across his knees and gave way to pent-up grief.

He held her gently, rocking her a little, making no effort to stem the tide of her tears. He had won.

A maid knocked and opened the door with a lamp in her hand. He shook his head at her frightened face, and waved her out with his free hand. The lamp went with her. He sat on, patiently, in the deepening twilight, shaken by Sarah's sobbing, his own cheeks wet with tears.

VII

Within a month after Ben's departure for Gibraltar, George IV had died. It was not unexpected, but no country is ever altogether prepared for the demise of its sovereign, and England's First Gentleman expired during a summer of grave political crisis all over the world. The Duke of Clarence became King William IV at sixty-five, and at first was very popular, largely because he was such a change from his brother's last years of bad temper and inaccessibility, and from the mysterious seclusion made scandalous always by the attendance of a shamelessly bored *maîtresse en titre*. People like a king to be a king. They like to have him on display. George had deprived them of all kingly spectacle for years—and if William came too much off his pedestal, to walk the streets with an umbrella under his arm, pause on the pavement to pass the time of day with an acquaintance, however humble, or stop the royal carriage to give a lift home to a friend, it was at least to many a human and endearing fault.

William retained a genial lack of formality from his seagoing days more than forty years before; even as Lord High Admiral he had once endorsed an official despatch to Admiral Codrington before Navarino with a hearty "Go it, Ned!" across one corner. Practically his first words as King, at the meeting of his first Council, when everyone was preserving a decent melancholy for the deceased sovereign, were to the cheerful effect that they had given him a damned bad pen with which to sign the declaration. His voice was high and shrill, and its quarter-deck language carried far in the impressive silences of his succession. George IV had once been heard to complain that naval officers never looked and never could look like gentlemen, and his brother William certainly looked—and talked—like an admiral to the end of his life.

As a further contrast to George he was honest and unselfish and genuinely wished to fill his difficult place well. And if he was a little too eager to please, at first, that also seemed an improvement. George had taken his ministers' every opposition as a purely personal affront. William actually desired the welfare of his subjects. But he was ill-educated and inexperienced in state matters, and he needed a firm and popular Prime Minister to advise him. Instead of which, he had Wellington, whose obstinate opposition to the agitating question of Reform was becoming the cause of violent dissatisfaction throughout the country.

The late Duke of Kent's only daughter, the Princess Alexandrina Victoria, was now the heir apparent, and the succession was still causing a great deal of uneasiness. One eleven-year-old girl was the sole product, except for German cousins in the younger branch, of those belated, judicious marryings off of the middle-aged sons of George III. In the event of the new King's dying during her childhood, England would have to be governed by a regency, and the discussion of this matter in Parliament always became acrimonious. The post would most naturally have fallen to the next surviving uncle, the Duke of Cumberland—but that alarming prospect was got round by the fact that Hanover observed the Salic Law and never recognized a female sovereign. On the extinction of the male line in England, therefore, the Hanoverian crown must again become separate from the English one, after more than a century of union under four Georges and a William. This meant that the Duke of Cumberland would become King Ernest I of Hanover when his niece ascended the throne of England, which would get rid of him peaceably, and Hanover could endure him or not as it chose. The rumoured accusations against him included both murder and rape, and he was meddlesome in a bullying way in politics. But at least the complication of his becoming the reigning sovereign of a foreign country precluded his even pretending to the regency of England.

The indications also were that in the event of William's death during the next seven years, the Princess's mother, the widowed Duchess of Kent, would try to run the country, and that would mean interference in its affairs by her brother Leopold, dead Charlotte's husband. Leopold had remained in England on a handsome settlement, and had recently refused the offer of the Greek throne, preferring his still somewhat anomalous position as uncle to the heir of England. There were the other uncles, too, left over from that long German family of George III and good Queen Charlotte—the Duke of Sussex was acknowledged to be eccentric, and the Duke of Cambridge, who never came to England now, was understood to be a very decent fellow. But the Duke of Kent's small daughter stood between them and the crown. Meanwhile England could only hope that William, who detested the Duchess of Kent, could hold out until his successor was grown.

The day the new King prorogued Parliament at Westminster in preparation for the General Election which must by law follow the death of the reigning sovereign—he wore his admiral's uniform under the royal robes—the people of Paris rose against the old-fashioned tyranny of Charles X, erected barricades, and plunged headlong into another revolution, with fighting in the streets under the tri-colour, and all the signs and omens of 1789 again. Charles X and his household fled for a second time to a refuge in England, and after three days of confusion Louis Philippe, Duc d'Orléans, took possession of the city, riding on horseback through the streets. There was not a great deal of enthusiasm for him; King of the Barricades, they called him; the Citizen King, as he preferred it. He was just as much a Bourbon as Charles X —descended from a brother of Louis XIV. He was fifty-seven, hardened and perhaps broadened by that same twenty-five years of exile which had taught the elder branch of his family so little.

Louis Philippe had had a rough trip altogether. During

the Terror he had escaped on foot into Switzerland with a
sole faithful servant, and they wandered about there under assumed names, selling their belongings one by one in order
to subsist, sleeping in cowsheds, with their shoes in shreds.
Then for a time his circumstances improved with a job in a
Swiss school, teaching mathematics as M. Chabaud. Finally
he was recognized there and driven on, incognito, by the in-
quiries of the French Directory following the death of his
father, Philippe Egalité, on the scaffold. He saw Brussels
next—Copenhagen—Sweden—Philadelphia—Niagara Falls—
Mount Vernon—the West Indies—Twickenham—and at last,
in Sicily, he married the daughter of the King of Naples.
Since 1814 he had been living in Paris, steadily opposing the
reactionary Royalist policy. And now it was suddenly his
turn to be King of France. This was in August, 1830, while
Ben was at Malta.

In England during the same month the General Election
took place amid terrific excitement. The English lower
classes were stirred by the successful revolt of the peasantry
in France, and Wellington's former friendship with the de-
posed Royalist minister Polignac was held against him as
proof of his despotic tendencies at home. The real reason
for the growing unpopularity of the Wellington administration was hard to come at. The Duke had offended his
anti-Catholic friends by the Emancipation Bill, but would
not take advantage of the new support he had won thereby
in the Whig camp, which he offended in its turn by his
brusque aloofness. The Whigs therefore hoped that if he
would not join them voluntarily they could force him to accept them by making it too hot for him to go on alone. Thus
the Government was absurdly in danger of being outvoted by
an alliance of parties who were actually more hostile to each
other than to the Ministry.

The new King's personal popularity and unassuming
manners were a blessing at this time. If George IV had still
occupied the throne the English Monarchy itself might have
been in danger. But the people were convinced that so
good-natured-appearing a man as William could not be re-

sponsible for their grievances, and blamed the existing administration for everything. The Opposition was careful to foster this idea. Nevertheless, the Tories were returned to office, with a diminished majority. The news reached Ben at Constantinople, where he read accumulated newspapers with avid interest.

The *soi-disant* second French Revolution had been immediately followed by the long-simmering revolt of Catholic Belgium against the oppressive Protestantism of the Dutch rule, with house-to-house fighting in Brussels in September, while Ben was playing at pirates in the Mediterranean. There were also local disturbances in Switzerland and Germany, and in November the brutal Constantine was driven out of Poland by an outraged people. The Papal States were given over to brigandage and insurrection. Portugal was in the hands of an effeminate usurper. Greek independence had been guaranteed by three great powers the year before, and there also was nominal peace in the Near East, but its progress there was retarded by brigandage, local wars, and reprisals. Ben found the Acropolis still littered with cannon balls from the Turkish bombardment, and the city of Athens unroofed and almost uninhabited.

The Tories had been retained on sufferance, but with the death of George IV their long domination was hopelessly broken. During that autumn the turmoil at home and abroad continued to assist the Opposition. Grey and Wellington were at loggerheads, as the feeling increased over the Reform issue, and the charges against rotten boroughs and borough-mongering grew more violent. Peel, by the death of his father during the summer, had become a baronet and a rich man, and was less than ever a crusader in any cause at Westminster.

At the opening of Parliament, Wellington, whose growing deafness made him always irritably suspicious of the half-heard talk going on all round him, announced flatly that he considered the representative system of England incapable of improvement and that he would regard it his duty everlastingly to oppose any such measure as Parliamentary Reform.

His colleagues, his opponents, and the country at large were more or less stunned at such a colossal conviction of omniscience, and most people now began inordinately to desire Reform.

By the end of 1830 Wellington's government had fallen and a Whig ministry came into power, with Earl Grey as Prime Minister. A remarkably consistent man, Grey had been patiently advocating Reform since 1797. His oratorical powers were always strongly sarcastic, as he had proved again by his castigation of Canning a few years before. William IV had not the personal antagonism for Grey that his brother George had shown, but William was attached to Wellington and was used to him. And now that William sat on the throne himself his earlier Whig tendencies had faded somewhat, just as George's had when he achieved the Regency. William regarded Grey with misgivings; especially as Wellington prophesied gloomily that now revolution would come to England at last.

Grey was an aristocrat, cold to strangers, handsome, unbending, but with an Old-World courtesy and grandeur of manner that was reassuring to those who dreaded that he was about to abandon the country to the will of the mob. He had an intense personal dislike of O'Connell and his foul language and his disorderly following. In Grey's ministry of fifteen there were several members of his own extensive family, and there was only one man without a title.

The new Whig Prime Minister announced his intentions at once. "Prominent and in the foreground I place Reform in Parliament," he said in his opening speech. "What out of office I have professed, I am now in office about to perform." Grey was sixty-six, and the times had caught up with him since the days when he and Fox had joined in advocating Reform in order to harry Pitt, who had a war on his hands. But Grey proposed confidently to evolve "a scheme which would be effective without exceeding the bounds of a just and well-advised moderation." He proposed to extend the franchise immediately to the unrepresented cities, and to deal drastically with the evils of borough-mongering. To all of which, in the course of the tumultuous debate which followed, Lord Sidmouth rose and shouted: "I hope God may forgive you on account of this Bill—*I* never can!" There was a scene in the Lords. Things had got beyond a well-advised moderation.

Grey had practically the whole House of Lords, as well as Lord Sidmouth, against him. It was an anxious winter in England, with rick-burning and riots and a general air of belligerent suspense, backed up by the revolutionary precedent established across the Channel. O'Connell, whose oratory played upon the masses like wind on an Aeolian harp, was whipping all Ireland into a state of frenzy on Reform as a means to Repeal, and pointing a triumphant finger at the success of the Belgian armed revolt against Protestant masters. Stanley, who was Grey's Secretary for Ireland, was not a meek man, and matters soon reached the usual crisis of a challenge, from Stanley to O'Connell. O'Connell as usual refused to fight, and their relations continued to be far more embittered than the old enmity between Peel and O'Connell had ever been. The O'Connell party proclaimed that they had "taken their coats off" to effect Repeal, and Stanley declared that he would resist Repeal to the death. And Stanley's own powers of invective were not to be despised.

Repeal, Reform, Revolution—and a world full of bad examples.

The instructions of the Cabinet to the committee entrusted with constructing the first Reform Bill recommended that the measure "should be large enough to satisfy at once public opinion and prevent any further change; but which should be based on and connected with the existing territorial divisions and rights." The constitution, it was added, was not to be encroached upon, but "the House of Commons was really to represent the intelligence, property, and feeling of the people." They could not make it even sound simple.

The first Bill was defeated in April, and England was roused to a pitch never seen since the Great Rebellion. The exciting echoes of Westminster reached Ben in old newspapers at Cairo while he waited for Meredith to arrive from

Thebes, and increased his impatience to reach home again. What had begun as an Opposition measure of the Whig party, a gadfly to sting Wellington out of office, had become almost overnight a fiery national issue. Even the Press lost its head and recommended the use of "brickbat and bludgeon" to intimidate the enemies of Reform. Unarmed mobs rose again about the country to do violence to machinery and property in a blind contagion of unrest, and the Home Office, under Lord Melbourne, acted promptly and severely with offenders. A howling London rabble threw stones through Wellington's windows, in defiance of the new civil police force which Peel had established in 1829, and swept on down Piccadilly, singing rude songs and shouting for "the Bill, the whole Bill, and nothing but the Bill!"

The *Quarterly Review,* entrenched in the smuggest of Toryism under Lockhart, declared that Revolution had indeed come unawares upon the land, and that England was a ruined nation. But Revolution was a word not even thought of by the hungry mobs who sought merely to express their dissatisfaction with the state of affairs, their desire for some sort of change immediately, and their reckless determination to achieve the millennium of peace and plenty which they had in some way got firmly affixed to the word *Reform.*

While O'Connell was forming a society for Repeal, which he declared no power on earth could prevent, he implied that all the purely social miseries of Ireland—famine, poverty, and disease—were due to purely political causes; and that if Ireland could but regain her independence all these inconveniences would miraculously disappear; which was to say that the throne of England had a direct connection with the failure of crops and the inevitable summer famine when the potatoes went bad. He spoke always as though all had been prosperous and halcyon in Ireland until the Union in 1782, and that all would be celestial again the instant that that connection was legally dissolved. Similarly the delusions which prevailed among the ignorant in England as to the probable fruits of Reform were profoundly fantastic—scarcely less so than Sydney Smith's satirical summary: "All young ladies expect that, as soon as this Bill is carried, they will be instantly married; schoolboys believe that gerunds and supines will be abolished, and that currant tarts must come down in price; the corporal and sergeant are sure of double pay; bad poets expect a demand for their epics; and fools will be disappointed as they always are."

Parliament was dissolved by the King (under protest) to prevent a resignation of the Government, and after a wild election met again in June with a heavier majority for the Whig ministry, and the debates on Reform were resumed with even greater vehemence than before. The Whigs were accused of a "corrupt compromise" with the O'Connell faction to secure their support in the election and the subsequent victory. This was angrily denied, but they had certainly used influence to return members pledged to vote for the Bill, and all anti-ministerial candidates had been very unpopular at the hustings. There was perhaps no organized intimidation, but undoubtedly there was violence and rioting.

For the first time the great Peel faced a thoroughly hostile House. He had given in on Catholic Emancipation in tardy necessity, and had got nothing but blame for deserting his principles. Very well, on Reform he would hold out to the end. Therefore he now found himself on the wrong side, in a false position all round, furious with the Ministers but on ill terms with his party and himself. "I shall oppose this Bill to the last," he said, "believing as I do that people are grossly deluded as to the political results to be derived from it."

But as the summer wore on he grew weary of so hopeless a struggle. His wife went to Drayton, the country house, and he was left to lonely meals and empty rooms—and he was a family man. Sometimes he sulked and would not go to the House at all. When there he spoke firmly but seldom brilliantly. His utter boredom gave rise to a legend among his own party that he was "wilfully cautious," or that he was playing some deep game. And all he wanted was to get away to Drayton, among his flowers and his children. His old ally Wellington could do nothing with him, and was in despair of the whole future of Britain.

During the hot weather too a new anxiety filled people's minds. Asiatic cholera had crept into England through St. Petersburg, Berlin, and the Baltic ports. Its form was not virulent, but there were periodic waves of panic, and endless discussions of means of prevention. The House was disinfected with chloride of lime, and the odour hung on the heavy air and caught the weary speakers at the back of the throat in the long debates.

It was not only the Opposition whose spirit flagged during those hot summer nights of 1831, while the battle went on in the Commons and bad ventilation and fatigue and sheer nervous strain took toll of the wrangling members, who were often in their seats till the early dawn glimmered in across the merciless artificial glare of the lamps, and while the fury of the crowds "out of doors" increased with the delay. Grey's favourite grandchild was dying.

William's coronation took place early in September; by his own orders as economical a coronation as possible, which was a discretion achieved almost to shabbiness. His carriage was greeted with enthusiasm by his subjects, cheers for His Majesty more or less drowning out the hoots and catcalls which were evoked by the appearance of the Duke of Cumberland in his escort.

Victoria, heiress of England, was not present in the Abbey. She had been taken to the Isle of Wight for a holiday, and she remained there during the sober festivities of her uncle's crowning; a prim, fair child in a cotton pinafore, watering her own flowers in the garden. It was no secret that the King did not approve of the Duchess of Kent and the influence of her brother Leopold. The Duchess remarked publicly that she kept her daughter isolated from the society of the Fitzclarence grandchildren lest Victoria should hear the word bastard and wonder what it meant; which raised a reasonable doubt if the jolly, informal infants who visited a kindly grandfather at Windsor were likely to discuss their antecedents while at play. And the King let it be known that he prayed God to prolong his life until his niece came of age, in order to defeat the Duchess's hopes of a regency.

Nevertheless, Victoria's sheltered life was opening out a little. She had begun to go on small tours "for her health" (which was excellent) and everywhere was received with affectionate interest and bore herself with quaint dignity and charm. Her education was in the hands of the Dean of Chester and a German governess, and proceeded along safe, uninspired lines. She liked music, and had a true, piping voice. Her water colours were excellent. She enjoyed her dancing lessons.

She was naturally gay and affectionate and uncritical of her elders' judgments in her small affairs. But now and then she showed alarming flashes of obstinacy, and there was one man whom she instinctively disliked—her mother's major-domo, John Conroy. She had already a royal tact with strangers, and a passionate loyalty to her friends. It was only recently that she had been made aware of her royal destiny, and she took it in with becoming seriousness, and set herself to learn. She had all the Hanoverian virtues, such as they were, and by reason of her sex and youth, none of the vices of her predecessors. It was merely a question now of whose influence would dominate. Her beloved Uncle Leopold had been persuaded to accept the Belgian crown during the past year. She missed his handsome presence and fatherly ways, and wrote him long, exclamatory, spontaneous letters and received affectionate, thoughtful replies full of advice and admonitions.

The second Reform Bill was passed by the Commons towards the end of the same September, and London went mad with joy. Church bells were rung and the city was illuminated, and windows were smashed in the houses which failed to show lights in honour of the Whig victory. It was now entirely a question of "What will the Lords do?" Ben, on the way home, was meanwhile marooned in quarantine at Malta.

The debates in the Upper House were magnificent, with Lord Lyndhurst's cold lucidity and commanding presence leading the desperate Opposition. Enterprise and industry throughout the country were at a standstill with suspense. Signs of intimidation of the Tory peers were visible. There was talk also of a sufficient creation of Whig peers to carry the Bill without more delay, but Grey disliked that idea intensely. More and more it became hopelessly apparent that some such step must be taken if the Ministry was to continue, and a great many people felt that if it retired now civil war was inevitable. Other people said that the term civil war was out of all proportion to a mere handful of obstructionists. The King was looking old and ill, and was almost in tears over the waning of his own popularity as it leaked out that the Bill had not his wholehearted support. Grey, who was not of a temperament to cajole his sovereign in any circumstances, made a genuine effort to soothe him, but William's original mistrust of the Whigs was now accentuated by his honest horror of what he regarded as spreading revolution.

The final debate in the Lords was attended by ladies in evening dress, who sat on the steps of the throne and overflowed into the corridors, and it lasted until seven in the morning. The Bill was defeated, but the Tories felt anxiety rather than triumph. London became strangely quiet, and very tense. Grey wanted to resign, but remained in office on a vote of confidence—a Whig government was surely better now than no government at all. Parliament was prorogued to allow the sponsors of the Bill time to make alterations in it before its re-presentation. There was more talk of creating Whig peers, which drove the King to open, hysterical revolt.

At this point Ben returned to England, full of a new ambition.

He spent the winter at Bradenham, however, cherishing Sarah's slowly reviving interest in life, working on the new book, with a great show of dependence on her opinions, and viewing the unsettled state of the country and affairs with oratorical disapproval. He was torn between London, where so much was happening, and Sa, who needed him desperately and whom he loved. But by Christmas time Sarah, who was as thorough as he was himself in moods and undertakings, was nearly her old self again. A certain sparkle and gay confidence had gone out of her, perhaps forever. But not once since the day of his homecoming did she relapse into the icy automaton he had melted to tears across his knees.

Her brave resumption of life's little things, her conscientious interest in the minutiae of existence which make up quiet country days, sometimes struck him to the heart, but still he recognized it as convalescence. The smallest matters can become of consequence to a mind which dares not turn inward on itself, a will power determined to be busy and sane and if possible cheerful. The last gallant dahlia in the wintry garden, the fall of a branch in the night wind, the illness of a puppy, the grey days or the fine, the prospects of a frost, the very direction of the wind—to Sa it was all something to think about, something to go on with. One felt that her mind chattered cheerily to itself in the dark, like an uneasy child who lies awake alone waiting for daylight.

She hung on Ben's words, made him repeat his stories, laughed in the same places, put the same questions, eagerly awaited the same answers. She cherished excessively the gifts he had brought her from far, exotic places, and received with more healing tears the presents accumulated for her by Meredith before his death. Her eyes were often wet through her laughter, but she was no longer ill and half demented. She was Sa again, white-faced, black-clad, but strong again, facing up to life, and always ready endlessly to discuss Ben's future plans. She did not cling on him. But there were evenings when she talked a little too fast as bedtime drew near, led him on a little feverishly to enlarge upon his prospects and intentions. And at such times he would build up the fire and sit with her after the family had gone to bed, holding back with his voice and his reassuring presence the wave of desolation which hung over her—until at last it receded from her again and she could rise with a sigh of relaxation and contentment and bid him a willing good-night. It was a taxing labour of love, with a world waiting to be conquered just beyond his reach, but he did not falter in it.

When Parliament reassembled the third Reform Bill was read, and though Peel still opposed it furiously, it was already regarded as inevitable in the House. Stanley was making a brilliant showing against him now, leading the moderate Reformers against the Radicals (including the Irish) who went much too far, and the old Tories who would follow the Duke of Wellington wherever he led, and whom Stanley called "sticklers for inveterate abuses under the name of the wisdom of our ancestors." Stanley was always better in a row than Peel could ever be, and while he did not altogether desire wholesale Reform, he saw that certain abuses should be remedied and that a headlong plunge into Radicalism might be averted by reasonable concessions. He was a glutton for work, and had become the hope of the Whig party, which Grey was striving to convert into a dominant buffer between the Radicals and the Tories. Peel was gathering about him a group of conservative Tories, but he lacked the energy and magnetism of a true leader, and was always absent when most wanted, to the annoyance of the men whom he could with a little effort have moulded into a unit of real weight and power. And the House still smelled of chloride of lime.

Much against his will, Grey was now prepared to force through a creation of Whig peers to ensure the passage of the Bill in the Lords—there seemed to be no other way. The King was half dead of horror. Coerce the Lords? Never! His womenfolk were in a perpetual flutter of alarm, and talked dismally of Marie Antoinette and the Princesse de Lamballe. His own health had dissolved into a perpetual fretfulness under the strain. Wellington assured him that he was prepared to put down any further disturbances with troops, which only frightened him the more.

Ben could bear it no longer. If the Government resigned there would be an election, and he might procure a seat. If it did not resign, Town was going to be exciting. Whatever happened, he must be there to see. He must hear what people were saying.

In February he went up to London and took rooms in Duke Street.

III. DUKE STREET

EDWARD BULWER had been quick to welcome him back, while he was still at Bradenham with Sarah. Bulwer had been elected in the spring on money borrowed from his mother, and had made a modest maiden speech supporting Reform, from the Radical ranks, though anyone less like a Radical than this fair, nervous man of proud lineage it would be difficult to imagine. Rosina resented Westminster as blindly and wholeheartedly as she hated everything else which distracted his attention from herself.

36 Hertford Street,
November 8, 1831.

My dear Disraeli,

If I am not the very first, let me at least not be the last to congratulate you on your safe return. I only heard of it yesterday from our common ally, Colburn. "Mr. Disraeli, sir, is home again—young Mr. Disraeli. Won't he give us a nice light article on his travels?"

I don't know if you ever got a long letter I sent you to Constantinople, acknowledging the safe receipt of the slippers, the tobacco bag, and the epistle. A thousand thanks for all.

Mrs. Bulwer has this day "presented me with a son," as the polite express it. So I have good reason for being brief in my communications to you. But pray write and let me know how you are. Adieu, my dear fellow. Take care of yourself and believe me,

Always and sincerely yours,
E. L. B.

Bulwer was genuinely impatient to hear new stories, laugh at new jokes, and warm himself at the dancing flame of Disraeli's generous friendship. He had missed Disraeli's volatile presence in London after a very short acquaintance, and to his own surprise, for he did not form attachments easily. All the ardent, uncalculating, spontaneous side of Bulwer's nature had been lavished on Rosina during their headlong, distracted love affair which had now dwindled so miserably into this unhappy marriage, from which there was never any escape. And now Disraeli had been as far as Jerusalem. To think that Jerusalem really did exist after all, with people alive in it today, and Englishmen arriving to look at it! Disraeli had stood on the plains of Troy and the sands of Egypt. To think that such a spirit of enterprise, such physical energy —and such freedom—could be had in this world! Bulwer had been to Paris when he was a boy, of course—he was twenty-eight now—and had done there most of the things boys did in Paris. But Disraeli had been to Constantinople.

Bulwer's starved imagination, draining for years down his right arm and off the tip of his hurrying pen, without respite or replenishment, strained toward that glorious moment at the end of dinner, when Rosina would leave the dining-room at last and he and Disraeli could draw their chairs together, with perhaps a few other choice spirits like D'Orsay, and a bottle of wine on the table—and the stories would begin. Disraeli was very good at telling a story. His gestures were superb, and often finished a sentence for him, deliciously without words. And his words were often odd and very pictorial, not the stodgy threadbare words of ordinary English conversation. In Disraeli's mouth English became as exciting as French, and as neat and apposite. This tradition that English was a poverty-stricken language which needed piecing out with other languages was all because the English did not know half of it.

And yet Disraeli himself was English. Well, yes, a Jew, but born in London and proud of it. His patriotism was intense. Germany he had considered amusing, and Italy beautiful beyond comparison; but England, he said with one of his swift swoops into classic simplicity after much rococo verbiage, was home. Now that he had been in the East, where his people came from in the beginning, would he bring back with him, perhaps, a sort of nostalgia for the cradle of his race? Would he be, perhaps, less English?

And here Bulwer's hypersensitive nature drew in upon itself like a snail, with a small familiar shudder. Disraeli had come back, yes, but might he not have changed? And this friendship, subconsciously cherished all these months of his absence, might it not dwindle too into a nothingness that rankled?

And so Bulwer's stretched nerves were at him again, jangling, distorting, scarifying. Rosina had changed, and left him without a sweetheart. Might not Disraeli change, and leave him groping for a friend? That odd, revivifying warmth round Bulwer's heart which had caused him to write impulsively that welcoming letter had all gone now, and there were only doubts, and a sort of dread. He always saw things out of proportion. And it seemed to him suddenly that Disraeli was all the friend he really had, and that if he lost him he would have nothing left—only the glitter, which must be kept up somehow, he had forgotten why, and the work, which never abated. And he began to wonder how he could postpone the meeting he had been looking forward to. Better not to know. . . . He was always afraid of facts.

Disraeli's first evening in Hertford Street came inevitably, and with it the stories and the laughter. Such laughter—when Rosina had left the dining-room—that tears rolled down their faces, and D'Orsay strangled on his wine and had to be pounded on the back and walked round and round the table, while they all cried with merriment again; foolish, abandoned, bachelor laughter, wholehearted and incomprehensible as children's, and very infuriating to Rosina in the drawing-room, playing with her dog. She snatched up a pen, and began one of her witty, complaining letters to her best friend, a Miss Greene, who understood her—pinning down in ink a phrase which pleased her about "that giant genus of bores yclept 'young men about town.'"

When at last they emerged from the dining-room she had gone to bed, and they sang as they passed up Hertford Street in the winter night. Rosina, lying in wait for Edward with her comments ready, whispered spiteful witticisms to the little dog which was curled up on the coverlet beside her. Edward would make it get down and go to its basket in the corner when he came, and together they listened to him moving about downstairs, putting out the lights—four large soft resentful eyes on the doorway in which he would appear.

Bulwer, snuffing dripping candles in the empty drawing-room, was suddenly very tired and a little drunk, and hated the thought of tomorrow and the unfinished manuscript of *Eugene Aram*. His life as he must live it seemed dull and narrow and futile, without zest or colour. The party was over, and now he must face Rosina's tongue. Next time Disraeli came she would make him give a proper dinner, with a dozen catty women to keep her company in the drawing-room, and mind the gentlemen do not sit too long over the port.

He found his bedroom candle on the table in the hall and lighted it somewhat unsteadily from the last taper, and turned toward the stairs. And there, gripping the bannister, he paused. It didn't matter. Nothing mattered. He had only just realized that Disraeli had not changed.

It was not long, however, before Bulwer became aware, painlessly, that there was a slight difference. Disraeli looked the same—always handsome, with health regained and spirits soaring he was more so, fresh from his tailors and moving with a careless, catlike grace which set off his exquisite clothes. But there was an added something, a poise, though God knows he was always self-possessed. Well, then, a—manliness. Bulwer, from his marital heights, chained by responsibility and dogged by debt, had regarded Disraeli as a stripling, untouched by tragedy, emotionally a child. Bulwer, who at twenty had been schooled by Lady Caroline Lamb at her worst, would hardly have considered Mrs. Austen an experience. But now—the perspective of travel, that awful business with Meredith at Cairo, his sister's sorrow—Disraeli had grown up, and Bulwer did not feel so fatherly any more. They met on an equal footing, and gained in understanding accordingly.

Ben in his turn was shocked and incredulous over the con-

ditions in Hertford Street as they transpired during the ensuing weeks before his tactfully averted eyes. He had known
from the beginning that Bulwer was not altogether happy—
but this was fantastic. Bulwer breakfasted in his library and
Rosina in her dressing-room. He never dined at home unless
there was company. They seldom met alone, and if they did
some domestic problem was sure to intrude and there would
be a quarrel, followed by a passionate reconciliation more
wearing than anger. They made each other preposterous
gifts which they could not afford, and then quarrelled over
the grocer's bill. Once they had thought the world well lost
for love, and having thrown the world away could not exist
in the same room without bickering. Bulwer's mother considered that Rosina did not treat her with sufficient respect
at their rare meetings and refused to relieve the financial
strain which was slowly killing her son. Rosina had exchanged a handsome, tender lover for a preoccupied, irritable
man who snapped at her if she showed her nose inside his
library door. Bulwer had lost a lovely, impulsive girl who had
cast her heart at his feet for a tearful, importunate woman,
idle and querulous, and with no slightest faculty of creating
an occupation or an interest in life apart from himself. Their
children only bored her, and got on Bulwer's nerves, and so
were left to their nurse, while Rosina lavished baby talk and
sweets and companionship on the small, ill-tempered dogs
she would not allow out of her sight. Though putting on a
little weight, she was lovelier to look at than ever, as some
women are after bearing a child, and if petted and flattered
into a good humour she could be enchanting, though she
never had and never would have any brains.

But what a way to live, thought Ben, whose domestic ways
had fallen in pleasant places.

I I

Young Mr. Disraeli, that much-travelled dandy, was
warmly received into the gay circle in Mayfair where Edward
Bulwer, the distinguished young novelist and M.P., was a

leading figure. At Bulwer's he met the political powers, and
the "blues," those brilliant, often disillusioned women of talent and fame who wrote novels and poems, edited ladies'
periodicals, and dabbled in politics and legislation. And in
Hertford Street his original ideas were somewhat stretched
in the matter of Reform.

Bulwer's Radical associations were largely a matter of expediency. He was totally opposed to the old-fashioned ultra-
Toryism of Wellington's administration, but being unac-
quainted with any of the great Whig houses behind Earl
Grey, being shy and proud and averse to patronage, he naturally gravitated to the Radicals. Like many others in that
party, he regarded Reform merely as a necessary means to
an end, which was to secure a real and not a nominal representation of the people in the House of Commons. The proposed Reform Bill would provide that seats in the House
could no longer be purchased or inherited as private property, but must embody by election the chosen candidate of
the people. The boundary line which indicated the classes
which would constitute "the people" was still flexible and
pretty vague.

Bred in the old Tory tradition, with country-gentleman
tendencies and land-owning sympathies, Ben was nevertheless quick to see that the old days had somehow mysteriously
vanished forever during his absence in the East, and to adopt
Bulwer's views on the need for improvements in the representative system. He had an ingrained horror of whiggery, having been taught from childhood that the Whigs were a
mutinous oligarchy opposed to the King. He was convinced
that the electoral reform they so virtuously advocated now
was designed merely to bring into power their natural supporters, the wealthier tradesmen and manufacturers, and
would still be far short of representing the actual opinions
and choice of the people. It would destroy the spacious ways
of the country-house gentlefolk and land-owners which he so
respected, in favour of noisy, smug materialism rooted in fac-
tories and trade, with nothing of beauty in it, nothing of tradition, nothing of dignity. And the people, the mobs who

clamoured and were hungry, would be no better off than before. But the Whigs would not care for that. The Whigs
never cared for anything so long as they were able to achieve,
and maintain, office.

Besides, the Whigs were snobs and would probably never
accept him.

The best of Toryism itself was still sound, he would tell
Bulwer earnestly—the benevolent feudalism of country estates
and large establishments, supporting dozens of tenants and
servants—and it made for romance and quiet beauty and cul-
tured, intelligent living. But the Tory leaders were old-
fashioned and pigheaded, and had got themselves thoroughly
unpopular by opposing tactlessly the magic word Reform,
which was least understood by those who committed the most
excesses in its name. That was where the Whigs had been
clever, to trade on that. But to join the Tory ranks now, he
realized, was to shoulder the sins of a past generation. One
must have a free hand. And freedom was to be found among
the Radicals, who came nearest, after all, to what was generally understood to be Reform. That way one would come
at the Whigs from the other side, and possibly steal a march.

Apparently Reform was inevitable in some shape very soon.
The Whigs had started it, and now they hardly knew what
to do with it. But if Reform must come, it must be controlled
by someone. It must accomplish something besides the ag-
grandizement of the Whig party. What was really wanted
was some happy compromise between old Toryism and Radicalism; a Tory Radical, a conservative Tory, able to progress
without destroying. There was no such party. Ben thought
there ought to be.

His letters to Sarah that spring were full of his gay doings
in London, and his new political convictions. Sarah read the
newspapers faithfully now, and knew all about what was
happening. He kept her with him in spirit, made her aware
of all that went on before his eyes and in his heart, determined that she should not be allowed to slip back into the
depths from which he had with such loving care drawn her
up.

London,
February 18, 1832.

My dearest Sa,

We had a very brilliant *réunion* at Bulwer's last night. Among the notables were Lords Strangford and Mulgrave, with the latter of whom I had a great deal of conversation; Count D'Orsay, the famous Parisian dandy; and there was a large sprinkling of blues—Lady Morgan, Mrs. Norton, L. E. L.,* etc. Bulwer came up to me and said, "There is one blue who insists on an introduction." "Oh, my dear fellow, I cannot, really, the power of repartee has deserted me." "I have pledged myself, and you must come." So he led me up to a very sumptuous personage, looking like a full-blown rose, Mrs. Gore. I avoided L. E. L., who looked the very personification of Brompton—pink satin dress, and white satin shoes, red cheeks, snub nose, and her hair *à la Sappho.*

Mrs. Bulwer was a blaze of jewels, and looked like Juno; only instead of a peacock, she had a dog in her lap, called Fairy, not bigger than a bird of paradise, and quite as brilliant. We drank champagne out of a saucer of ground glass mounted on a pedestal of cut glass. . . .

London,
April 28, 1832.

Dear Sa,

The *soirée* at Bulwer's last night was really brilliant. There were a great many dames there of distinction, and no blues. I should perhaps except Sappho, who was quite changed; she had thrown off her Greco-Bromptonian costume, and was perfectly *à la française,* and really looked quite pretty. At the end of the evening I addressed a few words to her, of the value of which she seemed sensible!

I was introduced "by particular desire" to Mrs. Wyndham Lewis, a pretty little woman, a flirt and a rattle; indeed, gifted with a volubility I should think unequalled, and of which I can give no idea. She told me she liked

* Laetitia Landon, the poetess.

"silent, melancholy men." I answered that I had no doubt of it.

With regard to politics, I really cannot pretend to say what is going to happen, although I may ascertain before tomorrow. If Lord Grey does not make peers he will go out, and perhaps finish his mortal as well as political career at the same time. . . .

By early spring the Reform Bill was indeed regarded as a certainty, which would necessitate a general election after it was passed, and Ben had now definitely fixed his eye on the borough of High Wycombe. It belonged to the Whigs, but he meant to invade it as a Radical, and all the time he continued to like the Tories best in his heart. But the Tories were sure of defeat. By becoming a Radical one went the Whigs one better, which was something.

Meanwhile he attacked the foreign policy of the Grey Government in a vigorous anonymous pamphlet entitled: *England and France: or a Cure for the Ministerial Gallomania.* It was hastily written, and was influenced by his sudden acquaintance—of brief duration—with a legitimist exile of Charles X's last ministry. The Baron was bursting with secret information, and he found an eager listener who loved an intrigue. The pamphlet dealt scathingly with "that mean and monstrous incident which hitherto we have been pleased to style a Glorious Revolution," which had brought Louis Philippe to the French throne.

They were not really his own views, they were the Baron's, but he was writing a political novel now, and this stripping off of "diplomatic decencies," this dabbling in foreign mysteries and overturned governments, fitted in with his mood. He regarded *Gallomania* as a step-child only, and while its style was to many people unmistakably the style of *Vivian Grey,* he never acknowledged its authorship. The *Times* honoured it with a leading article, pointing out that its concealed motive was actually hostility to the Reform Bill. Ben, who was scarcely aware of a concealed motive, and who *was* secretly hostile to the Reform Bill's more drastic details, did not bother to contradict.

Sarah wrote from Bradenham that she feared the pamphlet would confuse his prospective constituents at High Wycombe, and prove him a Tory after all. Sarah, gravely reading all the newspapers, was a little confused herself by his wayward avoidance of any definite party label. But his impatient spirit refused to be bound down by the usual lines of party demarcation, and his Tory soul shied at some of the more radical articles of Reform. He was able to sympathize on the whole with the movement which he termed "the general measure of Reform"—to broaden the electorate and bring the House of Commons more into touch with the actual needs and wishes of the populace. It was to his interest that the electorate should be broadened, if he wished to get a seat, for there was very little influence he could bring to bear to obtain one in the old way from men who had boroughs at their personal disposal. But at the same time he would suspect the Whigs of being nowise concerned with the welfare of the populace, and he nursed a growing distrust of their motives in reconstructing the electorate as they proposed to do.

Isaac wrote objecting to secret agents on principle, and refugee barons in general.

The third Reform Bill was carried in the Commons in March, and once again only the Lords stood in its way. The Lords, led by Lyndhurst and the Duke of Wellington, were still obdurate. It was only too plain that the Bill would never pass the Lords without a large creation of peers to outvote its old opponents. It would take about sixty new Whig peers to make a majority—which the King declared was to create a new Lords, and he held out stoutly against any such wholesale measure. As for Grey, who had been advocating Reform all his life, it would break his heart to achieve it only at the cost of so humiliating the Upper House. He saw that it would mean important resignations from the Cabinet, and the Government would probably drop apart soon after that. He began to feel that perhaps it might be better for him just to resign after all, if they were beaten again in the Lords.

There were murmurings among his party at the delay and his own apparent indecision. And Wellington, once the idol of the mob, was assaulted in the streets and would have been dragged from his horse but for the intervention of his groom.

Tied hand and foot by the King's tearful horror of degrading the Lords, and the Prime Minister's own disinclination, the Ministry resigned in May—made a clean sweep, and left the way dramatically clear for the anti-Reformers. Let them show what they could do.

There were popular demonstrations against the resignation of the Government. The mob waited, sullen and defensive, for the next move. Cornered at last, and badly frightened now, the King sent for Wellington. It was all he could ever think of to do in a crisis. But everybody, even the Tories, knew that if Wellington came in again as Prime Minister there might be civil war. Nobody among his advisors and associates had the courage, or the lack of tact, to put this into words. But even Wellington understood, and it went very hard with him. His decision was that he would not take office, but would act in a purely advisory capacity. At the same time he said unwisely that if the people of England would not be quiet there was a way to make them be—and he had the troops at his back to do it. Fears of a military government by him were born.

The panic-stricken King's instructions were that whatever ministry was got together now, some sort of Reform must be conceded at once. Wellington suggested Peel, and Peel refused to touch Reform. A Tory Government which did not include Peel was inconceivable, but Wellington persisted in trying a few days more, meeting refusal from almost everyone he had counted on, while the Commons made remarks about an anti-Reform party who would pass Reform as the price of office—whereas Wellington was only trying to save the King's face and his own, by tactics similar to those which had passed the Catholic Emancipation Bill.

But this time Peel would not join in the compromise, and the Lower House was utterly unmanageable. The King's carriage was hooted in the streets, now that it was known he wanted Wellington back. A run on the banks was threatened, petitions and political meetings abounded. After a chaotic week in which there was no Government at all to deal with revolution if revolution had broken out, Wellington gave up.

Fuming, the King recalled Grey, with full power to pass Reform any way he chose. Opposition was at an end.

Ben's hopes of an election had risen, with news of the resignation, but now there was no immediate prospect.

London,
May 15, 1832.

Dearest Sa,

I very much fear the Whigs are in again, and on their own terms.

Yesterday I dined at Eliot's, a male party consisting of eight. I was between Peel and Herries, but I cannot tell you the names of the other guests, although they were all members of one or the other House. Peel was most gracious. He is a very great man indeed, and they all seem afraid of him. By the bye, I noticed that he attacked his turbot almost entirely with his knife. I can easily conceive that he could be very disagreeable but yesterday he was in a most condescending mood, and unbent with becoming haughtiness. I reminded him by my dignified familiarity both that he was ex-Minister and I a present Radical.

Herries—old, grey-headed, financial Herries—turned out quite a literary man. So false are one's impressions. The dinner was sumptuous and we broke up late. . . .

Sarah's book, which he had been at work on for nearly four years and which was to be dedicated to her, was still being polished—*Alroy* was to be quite perfect before it saw the world. But in the meantime, for the sake of ready cash, he had thrown his political novel, *Contarini Fleming*, on the market. He had begun it abroad, as the natural expression of his new determination to enter Parliament, like Bulwer, when he got back. Its hero was the son of a Court noble in some fictitious northern kingdom, who as Under-Secretary-

of-State distinguished himself in a brilliant diplomatic *coup*
which amazed the ambassadors of the great powers; and his
father, returning from a conference with the King, linked
his arm in his son's and said—"My boy, you will be Prime
Minister; perhaps something greater." After which conversation, Contarini, left alone, in imagination "shook thrones
and founded empires."

Described as a "Psychological Romance," published while
England was on the verge of civil war, the book was very
nearly stillborn. The reviewers, who gave it perhaps their
divided attention, seemed to the author to have not the
slightest idea what it was about. And the *Monthly* accused
him of atheism; apparently, as he pointed out to Sarah, because he retired into solitude to write novels.

Although the King had not actually created the sixty peers,
it was well known that Grey now had the power to get them
if they were needed. Once more, Wellington's practical good
sense and knowledge of when to retreat came to his country's
rescue. He would not give in, but he could retire. Once more
he stamped off the stage with his followers, leaving his opponents a free hand to do their worst.

And so at last the great Reform Bill was passed, and received the reluctant Royal sanction on the 7th of June. The
King was never popular again. But the Whig Ministers
were idols in shrines.

And at last an election! Bulwer who had been through all
the flurry of his own first campaign while Ben was in Egypt
and considered himself an old hand at it, advised him to lose
no time in getting to know his constituents, and volunteered
to go to Wycombe with him and see him started. They posted
down from London together, in divine summer weather, to
begin Disraeli's first canvass.

I I I

Isaac was troubled, but saw that he could do nothing to
dissuade Ben from throwing himself headlong into this new
enterprise, which seemed doomed to certain disaster. All very

well for Bulwer, with his unexceptional English fairness, his unaggressive English personality—Bulwer could be as Radical as he liked. But then Isaac would think of Ben, frilled and jewelled and pomaded, with his un-English face; not essentially a Jewish face, perhaps, with its odd Latin quality as well, but—foreign; his wealth of dramatic gesture, his unconventional vocabulary; and Isaac would sigh and his pen would hang idle above the page. More heartbreak? It seemed inevitable. This was what came of those nationally chameleon qualities of the Jew, about which he had once been so enthusiastic.

Well, but suppose the boy succeeded. Suppose he did become the member for High Wycombe. Then he might never write another book. The whole pitch and colour of his life would change, from the scholarship dear to Isaac's contemplative soul to action on a grand scale, in a blaze of publicity. A man who took his politics seriously these days—and Ben took everything he went into seriously—was never his own master again. Look at Peel, exiled from the country house he loved, yearning for his children, separated from his wife, eating his heart out making speeches night after night. Look at poor old Grey, even at his age, cooped up in the Lords these hot summer nights instead of enjoying the air on the terrace at Howick amongst the myriad female relations who adored him. Of course Ben had no family of his own—not yet—but there was Bradenham, and it would miss him.

A passive M.P. was, or should be, a contradiction in terms. And anyway it was not in Ben to be passive. He would be constantly exposing himself to censure—abuse—derision. And he took things like that so hard. Yes, if Ben was elected they were in for a stormy time. It would be the end, too, of the pale, bookish boy who wrote clever novels. Bulwer went on writing, of course, but Bulwer was killing himself with overwork, and neglecting his duties in the House to make money at his desk; except for his pet hobby, a dramatic censorship Bill, which he kept hammering at whenever he got a chance.

Well, the chick was leaving the nest forever now. Going

into politics was like marrying a wife, or being called to the
Bar. One's life could never flow the same. One became hopelessly involved. Isaac had spent his life in an effort never to
become involved, and had pretty well succeeded, if it came
to that. But Ben was sure to be in the thick of this Reform
fight if he was elected. And on the wrong side. That was the
rub. To Isaac, Ben's alliance with the Radicals went against
the grain. And it was not real. Ben was a Radical only because
he would not be a Whig and could not be a Tory. It seemed
all very odd to Isaac.

Ben lost the election. The Whigs opposed him on principle and the Tories tolerated him merely because he was
not a Whig. His victorious opponent was the official Whig
candidate, the second son of the Prime Minister.

High Wycombe was nevertheless vastly entertained by
young Mr. Disraeli and his speeches. He had addressed them
from the roof of the portico of the Red Lion Hotel, where he
stood for an hour and a quarter while his magnificent, unembarrassed, effortless voice carried to the edge of the crowd
across a spellbound silence; a young, picturesque figure in
ultra-fashionable clothes, covered with lace and gold chains,
his dark curls blown about his pale face, and the unblinking
life-sized red-painted lion in effective immobility beside him.
"When the poll is declared, I shall be there," he cried, pointing to its head, "and my opponent will be there!" His
jewelled fingers flashed round to its tail. Laughter, and a
shuffling nearer in the crowd.

The county organ of the Whigs flayed him—popinjay
was the least of the epithets hurled at him by the Press;
charlatan—adventurer—all the words they had used for Canning. And they openly accused him of Tory connections. He
replied recklessly in another speech that the nearest thing
to a Tory in disguise was a Whig in office, and received a
challenge from a gentleman in the crowd who considered
himself pointed at as the gibe was flung. (This blew over,
something to his disappointment, for duelling was in the
high Tory tradition of Canning, Wellington, and Peel.) He
wore, he declared, the badge of no party, and the livery of

no faction. (All the women had adopted his colours, pink and white.) But the constituents were, perhaps, a little confused.

His speeches were clarifying, at least in his own mind, his conflicting political tenets, and as he understood and expressed himself more fully his divergence from any one of the cut-and-dried political doctrines became even more apparent. He not only admitted this, he called attention to it. He did not conform to any one party because the right party for him did not exist. To his fresh, logical mind, the demarcations of political opinion were outworn, inelastic, hampering. They trammelled his independent spirit. They were unnecessary. He could not be bothered with them.

Basically, he was fighting for romanticism against the encroachments of the middle class mind. He said that he was a Conservative to preserve all that was good in the Constitution, and a Radical to remove all that was bad. "I care not for party!" he declared at High Wycombe. "I stand here without a party. I plead the cause of the people and I care not whose policy I arraign!" He was still trying to reconcile the two extremes in his own person, making a fourth party, a conservative Tory party, of himself. "Rid yourself of all that political jargon and factious slang of Whig and Tory," he exhorted them, at High Wycombe. "Two names with one meaning, used only to delude you—and unite in forming a great national party which can alone save the country from impending destruction!"

The constituents cheered and flocked to hear him, but young Colonel Grey was elected. The Whigs were still in, with an overwhelming majority.

It seemed inevitable that the Whigs should remain in power now, perhaps for years, resting on their laurels for having brought about the supposed millennium of Reform. No matter that the Whigs themselves had dark presentiments as to where the ball which they had set in motion would stop rolling—or that Earl Grey was already an anachronism in his own party and must strive henceforth to brake the headlong progress of the measure he had himself introduced—or that

the Government was helpless before the eternal Irish question as always, especially now that their dangerous ally
O'Connell had assisted them with the Irish vote to retain
office. It was openly acknowledged that O'Connell would
have his pike perpetually in the Ministry's side, agitating for
Repeal and for the abolition of tithes. But the Whigs were
in. It might be years before they could be ousted again, by
another general election.

Ben had tasted blood now, and knew where his future lay.
"If I had let money fly I should have come in. I make no
doubt of success another time," he wrote cheerfully to
Austen. It was true that he had not had money to throw
about. Colonel Grey had spent £800 on his victory—Ben less
than one tenth that amount.

Alroy was finished at last and in the hands of the printer.
He was working on a new political pamphlet, which was to
be accredited to "the author of *Vivian Grey*" and was to be
entitled *What Is He?* in answer to a supercilious question supposed to have been raised by the Prime Minister when he
learned the said author was contesting his son's seat at Wycombe. Its text was mainly the subject which was fast becoming Ben's own private political creed. "A Tory and a
Radical, I understand," he explained therein. "A Whig—a
democratic aristocrat, I cannot comprehend. If the Tories
indeed despair of restoring the aristocratic principle, and are
sincere in their avowal that the State cannot be governed with
the present political machinery, it is their duty to coalesce
with the Radicals, and permit both political nicknames to
merge in the common, the intelligible, and the dignified title
of a National Party. . . ." It was at least a suggestion too
startling to be ignored by anyone who met it.

At the beginning of the new year he packed up the unfinished manuscript and went off with Bulwer for a fortnight
in Bath to recuperate. Both were lionized, and thoroughly
enjoyed themselves.

I V

London,
January 29, 1833.

Dearest Sa,

I dined with the Bulwers *en famille* on Sunday, "to meet some truffles"—very agreeable company. His mother-in-law was there, Mrs. Wheeler; not so pleasant, something between Jeremy Bentham and Meg Merrilies, very clever, but awfully revolutionary. She poured forth all her systems upon my novitiate ear, and while she advocated the rights of women, Bulwer abused system-mongers and the sex, and Rosina played with her dog.

Yesterday I dined with the Nortons; it was her eldest brother's birthday, who, she says, is "the only respectable one of the family, and that is because he has a liver complaint." There were there, her brother Charles and old Charles Sheridan the uncle, and others. The only lady besides Mrs. Norton, her sister, Mrs. Blackwood, also very handsome, and very Sheridanic. She told me she was nothing. "You see, Georgy's the beauty, and Carry's the wit, and I ought to be the good one, but then I am not." I must say I liked her exceedingly, besides she knows all my works by heart!

In the evening came the beauty, "Georgy" Lady Seymour, and anything so splendid I never gazed upon. Even the handsomest family in the world, which I think the Sheridans are, all looked dull. Clusters of the darkest hair, the most brilliant complexion, a contour of face perfectly ideal. In the evening Mrs. Norton sang and acted, and did everything that was delightful. Old Mrs. Sheridan—who by the bye is young and pretty and authoress of *Carwell*—is my greatest admirer, in fact the whole family have a very proper idea of my merits! And I like them all. . . .

It had occurred to Ben somewhat whimsically that if the Bulwer and Norton households could have been shuffled and dealt again the results might have been more peaceable on both sides. Rosina Bulwer, nearly as great a beauty in her way

as Caroline Norton, but uneducated, elemental, and affectionate, might have made George Norton a supportable wife,
might even have failed to rouse in him those murderous
rages which had more than once left their mark on Caroline's
throat. And Caroline, brilliant, talented, high-spirited, with
a truly noble side inherited from her grandfather Richard
Brinsley Sheridan, would have understood Bulwer's need
for creative solitude, and moreover would have supplemented
the Hertford Street income with the earnings of her own
capable pen.

One of three exquisite daughters of a widow whose income was not large, Caroline had married George Norton
in 1827, at the age of nineteen. She was in her second season
then, with another sister waiting her turn, and the only love
affair which had meant anything to her had gone wrong.
Norton had no personal fortune and was not a very engaging personality, dull and lazy, with a passion for killing
things in the autumn shooting season. In some mood of reckless despair or pique the thing was done. Caroline found
herself tied to a jealous man with a genius for nagging and
a capacity for patient revenge—and a thirst.

The first few months were dreadful. She wept and stormed
and wrote to her mother, while he drank and tried various
ways to teach her not to brave him. His female relations all
disliked her. He was not above reminding her in their
straitened circumstances that she had brought him no dowry
and had only £50 a year of her own, which was naturally
appropriated by him on their marriage—and that therefore
she could not expect much of him.

She was barely twenty when the first baby was born, and
its expenses were paid by the proceeds of her first book, *The
Sorrows of Rosalie*. They were settled in a small house in
Storey's Gate, with a balcony over Bird Cage Walk, where
Caroline grew flowers. She had admirers, as any Sheridan was
bound to do, and soon the tiny drawing-room housed what
was very nearly a *salon*. The young Duke of Devonshire,
handsome but very deaf, came to her regularly, and she was
invited to visit at Chatsworth; Leopold, the Princess Char-

lotte's somewhat aimless widower, was devoted to her until
he went away to be King of the Belgians; Fanny Kemble
adored her. But the greatest friend of all to George Norton's
unhappy, obstinately gay young wife was Melbourne.

William Lamb, Lord Melbourne, was past fifty and had
known her famous grandfather. His own marriage with Lady
Caroline Lamb, before he had come into the title, had been
a stormy one; that unfortunate Lady Caroline who had loved
and tormented Byron, but never bored him—he said so himself—and who later on, during the long estrangement from
her husband, had out of sheer mischievousness and vanity
enslaved Edward Bulwer in his Cambridge days. After her
death in 1828 Melbourne had figured as co-respondent in a
divorce trial, which was hushed up except for the drawing-
room gossip, and had amiably lived it down and gone his own
way as always. Lady Caroline had a faculty of leaving men
depleted, cynical, raw to the touch of another woman's hand.
Melbourne survived association with her better than most
of them, by cultivating a cheerful cynicism. He was an excellent sportsman and naturalist, and a scholar; an indolent
politician in that he never made memorable speeches, nor
laboured in any cause. After twenty years of Lady Caroline's
passions and hysteria, and the birth of a half-imbecile son,
Melbourne was still able to savour life, but he took it now
pretty much as he found it.

Lonely and sensitive and younger than his years, he had
always a need of women's society and could be an enchanting
companion. When he was named Home Secretary to the
Grey Government, Caroline Norton had written to him as
a friend of her family and at Norton's own request, to ask for
a place for her husband (who was an unabashed Tory) in
the new Whig régime. On an impulse, Melbourne called at
the house in Storey's Gate instead of writing a reply. They
liked each other at the first glance. He kept on coming.
She grew to count on him more and more. In his mature
philosophy, his lazy good humour, and his utter lack of
meanness, he was the last antithesis to the man she had
married. A small magistracy was found for Norton as per his

request. And by the time Ben arrived in London, Melbourne of the Home Office was a fixture in Storey's Gate.

Caroline, whose family was old in the Whig tradition, was an ardent Reformer. Melbourne, who was not by temperament a crusader in any cause, spoke and voted for Reform because he saw clearly that it was inevitable. Political discussion was pungent and enlightening in Caroline's drawing-room during the exciting years of 1832 and 1833, when the Whigs were trying desperately to cope with their own Frankenstein as the first flush of triumph wore off and the practical aspects of their reckless undertaking began to show.

Melbourne was amused. Everything amused him now, who had taught himself long ago that nothing was worth agonizing over. His attitude of wayward indifference to pressing issues, his perverse affectation of ignorance on difficult subjects, his invariable "Why not leave it alone?" when some energetic new political proposal was made to him, exasperated and deceived his colleagues as well as his opponents. At his desk at the Home Office Melbourne dealt firmly and wisely with his responsibilities and got through an incredible amount of painstaking toil; but he refused ever to admit that he exerted himself, and scorned to raise a dust about it.

Meanwhile the popularity of the Reform Ministry mysteriously waned, as the promised millennium did not occur. People were still cold and hungry, during the winter which followed the passing of the Bill. There was no single commanding figure at Westminster. Grey was swamped. Peel was leading a small band of his own amid profound gloom—they were known as Conservatives, and sometimes voted with Grey against the extremes which the Radical element was trying to force on the bewildered Ministry. Peel was now twenty-three years in Parliament, and without any question was the foremost man in the House, but he seemed after all to take very little trouble. Forced into the position of leader, he still would not lead. Stanley's somewhat erratic talent was concentrated on the Irish question, and his drastic Coercion Bill had Peel's support, though they never got on well together. O'Connell and his gang had by now seceded from

the Whigs and were fighting Stanley's Bill to the death, de-
nouncing it as "base, bloody, and brutal." The words, which
were O'Connell's, became a monotonous catch-phrase. Ireland was torn with internal dissension, in which even the
priests took part.

The Radicals slated the Government for inactivity and
feebleness, the Tories hated and opposed it, and believed
they would soon return to power. The King had never forgiven it for forcing his hand. There was a general feeling that
its days were numbered.

Ben, still smarting from his recent encounter with the
Whigs at High Wycombe, nevertheless fell under the influence of the Home Secretary's kindly interest and good humour, and when presented to him after dinner at Caroline
Norton's found himself to his own surprise pouring out the
grievances of his recent campaign. The Whigs had behaved
abominably to an unknown genius, and by so doing they
had thwarted his dearest ambition and retarded the good
of the country. And now he would have to wait—how long?—
for another opportunity.

Melbourne, who viewed life always with a leisurely and
speculative eye, was strangely attracted by the uncommon-
place language and flaming spirit of this odd-looking young
man in excessive clothes, who spoke with such un-English
unself-consciousness of his own capabilities. Melbourne was
amused. He wanted more of this. Having no personal ambition himself, the spectacle of such a large itch to be and to
do fascinated him.

"Well, now, tell me," he put in gently during a moment
while Ben drew breath, "when all is said and done and all
obstacles miraculously removed—what do you want to be?"

Ben looked back at him gravely, his large eyes larger
with the solemnity of the moment. There was no embarrassing patronage in the question—merely an honest and friendly
desire to know. He could be honest too.

"I want to be Prime Minister," he said simply.

For a moment Melbourne's habitual composure was frac-
tured. He stared. The boy actually meant it. In so many

words of one syllable he had stated his astounding goal. To Melbourne, with his lifelong training in decent reticence and his naturally self-contained turn of mind, to this most English of Englishmen, Ben's quiet statement was a nakedness. It was incredible. Why, the fellow had not even won his seat! But Melbourne was usually kind.

"No chance of that in our time," he said with all seriousness. "It is all arranged and settled. Nobody but Lord Grey could have carried the Reform Bill, perhaps. But he is an old man and when he gives up he will certainly be succeeded by one who has every requirement for the position, in the prime of life, old blood, high rank, great fortune and greater ability—I mean Stanley. Nobody can compete with Stanley now. I heard him the other night in the Commons, when the party were all divided and breaking away from their ranks, recall them by mere force of superior will and eloquence. He rose like a young eagle above them all, and kept hovering over their heads until they were reduced to abject submissiveness. There is nothing like him."

"Stanley," said Ben thoughtfully, his eyes on the older man's face, bright and full of attention.

"If you are going into politics and mean to stick to it, I dare say you will do very well," Melbourne added, hoping he had not thrown too much cold water, "for you have ability and enterprise. And if you are careful how you steer, no doubt you will get into some port at last. But you must put all these foolish notions out of your head; they won't do at all. Stanley will be the next Prime Minister, you'll see."

There was a little more of this, and then Ben drifted away, pensively. Stanley. Eton and Oxford again. How they hung together, that breed. Melbourne was Cambridge, but it was all one at Westminster. Stanley, was it! With nearly fifteen years of membership behind him, and the Canning tradition, Stanley had stood up against the Duke of Wellington, faced out O'Connell, and contrived some sort of *rapprochement* with Peel. The Whigs were notoriously lacking in young men of talent. Yes, and Stanley would be the Earl of Derby one day. . . .

"That's all very well, but how does he *know?*" said a light, sweet voice beside him.

He glanced down in surprise, for it was as though she had heard his thoughts or seen inside his head. It was Mrs. Wyndham Lewis, looking very pretty in pink silk with a lot of lace and bows. He had heard other women say that she did not know how to dress, but he admired her expensive appearance; and there was a remarkable freshness about her always, her roseleaf skin and small white teeth. And she had a way of looking up.

"Did you hear all that?" he murmured ruefully.

"I listened," she said shamelessly. "After what you said to him, I had to listen. *I* think he's wrong, though. Wyndham says Peel will be next."

"Ah," said Ben with interest, and thought that over. "I could bear Peel, couldn't you?"

She drew her shoulders together, half shiver, half shrug.

"He's such a *chilly* man," she said, her gaze as candid as a child's.

He laughed.

"Won't he flirt with you?" he said.

"Mr. Disraeli!" She was shocked and pleased.

"You women all like Melbourne best," he accused. "That's because he is handsome and footloose and makes a fuss of you. But Peel will get there all the same, I think. I suppose I must try not to grudge it him."

"There's plenty of time!" she cried. "Let him have a year—five years—what does that matter to you? You're young enough to wait!"

"Nobody is young enough to wait!" he cried passionately.

"That proves how young you are." Her eyes were wistful on him.

"And what right have you to talk as though you were my grandmother?" he demanded with a frank, admiring glance.

"Me! My dear boy, I very nearly could be! I was married the year of Waterloo!" And laughing back over her round shoulder at him, she left him.

Laughing too, he made her a little bow, while his mind

did a swift calculation—1814—why, she must be about ten years older than he was. It didn't seem possible, her cheeks were as smooth as a babe's.

He watched her cross the room and lay her hand on her husband's arm, and noted with a twinge of something like envy how the man's whole face softened as he turned to her. Apparently there was not so much difference between her age and Wyndham's as one would suppose. Wyndham was the Tory member for Maidstone, a strange, stern, uncommunicative man in his fifties. But they had something, those two, that made one feel an outsider—lonely, like looking in at a lighted, cosy room where one had no right to enter.

And yet at the same time he felt somehow comforted. Well, yes, let Peel have it a year or two. . . .

V

There was one name which did not appear in his letters to Sa.

He was seated one night at dinner between two dull women —one of them, he reflected, was dull because she had had no education and the other because she had had too much— and his eye wandered along the other side of the table to where someone had laughed. He had never seen her before, and for a minute his gaze remained riveted, incredulous of her sheer beauty. She was young, but not miss-ish, exquisitely curled and dressed, fair but not insipid, a honey-blonde with eyes which might be brown or violet. Her mouth was red and wise, her teeth were perfect, her throat was long and round—one glance was never enough for her, one must look and look, unable to wrench one's gaze away. And—she could laugh. One felt that it had not been an altogether proper joke.

While her eyes still slanted with that very knowing mirth, they met his by accident across the table, for a moment only, and then returned with a sweep of her dark lashes to the man on her right, the man who had made her laugh, and whose eyes as they rested on her were impudent and at their ease. Ben's fingers closed on the stem of his champagne glass—he waited—her glance came back in time to catch his across the brim. Without losing a beat of her conversational duet with her partner, she reached for her own glass, and as it touched her lips she glanced again across the table, and away.

"Yes, very cold," Ben heard himself agreeing automatically to the voice on his left. "But spring always arrives, I find, eventually." The resulting giggle revolted him.

What had happened across the champagne glasses was nothing, of course. He thought less and less of it as a gesture —a wholly childish idea of flirtation—a silly, banal, contemptible performance, to catch a woman's eyes over a lifted glass and call it a beginning. Such things were only taken seriously by second-rate novelists. And yet—it was not just champagne in his pulses now. He had an unreasoning, elated sense that the evening was made; that tonight was different from, better than all other nights, that something was going to happen. . . .

He was silent and preoccupied after dinner, when the men closed in round the port. He wore the mask. For as the ladies left the room he had seen her arm linked through her hostess's, and had heard his name on someone's lips. So she had asked who he was. He knew now that when he could get away upstairs he would be presented—there was to be dancing. He felt a tingling in his veins, his fingertips curled inward underneath the table, and his face was sombre and secretive among the jests which flew past his head.

Escaping from the dining-room at last, he sought his hostess. Her smile was enigmatic.

"You too?" she said, which left him speculating as he crossed the room at her side.

His head was suddenly very clear as he made his bow. Why must he flutter like a girl in her first season because a beautiful woman had not snubbed his impertinence? And so they were very formal. They agreed that it was a late spring, and that grate fires were still delicious. They discovered that they both loved the sun. He spoke of Italy with feeling, picturesquely—she had always wanted to go there, but had only got

as far as Paris. She was pleased that he knew Paris too. She
said she hoped the dancing would start soon as the wine had
made her sleepy. He said the champagne was very good
in this house—and when she laughed he realized that she had
construed the reference into a gallantry over the lifted glasses
and he felt rather clever. So she wanted to play. He smiled
audaciously into her eyes and claimed the first dance.

It was a waltz, and as his arm went round her waist her
perfume reached him, fresh and sweet and somehow familiar,
but nameless. As they circled the room it persisted. Above
the rival fragrance of the flowers and the other women, her
own was with him, tantalizingly familiar, but elusive. They
hardly spoke until the music stopped, and before they had
reached any kind of conversational footing again, she was
carried off by a new partner.

It was a part of his detachment as a rule never to dance. He
stood inscrutable against the wall, or bent a respectful ear
to ladies who weren't dancing, or resisted the efforts of fellow
bachelor strays to engage him in conversation. But he did
not take the floor with anyone else.

Whatever it was, it had happened. Life stood still until he
could be with her again. He noted with disparaging eyes that
all the other women's faces were dull and their waists were
thick. They existed, merely, but she was *alive,* she had solved
the riddle of the universe, and her eyelids were heavy with
wisdom. He craved impatiently to learn from her what it
was that she knew and all these other women did not. She was
different. He must know why.

He lost her at supper and was polite to his hostess.

"So you're still mooning after Henrietta," she said. "Take
care, my boy—put cotton wool in your ears, lash yourself to
the mast, and sail by on the farther side!"

He looked at her with aversion, behind the mask. Cat.
Because she did not know how to enjoy her own life, she
must belittle any woman who made the most of hers. Perhaps
that was it. This Henrietta *used* life, took tribute from it
hourly, with all her five senses. A man whispered a gun-room
story with a point, and she threw up her chin and laughed.

A stranger stared with delight and she—encouraged him. Or
had she? Yes, decidedly, he was encouraged. Or perhaps—it
was not impossible—she had thought Disraeli worth looking
at twice. He remembered acutely the yielding weight of her
on his arm in the waltz. Their steps were perfectly matched,
they seemed positively to breathe in unison, and she had
raised no barrier of words against their mutual surrender to
the music. There was no false modesty in him to deny that
she had felt the same throbbing satisfaction that he had.

"They give the most delightful water-parties," someone
was saying. "I wish *my* husband had a yacht! They serve the
most exquisite food, at a big table on deck, with a canopy—
I must say, Henrietta does do things well!"

"But mind you, Mr. Disraeli," his hostess pointed out
with some satisfaction, "she hates men who talk politics. She
told me so."

"Thank you, I shall remember," he said gravely, and raised
his brows at their laughter.

The evening had suddenly come to an end, and he had
not had another word with her. It was insupportable. He
took up a position at the foot of the staircase and at last she
came down, wrapped to the chin in a fur-trimmed pelisse, her
honey-coloured curls gleaming above it. She saw him there
without surprise, accepted him with her wide, straight look;
there was no coquetry in her, nothing sidelong, but rather an
appraisal embarrassingly frank in that steady look. A school-
boy would have flushed and fidgeted under it. He stepped
forward and she gave him her hand—"I must see you again,"
he said very low as he bent over it.

"Tomorrow at four," she murmured, and added an address in Curzon Street, and was gone.

He stood looking after her. He had no idea which of the
three men who closed in behind her was her husband.

A brisk walk along Piccadilly to his rooms did nothing to
put him in the mood for sleep. He poked up his fire, smoked
a pipe, and prowled about in a splendid dressing-gown. He
had no thoughts, only a state of mind. At last he put out

the lights, firmly, and firmly put himself to bed. As the sun
came up, he slept.

Over a late breakfast—with a slight headache—he suffered
a thorough reaction. A white night usually looks abominable
the next morning. Not many emotions can weather a boiled
egg and muffins. He began to think back cautiously to see if
he had made an impetuous fool of himself. He was certainly
not drunk last night, he could swear to that. And after all,
what had happened? He had caught a woman's eyes across the
table, and later they had discussed the weather and danced
one waltz together. Well, what would he have expected to
talk to her about—the state of his soul? And yet she had whispered through guarded lips the address in Curzon Street.
At this point the case for the prosecution broke down.

He arrived in Curzon Street that afternoon very calm, with
an active sense of proportion. One must not imagine things.
One was not in a novel. Doubtless the room would be full
of other people, having cakes and wine and gabbling. . . .

The house was very still, as he followed the footman up the
carpeted stairs.

The Empire drawing-room was empty, with a table ready-
laid beside the fire. He saw with surprise and satisfaction that
she had adopted the very new fashion of afternoon tea. It
was so like her to be among the first. He wondered with an
idle corner of his brain why even Sa seemed faintly scandalized at the idea that anyone who was not an invalid would
want tea in the middle of the afternoon. His mother said contemptuously that it was a habit for nurseries and sick-rooms.
But gazing down at Henrietta's French china, classic Adam
silver, and fine Irish linen, the hissing urn, and something
keeping hot under a silver cover, he considered it quite the
cosiest and most intimate custom ever invented. After all,
one had wine with one's meals. . . .

The door closed softly behind him, and the waft of her
perfume and the whisper of her silk skirts preceded her;
women's clothes had begun to billow again, after the skimpi-
ness of Regency fashions. He sternly repressed the singing
thrill which ran through him and bowed silently above her

hand. Someone else might come in at any moment—his glance swept the table again—two cups.

"I wasn't at all sure you'd come today," she said.

"Weren't you?" It told her nothing.

"I thought perhaps—well, that you had had just an impulse last night—"

"Or too much champagne," he suggested gravely, watching her.

She laughed, chin up, eyes aslant, and his heart skipped in his chest. It was thus he had seen her first.

"Tell me it wasn't champagne," she commanded.

"No, it wasn't. But it went to my head all the same."

He was standing before her correctly, his feet together, his elbows in, his face a miracle of sobriety—a man who has just made a bow and is prepared to make another. She sat down on the sofa by the fireside table, and her candid gaze, which could have passed for innocence and was not, ran over him slowly. He had again the ghostly feeling of a vanished school-boy awkwardness underneath his composure as he endured it.

"You were going to tell me more about Italy," she remarked.

"Was I?" Formally, he accepted the place beside her on the sofa, and watched her begin to make the tea. Sleeves were enormous that year, caught into tiny wristbands, and her narrow hands were long and languid with the silver. "What do you want to know about Italy, then?"

"Well, the climate, for one thing. Does it really make one go all soft inside—*dolce far niente*—that sort of thing."

For a moment his thoughts dwelt on a balcony in Venice.

"Most decidedly," he said, and smiled. How long ago. He had grown up since then.

"So that one makes a fool of oneself?"

"Voluntarily," he assured her, smiling.

"How very alluring." She handed him his cup, a shallow egg-shell in a shallow saucer, crusted with gold.

He was still incredulous of this delicious thing which persisted in happening to him. He began to talk somewhat at random of Verona's market place and Roman remains, of the white moonlight at Venice, of Byron's name scratched on the wall at Ferrara, and the crescent bay of Genoa. She listened, her eyelids a little lazy, as though the weight of the long lashes wearied them; and he knew unerringly that it was his voice she listened to, and not his words. He began to play on it then like an instrument, as he had learned to do before a crowd at the hustings, only now it was low and tender in all its notes, attuned to the small distance between them, sliding smoothly from humour to gravity, caressing, wooing—in his quiet, detailed sentences about the enchantment of Italy, he told her that she herself was lovely and that he was hers.

There were pauses, when the whole house seemed silent and empty, waiting. And still he could not believe. It was a situation not even a novelist would dare to depict, but he was living it, and everything that he had lived before seemed second-hand, childish, negligible, stale. Reason said that she was a married woman with a husband who was—presentable. Common sense pointed out that after all her husband was her own affair—not his. Doubtless she knew perfectly well what she was about. Doubtless the man could look after his own interests, if he had any. . . .

The early spring twilight had begun to draw in, and no one came to light the lamps. He rose with one of his quick, lithe movements, smooth and effortless as a cat's.

"I'm boring you," he said, with every inflection of penitence. "Do forgive me. If I don't take myself off at once you will never let me come again."

She sat still, looking up at him.

"Do you want to come again?"

"I shall count the hours."

She smiled up at him, as it were drowsily in the dimming light, with that odd, sleepy look as though her lashes dragged down her eyelids.

"Am I—just as you thought I would be, then?"

"You are even more beautiful by daylight," he said simply.

She stood up slowly and came toward him across the carpet,

drifting on invisible feet beneath the bell of her blue gown—
till she was nearer to him than in the waltz.

"Is that all you care about—beauty?"

"No. For me, beauty must be alive—vital—*breathing*
beauty. And I think you are more alive than anyone I ever
saw." Still she smiled at him, and the pause grew endless,
and she would not speak. He could have touched her by
lifting his hand. Common sense went on to say that she was
not an untried girl in the grip of a new emotion. She was a
woman, wise in the ways of her world, supremely sure of
herself and of what she wanted. It was fairly clear now, what
she wanted. . . . Her tantalizing perfume reached him
again, fresh and sweet and somehow unartificial, as though
she wore flowers—there was a low brick wall at Bradenham,
overhung with climbing pink roses and white jasmine—in
the evenings the jasmine scent was strongest—and that was
the fragrance which hung about him now. He had still some
shreds of sanity which insisted that this was not happening
at all, and that he would soon wake up and find it was tomorrow morning. . . . "And what about me?" he got out.
"Have I disappointed you?"

"Not yet," she said through her smile.

Was there something—derisive—in it? Was she laughing at
him for a prig or a dolt? Did she think him just a backward
boy who could be played with? He caught at her recklessly,
and found her lips waiting. . . .

"When do I see you again?" he demanded. "When?"

"Where do you live?" she whispered.

He told her, his face against hers.

V I

London,
March 26, 1833.

Dearest Sa,

Of *Alroy* I hear golden opinions, and I doubt not of
its success. I send you the review in the *Atlas*. There is
one in the *Town* still more eulogistic. I hear no com-

plaints of its style, except from the critics. The common readers seem to like the poetry and the excitement. Mrs. Jameson told Otley that "reading it was like riding on an Arab." Slade, the traveller, said it was "the most thoroughly Oriental book he ever read."

I have done nothing but go to the play lately, one night with Mrs. Norton to see Sheridan Knowles' new play, which was successful. Public amusements are tedious, but in a private box with a fair companion less so—a capital fire, our own tea, and really very amusing. Mrs. Norton has given me her portrait. Tomorrow, great breakfast at the Wyndham Lewises', when magnificent plate is to be presented from Maidstone to our host, the defeated Conservative. . . .

London,
May 22, 1833.

Dearest Sa,

There was a review in Hyde Park, and the Wyndham Lewises gave a *déjeuner*, to which I went. By the bye, would you like Lady Z. for a sister-in-law, very clever, £25,000, and domestic? As for love, all my friends who married for love either beat their wives or live apart from them. I may commit many follies in life, but I never intend to marry for "love," which I am sure is a guarantee of infelicity. . . .

London,
August 4, 1833.

My dear Sa,

My letters are shorter than Napoleon's, but I love you more than he did Josephine. I shall be down tomorrow, but very likely by the mail, as I have a great many things to attend to. . . .

"I wish," remarked Isaac plaintively when Ben arrived that summer at Bradenham, full of stories and gossip and laughter, "that your organization allowed you to write calmer letters—or that you could sober yourself down to a diary before you went to bed."

"A diary?" Ben crooked derisive eyebrows. "But there's so much one mustn't put in it!"

"I should like to know more," said Sarah, "about Lady Z."

"She was a great admirer of Southey," he informed her gravely. "So was I—that night."

It became a lasting family joke that summer, the possibility of Lady Z. Behind her innocent, sheltering skirts he hid Henrietta and all that she had come to mean to him. He felt safer with Lady Z. about, in case they noticed a difference in him. He gave them Lady Z. as a peg to hang suspicion on.

He bought a notebook. And feeling, he said, rather like a miss in her teens, he began methodically on the first of September to cast his mind back across the months which marked his absorption into that social swirl which was the curious blend of literature, politics, fashion, and bohemianism where he found himself so much at home.

"I have passed the whole of this year in lounging and pleasure," he wrote. "And one incident has indeed made it the happiest of my life. How long will these feelings last? They have stood a great test, and now absence, perhaps the most fatal of all." These were the things one could not put in. The test of intrigue, precarious, hurried meetings, secrecy, had not diminished the flame which had flared so suddenly between him and Henrietta. It was an exhausting business altogether—for though her husband appeared to have a life of his own which occupied him, and showed no inclination to observe things or be in the way, they still strove elaborately for a pretence of disinterest in the eyes of the world. He had felt the strain. The peace of Bradenham, the utter frankness of its atmosphere and inhabitants amounting to naïveté, enfolded him gratefully. It amused him to feel old and sinful, come back to Eden again.

"My disposition is now indolent," he noted. "I wish to be idle and enjoy myself, muse over the stormy past and smile at the placid present. All men of high imagination are indolent. My career will probably be more energetic than ever, and the world will wonder at my ambition. . . ."

And then on October 21—"Seven weeks! And not a line in my book!"

He was at work on a new venture which he called a *Revolutionary Epick,* and which bore marks of Miltonian influence. It dealt in verse with Napoleon's career, and the Genius of Feudalism and the Genius of Federalism each pled their antagonistic causes before the Almighty Throne. It was roughly ten years since he had given serious effort to poetry, in his Frederick's Place days. And now he sat at a flat-topped desk drawn close to the wide window of his room at Bradenham, with thin autumn sunshine faintly warm athwart his shoulders, writing of Athens:

> Blue ocean, bowery plain, and azure sky,
> And marble walls, and free-born citadel,
> Glittering with snowy columns in the sun;
> And gardens of delight, in whose green glades
> And fragrant groves—

The *Epick* was published during the following spring, and was a prompt failure, as it no doubt deserved to be.

This did not for once depress him. He was by then enjoying himself again rather expensively in society. Opera, balls, suppers, water-parties were his chief concern during the early summer of 1834, while O'Connell became more and more unmanageable at Westminster, and the Reform Government viewed with dismay its steadily diminishing popularity.

He did his best to re-create for Sarah's hungry imagination those bright scenes in which her butterfly brother moved. Sarah loved parties and seldom saw one now. Isaac's eyes were bothering him again, and she spent long hours in his library reading aloud to him the endless books which were necessary to his being, so that he might make his notes and write his considered commentaries without too much fatigue. Sometimes in a spasm of conscience he would apologize for confining her to the side of an old man's armchair, and she would point out that she had nothing else to do. They were drawing very close together—the girl whose life was over, and the old man who had never really lived.

London,
May, 1834.

Dear Sa,

On Monday I dined with Lady Blessington—the Prince of Muskova, Charles Lafitte, Lords Castlereagh, Elphinstone, etc. Hope's ball was the finest thing this year—we supped off gold and danced in the sculpture gallery. To-day is the Drawing-room. But nobody thinks of anything but politics. The Ministry at present are quite broken up; there is no Government, and perhaps there will be a dissolution. I dine with O'Connell on Saturday, and breakfasted with Castlereagh a few days ago. He has a fine collection of turquoise Sèvres. . . .

London,
June 4, 1834.

Dearest Sa,

There is a lull in the political storm; it is supposed that the session will now be hurried over quietly, and then something must be determined on. The Tories will not take office unless the Whigs give up in despair. My own opinion is that in the recess the King will make an effort to form a Conservative Government with Peel and Stanley.

I have had great success in society this year in every respect. I make my way easily in the highest set where there is no envy, malice, etc., and where they like to admire and be amused. Yesterday Lord Durham called on me, being the first day he has been in Town since we met. I was not at home; but this Lady Blessington told me. I am also right in politics as well as society, being now backed by a very powerful party, and I think the winning one. . . .

London,
July 7, 1834.

My dearest,

I have quite recovered from my influenza, but I am taking quinine and shall yet for a few days. I was very unwell until Friday morning. I had promised to join a water party in Sir Frank's yacht, which has returned with-

out its master, to witness the Royal embarkation on Saturday morning, and the exertion, which I dreaded, cured
me.

It was almost the only party of pleasure that ever turned
out pleasant. Lady Sykes, and Sir M. and Lady Georgiana
Cholmely, the Burdett daughters, Castlereagh, Ossulston,
and myself. The day was beautiful. The ladies went off
the night before. Ossulston drove me down in his cab. We
arrived just in time, half past 9, in spite of a long debate on
tithes which had kept him and Castlereagh up till 2. Castlereagh rode down and arrived covered with dust and sulky,
but just in time also; and regained his good humour after
breakfast. After the show we breakfasted and sailed up to
Greenwich. After lionizing the hospital and sentimentaliz-
ing in the Park, we had a magnificent banquet on deck, and
had nothing from shore except whitebait, piping hot.
Ossulston was our minstrel and a most musical one; and
we all arrived in Town in time for the ballet. I never
knew a more agreeable day, and never drank so much
champagne in my life.

I woke quite well, and after a very dull dinner party
at the Wyndham Lewises' went on to Lady Salisbury's. So
you see I am on my legs again. I am sorry for dear Jem,
but he has many fellow sufferers. The influenza, however,
is not so severe as last year. . . .

London,
July 11, 1834.

Dear Sa,

We remain here in breathless agitation. I can give you
no idea of the state of excitement. At this moment nothing
is settled. Lords Lansdowne and Melbourne were with the
King all yesterday. Massey Stanley brought the news of
Grey's resignation to the opera on Tuesday at nine o'clock.
I was in Lady Blessington's box. No one would believe it.
On Wednesday I met the Duke of Wellington at Lady
Cork's, in his blue ribbon. He was in high spirits, but say-
ing everywhere that the Tories would not take office. "He
always wears his blue ribbon when mischief is going on,"

whispered Ossulston to me. Fonblanque, who was there, said the Tories were like a woman who fancies herself *enceinte* and goes about saying it is not yet her time.

Yesterday I met Lord Lyndhurst, whom I like very much. The next time he goes the Norfolk circuit he is to sleep at Bradenham. . . .

On the 7th of July the Prime Minister, his Cabinet weakened by Stanley's resignation a few weeks before, battered by the storm of the Irish Coercion Bill, beset by internal dissension and plagued by criticism, abruptly resigned. He said he was too old to go on. He said it was the times moving too fast and not himself too slowly. He was tired, and Reform had proved a delusion and a snare. He wanted to go and live in the country with his devoted family. After all, he was seventy.

Only the year before, Melbourne had said that when Grey gave up no one could compete with Stanley for the premiership. And where was Stanley now? Stanley, who had every requirement for the position, said Melbourne on the hearthrug at Caroline Norton's in 1833—old blood, high rank, great fortune, and greater ability—politically speaking, Stanley was to seek. He had resigned over the matter of Irish church revenues, and had withdrawn himself permanently and conclusively from the Whig camp, which was a crippling loss to them and no gain to the Tories, as he was now speaking and voting as an independent member, holding aloof from any party affiliations whatever. And so it was not Stanley, but Melbourne himself, who became the next Prime Minister.

Grey had recommended Melbourne to the King, as it were on his way out. William liked Melbourne, and spoke of him as "a great gentleman." Whatever happened now would probably be a temporary arrangement, and the man who had held the Home Office throughout the alarms and disturbances of the past few years must logically be well fitted to take charge of the Government. The King hoped for a strong coalition ministry to check the Radicals, who horrified him. The King hoped for Peel and even Stanley to hold office under Melbourne. And Wellington, of course. The King always wanted Wellington.

Melbourne, his inherent tact stretched to the uttermost, wrote a long memorandum explaining to His Majesty why coalition was impossible. In the first place, Peel was not willing, and Stanley swore he had done with the Whigs forever. The King was disappointed and showed it, but Melbourne as Prime Minister philosophically reconstructed Grey's old Whig Cabinet with promotions and new blood, and prepared to carry on. Henceforth a franker and more genial atmosphere seemed to pervade the administration.

No one was any more surprised than Melbourne at his sudden elevation to the premiership, and he had hesitated long about accepting it. He hated trouble, and the things which seemed to him insufficiently important. He loved leisure, and cheerful conversation with people who had no ulterior motive, about things which did not matter very much. He had no desire for change, and liked things pretty well as they were. There was nothing in it for him, who had no personal ambition and whose thankless job it would now be to act as a brake on a coach which seemed destined to run down hill.

However! Stanley was sulking in his tent, and somebody had to do something. Resigned to his fate, Melbourne cheerfully shouldered the Government. His welcome, even among the Opposition, was cordial, even though they knew he had declined coalition with their chiefs. If it had to be a Whig Government, they preferred to have Melbourne at its head.

There were those even among his own party who wondered audibly if he was not too indolent to fulfil the duties of a Prime Minister, deceived anew by his unruffled "Why not leave it alone?" and his wilful "I really know nothing about the matter," which was so seldom true. The irrepressible Sydney Smith saw through him: "Everything about him seems to betoken a careless desolation; everyone would suppose, from his manner, that he was playing at chuck-farthing with human happiness, that he would giggle away the Great Charter, and decide by the method of tee-totum whether my lords the bishops should retain their seats in the House of Lords. All this is the mere vanity of surprising, and making us believe that he can play with kingdoms as other men can with ninepins. I cannot, however, allow to this minister the merit of indifference to his actions; I believe him to be conscientiously alive to the good or evil he is doing. I am sorry to hurt any man's feelings, and to brush away the magnificent fabric of levity and gaiety which he has reared; but I accuse our Minister of honesty and diligence; I deny that he is careless or rash; he is nothing more than a man of good understanding and good principles, disguised in the eternal and somewhat wearisome affectation of a political roué."

The crisis safely past once more, the gay season went on.

London,
July 23, 1834.

Dearest Sa,

I adhere to my plan of being down with you in a week or ten days, and tell Tita to get my pipes in order as I look forward to a batch of smoking with great zest.

I go every day to fêtes and water-parties. Lady Tavistock's at Richmond on Saturday. Monday another party to Blackwall with D'Orsay. Tomorrow we go to Lord Hertford's. I find the end of the season more fatiguing than the beginning, owing to the morning festivities.

The water-party at the Cedars most delightful. We embarked at 5 o'clock, the heavens very favourable, and sang all the way down, wandered in beautiful gardens, worthy of Paul Veronese, full not only of flowers but fountains and parroquets; the dinner first rate and much better than cold, miserable picnics, in which all bring the same things. People are still in Town, but Goodwood will, I think, clear us. . . .

VII

In his desk at Bradenham he found the notebook which he had begun on his last visit, at Isaac's suggestion. Lady Blessington too had advised him to keep some sort of record of his doings. He opened the book to a fresh page and dipped his pen, his face, in the solitude of his room with the mask laid aside, rather like the face of an absorbed child with a copy-book.

"And now nearly a year has elapsed," he began conscientiously. "And what an eventful one! A season of unparalleled success and gaiety. What a vast number of extraordinary characters have passed before me, or with whom I have become acquainted. I sat next to Lyndhurst at dinner at Henrietta's. We took to each other instantly. He said that if he were to choose a career now it would be to be at once editor and proprietor of a first rate newspaper.

"Interviews with O'Connell, Beckford, and Lord Durham, three men all making a great noise. Will they be remembered when this book turns up, if it ever does? Perhaps O'Connell. A man of the greatest genius. I sat next him at dinner. Very communicative. Said that from being the son of a gentleman farmer he had raised himself to be *une des puissances du monde* (his very words).

"How sorry I am that I did not keep some record of the last four months. I revived my acquaintance with the Sheridans, with whom I was so intimate last year, Mrs. Norton, Helen Blackwood, Lady Seymour—three matchless sisters and the mother. Bulwer is one of the few men with whom my intellect comes into collision with benefit. He is full of thought, and views at once original and just.

"I have this year become very popular with the dandies. D'Orsay took a fancy to me, and they take their tone from him. Lady Blessington is their muse and she declared violently in my favour. What a happy, or rather amusing, society Henrietta and myself commanded this year. What delicious little suppers after the opera! Castlereagh ever gay, a constant attendant, and Ossulston, the pet of all the women, with his beautiful voice. Then we made it a point always to have some very pretty women. How much I could write of this singular coterie! But this is a mem. which will recall them to my memory. . . ."

His introduction, through Bulwer and D'Orsay, to Lady

Blessington's gay evenings in Seamore Place was one of the prizes of this extraordinary season. Lady Blessington was not received by the ladies of London society, and so she was at home every evening from eight until twelve, unless she went to the theatre or the opera, when her box was a rallying point for the gentlemen, to the chagrin of beauties who considered themselves more respectable.

In Lady Blessington's octagonal dining-room lined with mirrors statesmen, soldiers, diplomats, painters, authors, men of rank and ability from every country in Europe were proud to gather. The food and the wines were exquisite. Bowls of fruit and flowers stood in the centre of the table, and the mature beauty of the hostess was framed by the carved gilt chair in which Louis XVIII had sat during his visit to London. When she left the dining-room at the end of the meal it was as though she took away the light with her, so that the ensuing hour seemed by contrast long and heavy, before they rejoined her in the red and gold drawing-room with its shaded candelabra and Marie Antoinette's own clock on the mantelpiece. Not even D'Orsay the magnificent had her knack of drawing out a guest and making him think well of himself.

It was because of D'Orsay that she was not received in London. D'Orsay had been married to the late Lord Blessington's daughter Harriet (by a former marriage) during the Earl's lifetime—people said in an attempt to regularize an already ambiguous situation à trois which existed in that household during their travels in Italy. The marriage was a notorious failure. The girl was shy and dull and hostile, apparently felt her position ignominious, and made no effort to improve it. Then Blessington died, and his widow and D'Orsay and D'Orsay's sulky wife returned to England together. Harriet soon left them, for her father's people, which made more talk; and D'Orsay and Lady Blessington went serenely on together.

The world was shocked, and said it was all very flagrant. But people who knew them shrugged and said, "Why not?" and went on going to Seamore Place. Lady Blessington was

years older than the perennially boyish D'Orsay, and she had
had a brutalized and wretched girlhood. He paid her the
elaborate laughing homage of a favourite son or a beloved
younger brother. They suited each other and were obviously
happy together. There was nothing visibly scandalous about
Seamore Place. And anyway—why should she not be happy
now, at last?

Lady Blessington probably knew more secrets than anyone
else in London, and kept them all. So of course she knew
about Henrietta, who was less of a secret at the end of 1834
than she had been.

Bradenham House,
August 5, 1834.

My dear Lady Blessington,

I was sorry to leave London without being a moment
alone with you; but though I came to the Opera on purpose Fate was against us. I did not reach this place till Sunday, very ill indeed from the pangs of parting. Indeed, I
feel as desolate as a ghost, and I do not think that I shall
ever be able to settle to anything again. I am quite at a
loss how to manage affairs in the future, as I find separation more irksome than even my bitterest imagination predicted. God, however, is great, and the future must regu-
late itself, for I can't.

My father I find better than I expected, and much
cheered by my presence. He is now very busy on his *History of English Literature,* in which he is far advanced. I
am mistaken if you will not delight in these volumes. They
are full of new views on the history of our language, and
indeed of our country, for the history of a State is neces-
sarily mixed up with the history of its literature.

For myself, I am doing nothing. The western breeze
favours an al fresco existence, and I am seated with a pipe
under a spreading sycamore, solemn as a pasha.

What do you think of the modern French novelists, and
is it worth my while to read them, and if so what do you
recommend me? What of Balzac, is he better than Sue and
Geo: Sand Dudevant, and are these inferior to Hugo? I ask

you these questions because you will give me short answers, like all people who are masters of their subject.

I suppose it is vain to hope to see my dear D'Orsay here; I wish indeed he would come. Here is a cook by no means contemptible. He can bring his horses if he likes, but I can mount him. Adieu, dear Lady Blessington, some day I will try to write you a more amusing letter; at present I am in truth ill and sad. . . .

Seamore Place,
August 20, 1834.

Dear Mr. Disraeli,

I am very sorry to hear that you have been ill and sad; we are all but poor machines easily put out of order when the mind and heart—or both, for they always like true friends sympathize—are deranged or chagrined. What poor philosophers even the wisest of us are proved to be, when influenced by some master passion, and authors who, like yourself, can make others think, are among those who can least govern their thoughts when once under the rule of love. . . .

The passion for Henrietta had twice survived the severe test of absence. Reaction from the stimulus of her presence now took the form of boundless languor. He complained of pains in the legs and retired to the sofa, a somewhat fractious invalid on a diet, with doses of ammonia.

But his mind would not stay quiet in his idle body, and before long he was writing again, a love story this time—his first. The heroine's name proved to be Henrietta, and the book was an impassioned argument for the cause of love at first sight: "Amid the gloom and travail of existence suddenly to behold a beautiful being, and as instantaneously to feel an overwhelming conviction that with that fair form forever our destiny must be entwined; that there is no more joy but in her joy, no sorrow but when she grieves; that in her sigh of love, in her smile of fondness, hereafter is all bliss; to feel our flaunty ambition fade away like a shrivelled gourd before her vision; to feel fame a juggle and posterity a lie; and to be prepared at once, for this great object, to forfeit and fling away all former hopes, ties, schemes, views; to violate in her favour every duty of society; this is a lover, and this is love!"

VIII

He returned to Town in the autumn, leaving the novel, *Henrietta Temple,* unfinished side by side with his journal in his desk at Bradenham. His health was restored with rest and peace—and ammonia. He felt again a craving for action. One mustn't altogether lose track of things.

In October a great fire swept Westminster, and he went to stand thoughtfully surveying the ruins. Gazing at the blackened shell of the chamber which had heard Canning's magnificent oratory, where Pitt and Fox had wrangled, where Cromwell had had his day, and so on back to Raleigh and Bacon, he felt genuinely bereaved. It was here he had dreamed his own triumphs to come, in an atmosphere rich with the memory of great men, sanctified by centuries of striving and, sometimes, success. And now it was all gone. A new building might rise, phoenix-like, from the ashes of the old—but it would be unhallowed by those long dead echoes of voices forever stilled. Saddened, he turned away, wondering in what surroundings his own voice would be heard when his turn came at last.

London,
November 4, 1834.

Dear Sa,

I dined on Saturday with Lyndhurst *en famille.* A more amiable and agreeable family I never met. The eldest daughter, "Sa," is just like her mother, and although only 13, rules everything and everybody, a most astounding little woman.

Yesterday I went to see the new actor Denvil. He is deplorable, and has not the slightest feeling, nor one physical or mental qualification for the stage.

D'Orsay has taken my portrait. . . .

His admiration for Lord Lyndhurst was growing, and it amused the elder man to talk politics with so ardent a listener. Lyndhurst had been a protégé of the great Castlereagh who killed himself in 1822, and after that he was Chancellor under Canning and Wellington. He was not so violent a Tory as the Duke, but he had little sympathy with Grey, and was now carrying on a joyous war with Melbourne's shaky government. Lyndhurst said the end of Whiggism was near, especially since they had begun to lean on O'Connell again, with various sub rosa intrigues to gain his support since the Stanley secession.

Lyndhurst was a magnificent man to look at, with a buoyant spirit and an irresistible smile. "You'll be a boy, Jack, all your life," his father used to say. And as Chancellor, Lyndhurst was the first to admit that his father had been right. "I am naturally a friend to gaiety," he would confess. "I love to see what is to be seen." He had turned sixty now, and his beautiful wife had died at the beginning of the year, bringing tragedy into a singularly devoted household. But his zest for life was still as keen as Disraeli's own.

He lived on a lavish scale, drove a smart cabriolet with a tiger, and his tailoring went beyond perfection. When his family outgrew his house in George Street he had bought the house next to it and knocked the two together into one sumptuous mansion. Rumours of insolvency clung about him periodically, but never came true. Wellington liked him, and therefore the King liked him. In fact, everybody liked him, except the Whigs and O'Connell.

In mid-November the still sulky King seized upon a technicality to dismiss the Whig ministry. It was a sudden exercise of the Royal prerogative which startled everybody. William was at Brighton and everything was going along as usual. Then Melbourne was abruptly sent for and dismissed, and when he had gone Wellington arrived post haste. When Wellington returned to London he was closeted with Lyndhurst, and Lyndhurst passed on the exciting news to Disraeli. The Whigs were out. Wellington had recommended Peel, and Peel was somewhere in Italy on a family holiday. A messen-

BENJAMIN DISRAELI IN 1835   *From a Sketch by Count D'Orsay*

ger had been despatched to fetch him home, which would
take a month. In the meantime Wellington was the Government, with Lyndhurst on his right hand. Things were very
quiet, very tense. Everybody was waiting to see what Peel
would do. If he failed, what was left?

He arrived in London early in December and went straight
to the King. He had travelled eight nights and twelve days
from Rome, over difficult roads, with a flood torrent at
Massa, and political riots at Lyons to delay him; his wife was
with him in the carriage during all that anxious, jolting
journey during which he sat silent, preoccupied, very nearly
sleepless, wondering what was before him, regretful that
Wellington could not be allowed to manage alone, and at the
back of everything nursing a grievance that it had had to
happen now, the minute he turned his back and tried to
enjoy himself a little.

On the road he had decided to take the premiership, and
anyway he had no choice this time. The King had left him
none. He would put Wellington into the Foreign Office, and
Lyndhurst must be Chancellor again. And Stanley really must
come in, with his little following of Independents.

In the end, he offered Stanley his choice of four different
Cabinet places, and Stanley refused point-blank with a reference to the evils of coalitions. He added, however, that he
hoped to be able cordially to support the Government from
his position out of office. Stanley was a thoroughly unpre-
dictable person, absorbed as often and as thoroughly in a
race-meeting as in a Parliamentary crisis. His refusal was not
an unfriendly one, but it was a refusal, and Peel resented it.
The hastily formed Cabinet was a weak one, but it was the
best he could do, leaning heavily on the aristocracy and Toryism. It was known as "the old odds and ends."

Peel found that Wellington had committed him to a dissolution, and election warfare had already begun when he
arrived. Rival mobs and bands were on the move, bribery,
influence and speechmaking had begun. It was given out at
once that a Conservative and not an ultra-Tory Government
was being formed, with a policy of moderation. That way he

hoped to hold Stanley on his side, in order to counterbalance the inevitable union of the O'Connellites with the Whigs which always took place in Opposition, no matter how bitter the feeling between them might rise while the Whigs were in office.

It was a lively Christmas, with Town very full. Peel was swamped with place-seekers, and betting ran high on every conceivable point. The clubs were packed with excited, over-worked members, and candidates. The Opposition laboured unceasingly. A bare, barnlike building was being hastily run up at Westminster, around and among the ruins of the old Lords and Commons, and with vexed problems of heating and lighting; but the new Government must be housed somehow, by February.

Disraeli's association with Lyndhurst had not made him any less a Tory, but he was still nominally unattached to a party, still gave the Whigs no quarter, was still feeling his way toward that happy mean between Radicalism and Tory-ism which he had given the "intelligent and dignified name of National Party." A hostile newspaper remarked of him on the day of nomination at High Wycombe that "to steer between the shoals of Toryism on the one hand and the quicksands of Radicalism on the other (for he was sup-ported by the two parties) required his utmost skill, and well did he acquit himself." Radicals and Whigs would draw to-gether again, and the result of this was a foregone conclusion —Disraeli would swing to the Tories. But not yet.

Once more he lost. And now he began to see that while to secede from a party, like Stanley, was possible, to build a career without one was next to impossible. He saw too that Toryism under Peel was not going to be like Toryism under Wellington. It was no longer stagnant. Peel turned the scale of political allegiance for many men, and Disraeli was among them. It began to look as though some of Peel's ideas closely resembled his own.

The election as a whole went against the Tories, owing to the Irish vote. While Melbourne was in office O'Connell had said that after four years they well knew that Ireland had nothing to expect from the Whigs but "insolent contempt, and malignant but treacherous hostility." Now the old alliance was formed again against the Tories, and references to "the base, bloody, and brutal" Whigs were out of fashion among the O'Connellites. Terrible threats were made against those who dared to vote against O'Connell's Radical or Liberal candidates. Even the priesthood joined in the intimidation of voters, and herded their flocks to the polls like sheep to obey their bidding. O'Connell was in his element, declaring that every Catholic who dared to vote for any Tory candidate should have a skull and crossbones painted on his door —"I will supplicate the Throne of the Almighty God that he may be shown mercy in the next world, but I ask no mercy for him in this! His shop shall be deserted—no man shall pass his threshold—let no man deal with him—let no woman speak to him—let the children laugh him to scorn—" And so forth.

It seemed that nothing could placate or tame the great Agitator, born to pit his strength against whatever authority was in existence. He had but two passions in life—the Catholic Church and Irish independence—besides his wife, whom he dearly loved. Witty, magnetic, passionate, and ruthless, he had waged his battle for more than twenty years and he showed no signs of flagging. His tongue was a whip-lash and his vocabulary seemed to consist wholly of epithet and invective. His career was dotted with challenges from men goaded beyond all endurance by his tongue, and he habitually fell back on those scruples against duelling which arose out of the death of an opponent years ago, until now his victims had almost given up calling him to account.

He was a master of the machinery of agitation and exercised a sort of hypnosis over mobs. England had hoped that Emancipation might keep him quiet for a time, but he only used that advantage to invade Parliament itself to continue his war for Repeal. No adversary was too big for him to tackle, and he even took on the *Times,* which objected to being called "the venal lady of the Strand" to the extent of some three hundred leading articles against him.

He had fought for Reform with the Radicals and the

Whigs because it was the first step to Repeal. After the Whigs were in, and Grey would not go all the way with him, he called them humbuggers and made their lives a misery. Now that they were out they must truckle to him again, and the balance of power was in his hands.

The Peel Ministry, with the small majority of the Irish vote against it, was thus doomed from the start, but it hung on desperately till April, 1835, and then resigned after less than four months of strife and grief for all concerned. Everyone knew that Peel had had no option about taking office prematurely, and that he owed his defeat to the treacherous union of the two conflicting wings of his Opposition. But still he was forced to resign, and William in desperation sent for Grey again. Grey simply recommended Melbourne, and retreated to the lawns and fireside of Howick and his flock of ministering women.

There was some confusion. But by May Melbourne was back in office with practically the same Cabinet as the one which had been turned out. Peel had lost, it was true, by the Catholic vote—but the tide of public opinion was beginning to turn against the revolutionary fervour so foreign to the English temperament. His skill in debate, his perfect Parliamentary tact under trying conditions, had enormously increased his popularity. His time would come.

Meanwhile, the change over at Westminster had made a vacancy at Taunton, and Disraeli went down to contest the seat. This time he entered the lists definitely as a Tory, with the Tories behind him. Naturally enough, he was accused of inconsistency.

"Gentlemen, here is my consistency," he said in his nomination speech. "I have always opposed with my utmost energy the party of which my honourable opponent is a member. That party I have opposed for reasons I am prepared to give and to uphold. I look upon the Whigs as an anti-national party. When I first entered political life I found the high places of the realm filled by the party of which my opponent is a member. I found they had an immense majority in the House of Commons, acquired by a system of nomination not less equivocal than that of the borough-mongers they affected to destroy. Believing that the policy of the party was such as must destroy the honour of the king-dom abroad and the happiness of the people at home, I con-sidered it my duty to oppose the Whigs, to ensure their dis-comfiture, and if possible their destruction.

"Had the Whigs remained in power—and it seemed to me, and the wisest men in England shared my conviction, that they were our masters for life—had, I repeat, they remained in power I considered the dismemberment of the Empire inevitable; and therefore I tried to root them out. But, Gen-tlemen, great, ay, almost illimitable as was my confidence in Whig incapacity, I confess they surpassed even my most sanguine expectations. The mighty Whig party which had consented to a revolution to gain power, fell to pieces; the vessel of state righted itself; and now there is no necessity to cut away its masts. Gentlemen, the object for which I la-boured is attained; the balance of parties is restored; and I do no longer advocate the measures in question, simply be-cause they are not necessary. Is this an answer? Is this in-consistency? . . ."

He then took up the case of O'Connell, which was a red rag to all Tory orators during that election, and in pictur-esque language described the reunion of the harassed Whigs with the man whom they had so recently regarded as a traitor and an incendiary, depicting them forcibly as grasping the "bloody hand" of the Agitator to hoist themselves again into office.

This tail-pulling of the great O'Connell by a political stripling who had not yet won his first seat delighted the reporters, who always enjoyed egging O'Connell on, and much space was devoted to young Mr. Disraeli's speech. He gained the show of hands at the hustings, but was defeated at the poll. At the same time he acquired undeniable popu-larity at Taunton, and was the central figure at a banquet given after the contest by the Conservatives of the district, where his speech was again received with tremendous en-thusiasm. As a Tory he was becoming a distinct success.

IX

O'Connell was in Dublin, but he saw the London papers there, and at once took occasion to allude at a public meeting to the recent attacks made on him, "particularly by a Mr. Disraeli." The speech which followed was one of his most terrible philippics, directed this time at the comparatively unknown young man who had dared to throw down the gauntlet to him, the great O'Connell; and in its turn it was faithfully reproduced in the *Times*. As usual the language he used was foul and personal to a degree. It was not the sort of punishment to be taken supinely by an ambitious politician with his way to make, though Disraeli knew that at least he was in good company, latest on the long list of victims of O'Connell's public opprobrium.

Peel had not been able to swallow it, nor Stanley, in their day. Neither of them had been able to bring the fellow to book, though, and the last challenge to O'Connell, lately made by Lord Alvanley, had been taken up by his son Morgan, who fought the duel himself on behalf of his father. O'Connell had as usual paraded his scruples against duelling, but this was too much, and the papers had been full of it.

With a sardonic smile Disraeli now addressed himself to Morgan, requesting him to resume his "vicarious duties of yielding satisfaction" for the insults which his father had too long heaped with impunity on his political opponents. Morgan declined. He was not responsible, he said, for what his father might say, and had only fought Alvanley because he considered that his father had been deliberately insulted.

Still smiling very sweetly, with D'Orsay looking over his shoulder and Bulwer fidgeting about the room, Disraeli wrote another letter—designed not for posting to its addressee but for publication in the Press. Peel and Stanley might both have failed to smoke O'Connell out—but what a triumph now to be the man who could contrive to force him to give satisfaction! If words had the power to draw him, Disraeli was determined that this time the Agitator would stand another man's fire.

Disraeli was living now in Park Street, Mayfair, within a stone's throw of Bulwer, the Lewises, and Lady Blessington, in the middle of the fashionable world he had made his own. There was nothing here of the usual dismal bachelor's lodgings. A sort of Turkish divan had been added to the sober Chippendale furniture; a soft, deep couch with a low back and a pile of bright cushions, near the fire. An exquisite prayer rug from Constantinople lay between it and the hearth, and instead of pictures there were oriental embroideries glowing on the walls. It was an individual and exotic room, full of the vitality of its tenant.

Bright-eyed and fresh in the late afternoon light from a long window facing his desk, he bent his head above the confident scratch of his pen, making no effort to guard the paper from D'Orsay's impertinent peeping, taking no notice of Bulwer's unhappy, gloomy prowlings. He had superlatively the gift of concentrating on the matter in hand, which was now the deliberate insulting of Daniel O'Connell.

" 'Although you have long placed yourself out of the pale of civilization,' " read D'Orsay aloud with delight to Bulwer, who could only blame the Frenchman for encouraging his friend in this foolhardiness, " 'still I am one who will not be insulted, even by a Yahoo, without chastising it.' Ya-*hoo*," repeated D'Orsay, tripping on his accent with excitement. "Oho, that is very good, *non?* Dizzy calls the Irishman a Ya-*hoo!*" He slapped his thigh, and Bulwer smiled perfunctorily. D'Orsay leaned again over the desk, his forgotten eyeglass dangling. " 'Eef it had been possible for you to behave like a gentleman—' " he read, and chortled. "But of course not, *non,* eet is a Ya-*hoo!* What a word!" He blew a kiss from the tips of jewelled fingers. "The very sound of it is a rudeness! *I* could never have thought of such a word!"

"Oh, come away, man, and let him finish it!" exclaimed Bulwer impatiently, from the window. "You're spoiling for a fight, I can see that! You'd enjoy acting as Dizzy's second, I suppose!"

"What, me? A foreigner?" D'Orsay waved the idea reluctantly aside. "No. They would say I am French. Well, they would be ri-ight!" He spread his hands to the inevitable. "But *I* do not say to Dizzy, 'You must challenge O'Connell!' No. Eet is his own idea, he who is born English. His own theeck head has thought of it, eh, Dizzy? No, no, his second must be English too—respectable—not me. Both feet on the ground. Somebody like you, perhaps?"

"I refuse to have anything to do with it!" cried Bulwer, his nerves on edge. "Suppose he gets killed?"

"Nonsense," said Disraeli from the desk. "I'm a fair shot, and I'm perfectly calm and perfectly ready for him." He signed his name, and laid down the pen. "There's a lot more, but how's this to finish?" He read from the paper before him. " 'With regard to your taunts as to my failure in election contests, permit me to remind you that I had nothing to appeal to but the good sense of the people. No threatening skeletons canvassed for me; a death's head and cross-bones were not emblazoned on my banners. My pecuniary resources too were limited; I am not one of those public beggars that swarm with their obtrusive boxes in the chapels of your creed, nor am I in possession of a princely revenue wrung from a race of fanatical slaves.' " (Here D'Orsay applauded loudly.) " 'Nevertheless, I have a deep conviction that the hour is at hand when I shall be successful. We shall meet at Philippi; and rest assured that I will seize the first opportunity of inflicting on you a castigation which will make you remember and repent the insults you have lavished upon—Benjamin Disraeli.' "

"Oh, very goo-ood!" said D'Orsay, nodding judicially. "That bit about Phileeppi—very good indeed! Eh, Bulwer?"

"Yes," admitted Bulwer sourly. "It's good enough, if it must be done at all."

"My dear fellow!" said D'Orsay, dismissing doubt with a gesture. "Eet will be in all the papers tomorrow. Then we shall see! And now—*bon Dieu,* it is time to dress!"

They were all at the Opera that night, to hear Mlle. Grisi sing Desdemona. The Princess Victoria was there, in a box, with her German governess, and thoroughly enjoying herself. She would be sixteen in a few days, and looked like a child still.

The next evening found Disraeli again at his writing-table, the curtains drawn against the spring dusk. He wore a sumptuous brocade dressing-gown over the snowy shirt-frill, black silk stock, and pearl-grey trousers of evening dress; on his feet were soft red Turkish slippers with upturned toes. He had intended to go out, and his plans had been suddenly abandoned.

The room was as usual brilliantly lighted. Newspapers open and folded back lay about the place untidily—*Times, Courier, Post, Chronicle,* etc. The floor beside him was littered with spoilt sheets of notepaper. But now his pen travelled steadily toward a signature, and his eyes were bright with derisive humour:

Mr. Morgan O'Connell,

I deduce from your communication that you do not consider yourself responsible for any insults offered by your father, but only bound to resent the insults that he may receive. Now, Sir, it is my hope that I *have* insulted him; assuredly it was my intention to do so. I wished to express the utter scorn in which I hold his character, and the disgust with which his conduct inspires me. If I failed in conveying this expression of my feelings to him, let me more successfully express them to you now. I shall take every opportunity of holding your father's name up to public contempt. And I fervently pray that you, or someone of his blood, may attempt to avenge—

The knocker on the outer door of his chambers sounded three times, then twice; a signal. He looked up incredulously, at the panels of the door. His manservant had gone for the night. Someone was tapping now—three times, then twice. He rose and went quickly to the door.

She slipped inside with a rustle of silk and a whiff of that fresh, sweet scent which always hung about her. He clapped the door shut behind her and leaned against it, staring at her in astonishment. He had not been expecting her tonight. He had *forgotten* her.

"Henrietta, for heaven's sake—!" he murmured, in protest at the heedless risk she ran in not warning him that she meant to come. Anyone might have been there—D'Orsay—Bulwer—a stranger—*anyone.*

"Why weren't you at Lyndhurst's?" she demanded tensely. "I expected to see you there."

"I sent regrets," he said, still leaning against the door watching her, his hand on the knob. "A bit late, I admit, but in the circumstances he would understand."

"D'Orsay was there," she told him significantly.

"Was he?" He smiled, his eyes very bright, his manner a little absent-minded. His thoughts had already flown back to the unfinished letter on the writing-table. Her presence to-night, though flattering, was an interruption.

"I cornered him. I made him tell me the truth."

"D'Orsay?" He laughed. "I wonder!"

"He said you were going to fight a duel with Morgan O'Connell!"

"I hope he is right." His defiant, amused gaze ran over her appreciatively. "You're looking exceptionally beautiful about it, it seems to me."

"Don't clown, please! I'm frightened. And *very* angry with you!"

"Are you? It's very becoming. Shall I take your cloak?"

His fingers found the fastening at her throat with practised ease, and she emerged exquisitely from her pink taffeta wrappings—a figure of porcelain and gilt, she seemed, an incredibly dainty doll of a woman, clad in stiff white silk painted with scattered rosebuds, her enormous puffed sleeves ending just above her adorable elbows, her shoulders rising whiter than the white tulle which bordered the top of her low bodice, her curls gleaming round a rosebud wreath set aslant; a perfection of beauty and style to dazzle the most critical eye. He folded the pink cloak gently across a chair, his long, ringed fingers unconsciously caressing the delightful fabric.

"Dizzy, how did this thing get started?"

He turned back slowly to face her, and his whole face tightened and closed in, his eyes looked enormous, very hard, very dark, with a dangerous glint. He spoke softly through his teeth.

"Mr. Daniel O'Connell called me a blackguard, a reptile, an egregious liar, a Jewish miscreant, *and* heir-at-law to the impenitent thief on the Cross," he explained. "Naturally it got into the papers. Naturally I replied. I—"

"But what *began* it?" she cried.

"One of my speeches at Taunton. But I wasn't the only person who has had uncomplimentary things to say about the recent—apostasy of the Irish. It only happened that *I* was misquoted, and *I* fell under Mr. O'Connell's blood-thirsty eye—"

"But if you had been misquoted, surely—"

"Ah, but he didn't wait to find out exactly what I had said," he cut in, speaking with an incisive, measured venom in every word, while his frightening eyes remained fixed on her, unseeing, unaware of her beauty. "He didn't send for the local papers where my speech was printed in full. He took some summarized version at its face value. If he had appealed to me as any gentleman would have done, he might have found his—comments—unnecessary. But, no. He goes off half-cocked and pitches into me at a meeting in Dublin. And the first I know of it is my—crucifixion—in the *Times.*"

"And you challenged him?" she cried, horrified.

"It's a waste of time to challenge him. I challenged Morgan. And he refused to fight."

She drew a breath of relief.

"Then you can let it drop," she said.

"Didn't you see the papers this morning?"

"Now, Dizzy, you know I don't read newspapers if I can help myself!"

Smiling a little grimly, he brought her one of the open newspapers and pointed to a column. She snatched it out of his hand and carried it to the mantelpiece lights, her eyes skimming the lines.

"Must you get on to religion?" she said at last.

"He began that too," he reminded her coldly.

"But you're not a Jew!" she cried quickly, at that. He only looked at her silently, his chin well up, his lips curled in a small, cool smile. She flushed, and then realizing that she had flushed, felt a crimson tide envelop her whole body —but how awful—she had said an unpardonable thing—that is, he looked merely Latin—but that pagan strain which made him so compelling a lover—was that the Jew?—she had heard somewhere that the wives of Jews always loved their husbands —but what had she said just now, because she had never thought of him like that? She stood before him, her eyelids down, hot with mortification. But he went to St. George's, Hanover Square, like everybody else—he was standing for Parliament—he—he ate everything—he—another blush ran over her—he was her lover. . . . "I mean," she gasped, desperately breaking the silence he would not ease for her, "I mean you—you—"

"You mean I've been baptized," he suggested softly.

"Well, I mean you've always—"

"The obligations of the synagogue bored my father," he explained, and there was amusement in his low voice, some bitterness, and a great patience. "When I was a small child he marched us all off to St. Andrew's and chucked us bodily into the Established Church. That makes me just as good a Christian as you are, doesn't it, my dear."

"You're making fun of me again," she said uncertainly, confused.

"On the contrary, I think you're rather sweet," he smiled, and she threw down the paper and came to him swiftly.

"Dizzy, don't go on with this, *please!* What's going to happen now?"

"Well, just to make sure, I'm writing to Morgan again, expressing the hope that I have now succeeded in insulting his father to a sufficient degree—"

"No, no, no, I won't have it!" she cried furiously, clutching at him with angry little white-gloved hands. "What if

O'Connell did use words about you? You've used them back! You're quits now. Let it go!"

He was amused.

"My dear girl, you don't understand. If I am ever to get anywhere I can't afford to stand for that sort of thing from anyone, let alone a professional bully like O'Connell."

"Dizzy, please don't send that letter!"

"I'm sorry to worry you, my dear, but the letter will be signed and sent off tonight."

"For my sake—?" She melted against him piteously, her hands creeping into his, her hair sweet against his face. "What's the good?" she coaxed. "What's to be gained by popping at each other before breakfast?"

He looked down at her, remote, unyielding, miles away.

"Satisfaction," he said, with a wicked gleam of laughter.

"But suppose you killed Morgan—that would make a horrid mess!"

"Of Morgan, yes," he agreed.

"Don't joke, Dizzy! Duelling is against the law. Couldn't they arrest you, or something?"

"They never find out till afterward, if one is clever."

"What if I warned them?"

"You wouldn't do that," he told her coolly. "They would naturally wonder—and guess—how you knew and why it mattered to you."

She gave him an upward look, defiant, guilty, shamelessly loving, admitting her own impotence, and then caught at him fiercely.

"Oh, Dizzy, he might kill you!"

"And would you mind so much?" he murmured, his lips in her hair, but making no move to take her in his arms as she clung to him, and she turned away from him fretfully, twisting her fingers together.

"I hate you when you're like this! You would sacrifice anything in these moods," she accused. "Even your life! Even me! To the great god Politics!"

"You are jealous of elections," he mused, smiling after her, "jealous of the House of Commons—jealous of my books—

jealous of my sister. Is it possible that now you are jealous of the O'Connells?"

She gazed at him sulkily from across the room. Immaculate in his evening dress, he was looking very well as he stood there, where she had left him—exasperatingly well, to her possessive eyes. Above the red plush collar of his dressing-gown his black curls lay shining round his pale face, the crisp white gills of his black silk cravat projecting at exactly the right angle across the young, clean line of his jaw, the cord at his slender waist drawn tight, his ringed hands long and graceful in the belling sleeves—she noted how the finger-tips curled inward tensely—a bad sign. It was not like this that she loved him best. His eyes were bright with an excite-ment which had nothing to do with her; his beautiful mouth was drawn tight at the corners—her gaze lingered—even now, that enthralling curve of his upper lip. . . . She sighed petulantly, and seated herself with a sweep of white silk on the divan. He must be brought back at once, to a conscious-ness of her presence. Did she or did she not detect a growing tendency on his part to allow politics, his preposterous ambi-tions, his preoccupations, in fact, to intrude on the time they spent together? Politics bored her. Surely he had learned that by now?

"The Lewises were at Lyndhurst's tonight," she said, with a seeming irrelevance. "*She* was asking where you were."

"I hope you didn't tell her it was none of her business," he remarked, following her trend of thought with ease.

"I wanted to," she admitted pugnaciously. Then she turned on him. "Oh, I know what it is! She encourages you, and tells you you can be a great man in Parliament, and your silly masculine conceit simply laps it up!"

"I am not conceited," he objected with his infuriating patience. "I wish I were, it makes one thick-skinned. A few years ago when the world called me conceited I was merely nervous and had self-confidence only by fits. So far, my life has been a struggle, with moments of rapture—a storm, with dashes of moonlight!" His fine gesture set his rings flashing.

"But it needn't be like that!" she cried, exasperated. "You

wear yourself out—you get those awful headaches—you make a slave of yourself to your hateful politics! I'm sick of the Tories, the Radicals, and the Whigs! Words, words, *words!* Melbourne or Peel—what does it matter *who* is Prime Minister? We all seem to go on just the same!"

"What heresies," he said, amused.

"Don't jeer at me, you know I'm talking sense!"

"Suppose I were Prime Minister," he suggested quietly. "Would that matter to you?"

"You!" She stared at him, astonished. This was a side of him which she hardly knew, so completely had he keyed himself to her atmosphere of gay leisure—until recently. It was as though a thoroughbred hunter had suddenly signified a desire to pull a city omnibus; or as though the handsome bay which carried her daintily round the Park each morning had entered himself in the Derby. Dizzy was all that was witty and charming. All the more reason why he should leave the hackwork of Parliament to stodgy bores like Peel. "But you can't even win an election!" said Henrietta.

It was brutally tactless, an impulse born of her savage need to smash this high mood of his which stood between them. But there was nothing on his calmly smiling face to show that it had got home.

"I shall probably get in the very next time," was all he said.

"Are you going to try *again?*"

"Of course."

"But *why?* Why do you go on fighting, fighting—"

"Because I must," he cut in sharply. "Nature has given me an awful ambition and fiery passions. I know I can never be really great except in action. I am never even well, except in action, and then I feel immortal! I haven't the money to buy my way into the House, nor the influence to get myself carried in over other people's dead bodies. I have only my wits and my will, and a tyrannous body that won't stand idleness and defeat, but demands action, adventure, tasks beyond its strength—superhuman endeavour—otherwise it collapses on a sofa and aches!"

"That's just living on your nerves," she accused.

"I'm ashamed of being nervous," he told her seriously. "Ashamed of ever having to knuckle under to this feeble envelope of flesh and blood, with its ailments and weaknesses. What right have my mere bones to interfere with what I want to do?" he demanded of the heavens. "Nerves—pain—fatigue—it's only in idleness that they can overtake me! A headache turns me suicidal in an hour! A touch of dyspepsia makes me long for civil war! But an election campaign, with two long speeches a day and a nine hours' canvass on foot in a blaze of repartee—puts me in the seventh heaven!"

"Yes, but you lose the election!" she reminded him triumphantly, ready to stab where she could to bring him back to a consciousness of her claims on him; desperately struggling against this odd, distant self-dedication to a bloodless idea, a dry-as-dust ambition in which she had no part—she who was accustomed to his whole attention. But again the thrust seemed to glance off.

"If ever I get the chance I can rule the House of Commons," he was saying gravely, with no hint of bombast, stating what was to him a commonplace fact, "though there will be a great deal of prejudice against me at first."

"Well, suppose you could!" Henrietta threw out her small gloved hands. "Is it worth it? Why bother about all that?"

"What could be more worth bothering about?" His eyes came to rest on her with a sort of impersonal surprise, and she leaned back against the cushions, making a picture of herself for his delight, smiling, inviting, entirely enchanting.

"I think we have a very pleasant life as things are," she remarked gently, and held his gaze with her own. "You could go on writing books—you say I give the nicest dinners in London—it's going to be a very gay season, if only the Whigs will settle in again. I want you to have time for *me*."

He regarded her appreciatively from the middle of the room, aware that she was using all her wiles. He saw through her, of course. He always saw through her, but usually he was content to surrender himself, body and soul—it was an enslavement he enjoyed, and which he did not begrudge her.

But there were times, which Henrietta did not recognize, when a man's brain had the better of him and could not be lulled into inactivity by the dearest enchantment he knew. Tonight, with his challenge to O'Connell still hanging fire, he stood firmly amongst realities. He knew with a sort of despair that she wanted him to make love to her, wanted to be consoled out of her very genuine fright over the duel, wanted to show, and feel, her power over him. And his mind was not on her. It was on O'Connell.

"My darling," he said, "you know you are everything to me —everything but a career."

"That's one of *her* words!" she pointed out instantly. "Mrs. Lewis's! I can hear her! 'Mark my words, Mr. Disraeli will have a brilliant career!' Just because you make her pretty bows and listen to her chatter with that solemn face of yours, she thinks you're bound to be a great man! If she knew you half as well as I do, she'd know that the more polite you look, the ruder you're being inside!"

"Really, Henrietta, sometimes you are surprisingly deep!" He was surprised into laughter.

"What you can see in her I can't imagine," Henrietta pursued her grievance swiftly. "She spends far more on clothes than I do, and somehow contrives to be the worst-dressed woman in London! That house of hers in Grosvenor Gate is a miracle of bad taste—her drawing-room carpet would drive me mad in a week! She makes the most appalling breaks every time she opens her mouth—she must be completely uneducated. Why, the other evening it was perfectly plain that she didn't even know that Swift is dead!"

"Is he?" he murmured maddeningly.

"Or even who he was!" cried Henrietta. "Oh, she'd drop you fast enough if you didn't flirt with her outrageously under her husband's very nose!" she added recklessly.

This went too far, and his smile faded instantly. She had her knife into Mrs. Wyndham Lewis in a way which puzzled and sometimes diverted him. But if ever friendship between man and woman was safe and innocent, his was with Wyndham's wife. Cynic that he was in such matters, he had had to recognize one happy marriage among his friends, made for love twenty years ago, and still sweet and honest. Of course Wyndham was a great deal older, and still treated her like a precocious child, encouraging her chatter, laughing at her impertinences, vastly delighted with her unique, unconscious wisdom. And really she was very charming, so small and pretty and gay on his proud arm, with that trick of looking up, round the bunched curls which clustered over each ear. . . . This time Henrietta had gone too far.

"She's devoted to Wyndham and you know it," he said severely.

"I never said she wasn't!"

"So am I devoted to him. Remember that. He's one of the oddest men I've ever met, but I like him."

"I don't see anything very odd about him—except his taste in women! He's a nice, friendly old stick."

He realized that it was no good going on like this about the Lewises. It was deliberately naughty of Henrietta, and very unwise, in a way he did not approve, to imply even in fun that there was anything very intimate between him and Wyndham's wife. In the first place, she was years older than he was. She said so, even if she did not look it, with her smooth cheeks and candid eyes—her shoulders were nearly as beautiful as Henrietta's own. Wyndham had kept her like that—young, with a kind of innocence, cherished, and modestly abloom. She knew nothing of life as Henrietta knew it —thanks to Wyndham.

"He's a very sound man, and my friend," he said, closing it.

"Well, just because he's in Parliament is no sign she can get you there as well. Aren't you sick of being defeated?" she prodded at his sensitive self-esteem again. "Taunton was the fourth time, wasn't it?"

He looked at her, a long, slow disenchanted glance, which missed nothing of her beauty, and held nothing of ardour. So little she knew him still. So little she cared to know him ever, with her heedless stabs at his vanity, and her heartless, wilful blindness to the nagging ambition which drove him.

Sick of being defeated? Had he concealed it so well? And did she imagine that he would give up for that, and stop short of success because his goal was difficult to gain? Had she not learned yet that he relinquished only what was not worth striving for?

"There was once an old Italian general," he smiled at her, "who was asked how it happened that he was always victorious. And he replied that it was because he had always been beaten in his youth."

"You made that up!" she accused him.

"I didn't, my dear, it's true. Anyway, I'm not disheartened. I don't feel like a beaten man. Doubtless because I'm getting used to it." He shrugged, and smiled, and drifted away from her down the room. "Last time I went to the House I heard Bulwer speak—and Macaulay, and Sheil. And between ourselves I could floor them all. I suppose you will call that conceit too. Very well. But I suffer from Pride, you see. Yes, it's Pride that drives me, as much as Ambition. They shall not say that I have failed! *The time will come!*"

"All right, all right, don't shout!" There was a silence, while he dropped wearily into the chair by his desk and she sought some means of turning his thoughts back to the small, secret things they shared, determined to pull him down from the heights to the sunny levels where they met and strayed together. "Edward Bulwer and Rosina have finally gone completely smash, did you know?" she said at last.

"Yes—" He sighed heavily. "Another marriage wrecked— two more lives uprooted—I tell you it's a fatal thing to marry for love!"

"Did I marry for love or money?" mused Henrietta. "I forget. There's little enough of either now, God knows!"

He looked at her aslant, under his lashes.

"How did you happen to get away from Lyndhurst's tonight? Wasn't there to be dancing after dinner?"

"There was a frightful crush, I shan't be missed. And if I am—" She shrugged. "Who cares? Not my husband!"

"Won't be missed?" he said, and his eyes ran over her dispassionately, taking in again the exquisite details of her dress

—the white tulle folds at the top of her low bodice, the pink satin rose at her breast, the intricate puffing of her big sleeves. "When half the beauty in the room left with you?" he murmured.

"Well, that's better!"

She sparkled at him, surprised and pleased, restored to good humour by one small absent-minded compliment. It smote him to see how easily he could please her, as it were left-handedly, with his mind elsewhere. And once, not long ago really as time goes, how he had striven to please her! His mind flew back to that first day in her drawing-room, and the dawning, incredulous wonder of their inevitable relationship —back even to the first time he ever saw her, and the lightly spoken warning that she hated men who talked politics. How very true. And now, how very unfortunate. Since then his life had become wholly indivisible from politics. Yes, and she still hated it. She would not compromise with his career, not an inch. Well, he had spoilt her in their early days; she had had things all her own way then.

There was speculation in his gaze as it rested on her. What was going to become of them now, he wondered. With a swift, painful cramp of his heart he saw, somewhere ahead, a parting of ways, and instantly he closed his mind's eye to it. No. Not yet. Not for a long time. Life would be desolate without her. She was a part of his soul and body, he could never do without her, he would be destitute. She was beauty, which he always craved, and she was love, which he had been without so long. . . .

From across the room she caught the flicker in his eyes, with a little triumphant quickening of her blood. Now. At last.

"Come and sit here," she entreated, and laid her hand on the divan beside her. "Unless you want me to go—?" And while the words were wistful, her eyes were confident again.

For answer he joined her on the divan, and she held out her gloved hands to him with a familiar gesture, to be unbuttoned. In silence he received them, one by one, and deftly stripped from each its white kid glove. She had the hands of a houri, pale and slender, with narrow nails. They lay on his like lotus petals—his nostrils flared slightly to her perfume— still he did not speak.

She watched him possessively, smiling a little, as he removed her gloves, delighting in the neatness of his touch, which never fumbled, noting for the hundredth time the way the very air about him seemed to quiver with a latent something which must emanate from his own nervous vitality. She, who was so alive herself, so greedy of sensation, responded like a harp-string to his nearness. True, he could be tiresome. But what did all that matter, really, so long as this obstinate rapture still flared between them?

"It's a new gown," she murmured, her hands in his, "in your honour. And not a word do I get!"

He gave her a long, sly look beneath his lashes, released her hands and blew into the fingers of one glove, to straighten it. "I've talked about nothing else since you came in," he remarked shamelessly.

"Kiss me," she commanded, leaning toward him.

He kissed her, but briefly, and his lips were small and cool on her parted ones.

"My dear, I must warn you not to come here again like this after next week," he said unexpectedly. "My sister is coming up to Town for a visit."

"Oh, bother! How long will she be here?"

"A fortnight or so, I hope. Till after the masked ball, anyway. She needs a change. My father hasn't been well."

"But that will bring us into June, and soon you'll be off to Bradenham!" She was jealous of Bradenham too.

"Yes—I must."

"Just when things have brightened up for the summer!"

"My father is getting old," he reminded her patiently. "Getting blind. I'm very fond of him."

She was silent a moment, chidden and resentful again. There were so *many* claims on him, she ruminated rebelliously. She might have put up with a family, or with politics, perhaps, or with novel-writing. But all three—!

"But you'll come to us for the hunting again—you promised."

"My dear girl, I don't fall off the horse, but you know I ride very badly. I don't think I'll hunt at all this year. Lyndhurst is coming to Bradenham in a month or so, and—"

"And you'll get them to ask me to Bradenham in September, as we planned?" she insisted.

"Yes. If you behave yourself."

"Oh, Dizzy, what a prig you can be! You were proud of me once!"

"My darling, I still am. But I don't want to start Sa thinking. She reads my mind."

"What would she think about me—if she knew?" queried Henrietta with a morbid curiosity.

"She likes me to be happy," he admitted wryly.

It was the wrong answer. He was not troubling tonight to make the right ones.

"I suppose that's all I'd seem to her—just something to amuse you for a time. A toy for the great man's leisure hours." She leaned to look into his face. "Is that all I am, Dizzy? Just—*divertissement?*"

"My dear, forgive me if I don't pay you brilliant compliments tonight—the day has been rather a strain, and—" Involuntarily his eyes returned to the writing-table.

"Now, never mind that beastly letter to O'Connell! It can wait till later." She ran her forefinger intimately down his cheek and along the edge of his collar. "Much later," she whispered.

"Thank heaven I can't marry you!" he said suddenly out of his thoughts. "I should get nothing done with you always in the house!"

"I think I'd better go," said Henrietta. She took her gloves from his knee and rose. He looked up at her, astonished, from the divan, and then got hastily to his feet, and slid an arm round her waist.

"Henrietta, don't be angry, my sweet—do forgive me, it was a mood—" His face as he laid it against hers was suddenly merry and charming and alight. "I didn't mean to bore you—" He buried his lips in her curls, and felt their silken coolness strike against his heart.

"I suppose I shouldn't have come here tonight," she conceded, still rigid and unfriendly in his arms. "You never take any notice of what I say, anyhow."

"Don't I?" he murmured, and then—"Forgive me!"

"Soon you'll be going to Bradenham—" Her arms went round his neck convulsively. "And life is so dull without you!"

"I know," he said, and drew her closer. "Each time I go away from you, it's much worse than I ever think it can be!"

"Then don't go!" She clung to him.

"I must. It's a great shame, isn't it, when people are happy together that they should ever be separated. But it seems to be the great object of all human legislation that people should never be happy together."

"Don't make speeches at me, Dizzy—when I want you to make love—"

"My dearest." He kissed her, long and hard. Their quarrel, such as it was, had ended, as their quarrels always did, in an acknowledgment of their delight in each other the more complete for having been withheld. It was not in his nature to hold her yielding in his arms and deny her.

At last she stirred, and looked up at him, his face between her hands.

"Why is it that every now and then I must teach you all over again that you love me?" she queried reproachfully.

"Because I'm stupid, and absent-minded, and tiresome," he confessed, and drew her down on the divan again, everything else set aside. "But give me credit, beloved—I can always learn again."

"I adore you when you smile like that." Her finger traced the line at the side of his mouth, and travelled on, audaciously, across his lips. "Oh, this being in love!" she sighed, relaxed and contented against the cushions, looking up at him. "It's been two years, have you thought of that? And still my life goes flat and stale unless I see you every day! What have you done to me? This is captivity! Why don't you speak?"

"Interrupt you?" he murmured. "When you are saying such beautiful things to me?"

"Dizzy—"

"Yes, my darling?"

"Promise you'll give up politics—and be happy, with me."

"Suppose I refuse." He looked down at her in his arms, daring her to resist him now and go on with her foolish tantrums. He was hers, yes, in this sweet drunkenness brought on him by the scent of jasmine and the swish of silk and the cool tingle of her curls against his face. She could always entangle his senses, and he was willing that it should be so. Up to a point. "Will you cast me off if I refuse?" he murmured, daring her. "Will you?" He crushed his lips on hers, and her arms slid up submissively round his neck. . . .

X

There was no duel after all, though the letter went to Morgan O'Connell in the morning. A friend of the O'Connells did what Henrietta could not do, and informed the police. An officer of the law arrived promptly at Disraeli's chambers, and he was bound over on £500 securities to keep the peace. He had come off at least as well as Peel had done fifteen years before.

The notoriety which the whole thing brought him was not unhelpful, and he received letters of congratulation on his firm attitude from all over the kingdom. And while his common sense recognized that here was the end of the matter, the romantic side of him regretted the lost opportunity for the traditional drama of the early morning appointment, the duelling-ground paced off, the grave presence of surgeons and seconds, the solemn count, and that breathless moment before the word to fire—he had been through it again and again in his imagination, to stretch his courage. It was a gesture he could have made in the grand manner, without faltering, and Mr. Peel's interfering new police had deprived him of it. There was very little chivalry left in the world, which was rapidly becoming commonplace. Philosophically, he returned to his pen.

The Whigs did settle in again, and it was a very gay season, though the King was sullen at having to take them back. "The Cabinet is not my Cabinet," he said darkly. They had better take care, or by God I will have them impeached!" The summer was a stormy one, politically, with the Irish question still up. Lyndhurst was mighty in debate, and there was talk of his becoming Prime Minister; even, it was said, hints of this from Windsor where the King was.

In the autumn at Bradenham Disraeli settled down to much the most serious effort he had made yet. There seemed to be no one to guide what he termed a "perplexed, ill-informed, jaded, shallow generation," and his new political pamphlet was entitled *A Vindication of the English Constitution, in a Letter to a Noble and Learned Lord, By Disraeli the Younger*. The noble lord was Lyndhurst. And the pamphlet—it was two hundred pages long—not only clarified its author's own ideas for himself, but gave him a recognized place henceforth as a political thinker and writer. There was little in it which he had not said in one way or another before, but here it was all gathered tidily between covers, arranged and set forth.

The *Vindication* attacked the Utilitarians, the Radicals, and O'Connell, who was now on a progress through the North, agitating for the abolition of the House of Lords; and Disraeli brought to bear on this new blasphemy all those years of historical reading and empire dreaming in his father's library, which had begun after his first trip abroad. It was impossible, he pointed out, to obtain a substitute for the House of Lords by merely collecting all the clever men of the country and giving them the august title of Senate. The King of England, he observed, might make peers, but he could not make a House of Lords; and in a hasty and factitious effort to get rid of representation without election, it would be as well if they did not discover too late that they had only obtained election without representation. "The

English nation," said the *Vindication* roundly, "to obtain the convenience of monarchy, have established a popular throne, and to enjoy the security of aristocracy, have invested certain orders of their fellow subjects with legislative functions; but these estates, however highly privileged, are invested with no quality of exclusion; and the Peers and Commons of England are the trustees of the nation, not its masters."

He perceived now that it would be necessary to re-create the Tory party as a bulwark against the destructive philosophies which beleaguered the old order of things where the national sanity was rooted. "Nations have characters," he reminded his readers, "as well as individuals, and national character is precise., quality which the new sect of statesmen in their schemes an. culations either deny or overlook. . . . This respect for precedent, this clinging to prescription, this reverence for antiquity, which are so often ridiculed by conceited and superficial minds, appear to me to have their origin in a profound knowledge of human nature."

The *Vindication* created a very respectable sensation. Even Peel read it, and wrote to congratulate the author, though he and Lyndhurst were at outs with each other. There were acrimonious reviews in the Whig papers, of course, and a long controversy went on between Mr. Disraeli in the *Times* and the abusive editors of the *Globe*.

Isaac was delighted with it as a literary production, and wrote from Bradenham in real excitement: "I never doubted your powers—they were not latent to me. With more management on your side they would have been acknowledged long ere now—universally. You never wanted for genius, but it was apt in its fulness to run over. . . . All that now remains for you to do is register a vow in Heaven that you will never write anything inferior to what you have now written, and never to write but on a subject which calls forth all your energies."

Early in the year there began a series of anonymous letters in the *Times*, signed simply "Runnymede;" open letters addressed to O'Connell, Melbourne, Palmerston, and revealing a splendid disregard for the laws of libel. O'Connell was accused of having "committed every crime that does not require courage;" Melbourne was said to be "sauntering over the destinies of a nation, and lounging away the glories of an empire;" and the scathing suggestion was made that the Cabinet might well go in for cricket as a choice eleven, with a talent for keeping in and being caught out. Peel and Stanley in their turn were praised—overpraised. The incognito was scrupulously maintained, but altogether it was not hard to guess who "Runnymede" was, and Disraeli's reputation grew in stature if for no other reason than his ardent opposition to the hateful O'Connell influence in Parliament.

In March he was elected to the Carlton Club—sacred stronghold of Conservatism. Not long after, he was unexpectedly congratulated by a fellow member on his speedy prospects of a Parliamentary seat, which made him stare. Socially he began to be rather lionized, and even went to the Duchess of Kent's, where the Princess Victoria was allowed to dance just one dance, and then was sent to bed.

The Parliamentary session of 1836 was mainly on Irish matters, and though it opened fairly well for the Government, they emerged from it with little credit. Wellington was heard to say that he daily expected a break-up of the Whigs, and thought that Peel and Lyndhurst would be next. The difficulty was to get Peel to take the trouble. Portly, handsome, intelligent, reserved, he went off to the Isle of Wight for a holiday, and read memoirs of the French Revolution for relaxation. There were signs that the crazy alliance which had driven him out of office might not last much longer. The Radicals and the Whigs were at variance with each other and quarrelling among themselves. The people at large had lost their intense interest in Westminster affairs again, in a gradual return of prosperity. There was little left for the Ministry to carry on with but a shaky majority in the House. The Court and the Lords were against them, the country was indifferent. Even Melbourne's urbanity was strained, and he remarked that a man must have the patience of an ass to stand against such odds. On the other hand, no one knew quite what would happen if the Whigs resigned or were turned out.

XI

The growing pressure of his debts drove Disraeli back to novel-writing, and he returned to Bradenham in August to shut himself up and finish *Henrietta Temple,* which had lain neglected in his desk for more than two years. He turned the half-forgotten pages of manuscript with mixed emotions. "There is no love but at first sight," he had written in 1834. "All other is the illegitimate result of observation, of reflection, of compromise, of comparison, of expediency. The passions that endure flash like lightning; they scorch the soul, but it is warmed forever."

It made him feel very old and disillusioned, to read that in his own handwriting. The passion for Henrietta endured, oh, yes; but love, he had found, was not exclusively an inspiration and an incitement to great deeds. Love could cease to exhilarate, and could torment and confuse, absorbing one's precious vitality like a sponge. And love at first sight, while it might last forever, could become a sort of maiming, to which one must be resigned, and which one must learn to ignore.

He turned the leaves. ". . . to feel our flaunty ambition fade away . . . to feel fame a juggle and posterity a lie . . . to be prepared to forfeit and fling away all former hopes. . . ." No. No, one was not so prepared, when the time came. Even then, when he wrote that, he had recognized that a man could not serve two mistresses. But then he had been wrong about the choice to which Henrietta's blind jealousy of his equally jealous career had finally forced him. His fierce pride drove him on. He knew with the cold, relentless sanity which was so inevitable in him that he was not one to count the world well lost for love. Not for long.

The half-filled volume of his Bradenham journal lay beside him. He laid it on top of the manuscript, dipped his pen deliberately, and wrote: "Autumn of 1836. Parted forever from

Henrietta. Returned to Bradenham at the latter end of
August. . . ."

The sylvan peace of Buckinghamshire was grateful to his
jarred nerves, and he buried himself in the devoted household with pathetic relief. There life ran smoothly, easefully,
bills were never heard of, the food was fit for gods, no one
worried, no one quarrelled, and the rooms were full of flowers. The tension and heartbreak and suspense which had surrounded him in Town seemed worlds away.

It had been a disastrous year among his friends, and the old
familiar gaieties had crumbled to bits all round him.

In the spring Caroline Norton's vindictive husband had
kidnapped his own children while she was out of the house,
and had given them into the care of a woman whose influence
over him was not the least of Caroline's humiliations at his
hands. Caroline took refuge with her brother, leaving all her
papers and clothes behind her in her flight. But within a few
weeks, after a futile attempt to steal her children back again,
she desired only to return to her husband's roof for the sake
of seeing them. In an almost daily correspondence Melbourne
was prudently urging her to try for any sort of reconciliation
with Norton. Driven to distraction by anxiety for the "chicks"
she adored, and by what seemed to her a lack of sympathy
and understanding on Melbourne's part, she wrote furiously
that he was always more annoyed that there was a row than
he was sorry for the people involved in it; to which he replied
patiently that whatever happened she could always count on
him.

Meanwhile Norton was naming Melbourne as co-respondent in a court action. He had searched his wife's papers for
incriminating letters and found among them a few notes
signed "M," bare of endearments or other evidence, and intimate only in their brevity and utter simplicity. From the beginning of their friendship Norton had encouraged it in his
own interests. He had often accompanied her to Melbourne's
door in Downing Street, and left her there, complacently,
and gone about his own obscure affairs. He had himself admitted Melbourne to her bedroom while she was still ill

after the birth of the third child. And now, with purchased testimony from servants and nobodies, Norton was trying to turn these innocent meetings to his own advantage: she had called at Melbourne's house alone, he alleged, and she had received him in bed and privately.

The so-called trial took place in June. Melbourne of course faced political ruin if Norton's charges could be proved, especially as it was the second time an aggrieved husband had brought his tattlings to court with Melbourne as the defendant. But the witnesses broke down under cross-examination or proved to have nothing worth telling, and the jury pronounced for the defence without leaving the box. The case was dropped. Old Lord Malmesbury remarked that the evidence only showed that Melbourne had had more opportunities than most men, and had made no use of them.

Caroline existed in a stupefaction of misery over being separated from her children. They had been transferred to the care of Norton's family, and she knew they were unhappy there, if not actually unkindly treated. Norton could not proceed with a divorce, and she could not take any action against him, as she had voluntarily left his house. Yet he could claim her earnings, and keep her children from her. There was nothing left but to find terms for a legal separation which would at least safeguard her from his society. Her beauty had suffered terribly, and her high spirit was mortified into bitterness, but not crushed.

At the same time Bulwer's home affairs had gone from bad to worse. His health broke down late in 1833, largely from overwork, and they went to Italy with friends. Rosina hated Italy at sight, and complained bitterly of the mosquitoes, smells, and bad food. "Poets ought to be strangled for all the lies they have told about this country," she wrote to her friend Miss Greene. But at Naples, in the midst of a snobbish English colony who were only too ready to welcome a distinguished author and lionize him, her sulky Irish beauty went to the head of a local princeling. She adored admiration and flattery, and Bulwer had for years been too busy or too cross to make love to her most of the time. Her conduct with the Italian in the circumstances was neither discreet nor dignified, and Bulwer emerged from his absorption in the ruins of Pompeii to drag her unceremoniously back to England. The effect of his moral indignation was somewhat marred by the ugly gossip which already linked his name with the woman who was one of their travelling companions.

When they arrived back in England in February their quarrels were an open scandal, and they gave up trying to live together. Bulwer took a country house for Rosina and the children, let Hertford Street, and moved into Byron's old rooms in the Albany. After that they carried on a correspondence alternately venomous and decorated by all the old foolish words—"My dearest Rosy"—"Teddens darling" —and so forth. A period of peace on paper would lead to an unhappy interview, and it was all to do over again. Three times he suggested a legal separation with a settlement. Each time Rosina melted into panic, made abject apologies, stormed, pleaded, and was pitiful. Each time he gave in to her, though he was in love now, miserably so, with a woman who knew how to bring some sort of peace to his lacerated soul.

One day early in 1836 he had promised to go down to the country to see Rosina, but was not well and so did not go and somehow forgot to send her any word. She waited a while and then, in a fever of jealousy and pique, went up to Town and knocked on his door in the Albany. The servant was temporarily out. Bulwer himself opened the door, and stood there staring at her in pardonable surprise. Rosina peered past him into the room. She saw a tray with service for two, and a dressing-gown lying across a chair which she mistook for a woman's shawl.

Rosina had hysterics in the passage, screaming at him dreadful words which no one would have supposed a sheltered woman had ever heard. The sacred bachelor silences of the Albany echoed to her fishwife epithets and Bulwer's angry denials and self-justifications. It was Fred Villiers who hovered uncertain and embarrassed inside Bulwer's rooms that day, and not a clandestine lady. But Rosina, forcibly ejected from the premises by a scandalized porter at last, while Bulwer leaned dizzily against the inner side of his locked door, covered her loss of the decencies for months to come by mad, circumstantial witticisms about a Muse in white muslin which she saw perched on Edward's knee when she herself opened the door. There was not a word of it true. But because it made for sniggers and knowing looks, the story lived.

That was the end of Bulwer and Rosina. The separation papers were signed in April. But even then Rosina could not let it rest, and seized every opportunity to damage Bulwer's reputation publicly, until in the eyes of credulous people he became a very monster of base deception and conjugal cruelty. And to a proud, oversensitive man, this bandying about of his name and this invasion of his emotional privacy was the worst agony of all.

Meanwhile his *Last Days of Pompeii* was selling better than anything since *Waverley*—an ironical result of the disastrous Italian holiday.

XII

The end of *Henrietta Temple* was visibly hasty and crude, but the book had long been promised to Colburn and he published it in December. The fire was burnt out. Bulwer thought the whole book very bad and said so, but added that it made the women cry and therefore would be a great success, which was a true prophecy. And anyway, it helped to pay Disraeli's debts.

Since his return from the East, four unsuccessful election contests, extravagant companions, and an expensive social environment had increased his liabilities to saturation point. He was generous, and loved to spend. And matters reached a stage where sometimes he dared not go out of his rooms in Town at all "from fear of the Philistines," whom his cheerful solicitor, Pyne, somehow contrived to keep at bay. What he owed was after all a comparatively small amount beside the financial involvements of men like D'Orsay and Lyndhurst;

a few thousand pounds, which it would not have seriously inconvenienced Isaac to pay off. But he obstinately refused to confess his needs at home. It did not fit in with the mental picture of the brilliant London dandy which was enshrined in the imagination of the simple-minded family at Bradenham. "Of all things in the world, preserve me from the sheriff's officer in my own county!" he implored Pyne during that autumn when he was trying to finish *Henrietta Temple,* in an idyllic atmosphere where the chief anxiety was whether the drought would damage Sarah's late chrysanthemums. Pyne was successful, and Disraeli spent Christmas at home, and wrote to Pyne of the roads being blocked with snow, and of the beech blocks burning on the Bradenham hearth, out of a vivid sense of sanctuary.

"Established my character as a political writer by the letters of Runnymede," he wrote in his journal. "Resumed my acquaintance with Sir Robert Peel. My influence greatly increases from the perfect confidence of Lyndhurst and the success of the *Vindication.* Stayed a week with Bulwer this spring and introduced him to Lyndhurst, against whom he was bitterly prejudiced. They became warm friends. . . ."

The *Vindication* and the anonymous activities in the newspapers did not bring him any substantial income, but his reputation did steadily increase. He was entrusted with a toast at a big Conservative banquet that winter, and made a witty, vigorous speech which was enthusiastically reproduced by the delighted reporters, and the applause was long and genuine. Here he again seized the opportunity of getting home on O'Connell. "It is as natural for Mr. O'Connell to cry, 'Down with the House of Lords!' as it is for a robber to cry out, 'Down with the gallows!' " he remarked, to the uproarious amusement of his hearers. "Both are national institutions very inconvenient to their respective careers. Ay, down with the only barrier between him and his disastrous machinations! But the House of Lords is a great breakwater that his waves of commotion will beat against in vain!" (Cheers.)

Sarah read it all in the *Times,* and was proud. This was

attainment, to make a speech which was published and talked of all over England! O'Connell did not reply in the papers, for which they taunted him. The Duke of Wellington was heard to inquire when young Mr. Disraeli would come into Parliament, and Lyndhurst assured his protégé that it would not be long now. But Lyndhurst—off to Paris for a spell of *la vie garçon*—was not the man to command the situation at Westminster, where Peel appeared to be in one of his periodic *rapprochements* with Stanley.

There was much Conservative activity that winter, but though the Whigs and Tories watched each other, as Disraeli wrote to Sarah, like cat and dog, neither would make the first move. There was no election in sight, and his creditors pressed. At last he was taken really ill from overwork and worry, and the doctors got at him. Put to bed at Bradenham and bled till he was weak, and fussed over by his womenfolk till he lost sight of the London dandy himself, he surrendered and confessed to Isaac that he owed a lot of money. Isaac was not altogether surprised, for Ben's wardrobe alone was impressive. Some of the worst bills were produced and dealt with. But even then, he was not clear.

While still in the bosom of his family, he suffered a violent reaction, perhaps remorse for having caved in, and wrote to Lady Blessington that though he was pretty well and had his rooms and his time to himself, and the family was an amiable and engaging one, nevertheless he was becoming more and more convinced that man was not a social animal; and in his despondency he turned against politics too, and regretted that he was too much committed to the fray to retire, because one's enemies would say that one had failed, to say nothing of one's friends; and he wished pathetically for the wings of a dove. In return he received a maternal lecture, charitably attributing such misanthropy to the influenza. And enclosed in it came a fraternal note from the gloriously bilingual D'Orsay, which began: "Je suis bien aise pour votre intérêt que vous vous soyez décidé à avouer à votre père l'étendue de votre scrape. Car les plasterings-over se demolissent toujours, etc. . . ."

Even so, because he had not told Isaac the whole story the next few months were dismal ones. Another new book, *Venetia*, was conceived and executed during that time of almost intolerable distress and worry, and he felt that it bore the marks. "My father advances daily with his great enterprise," he wrote unhappily to Lady Blessington, "but works of that calibre are hewn out of the granite with slow and deliberate strokes. Mine are but plaster-of-Paris casts, or rather statues of snow that melt as soon as they are fashioned." The critics liked *Venetia* better than *Henrietta Temple,* and the public not so well.

He returned to London early in 1837, and was D'Orsay's guest for a time in the little mansion next to Gore House, where Lady Blessington now held her cheerful court. He wrote to Sarah that there was not much news, and that the Government would probably crawl on a little longer and then dissolve. Things had reached a sort of deadlock of stagnation. There was much speculation about the King's health during the spring. He was known to be ill, but people said it was only hay-fever. Melbourne murmured to someone that the King was now quite crazy. By June everybody knew that William was dying at Windsor, and the dissolution of Parliament would soon be obligatory. The prospect of a general election, now that it had come, was singularly intoxicating to Disraeli.

London,
June 19, 1837.

Dearest Sa,

There was an agreeable party at Madame Montalembert's last night; but whether la comtesse had taken an extra glass of champagne, or what might be the cause, she lionized me so dreadfully that I was actually forced to run for my life. She even produced *Venetia,* and was going to read a passage out loud, when I seized my hat and rushed downstairs, leaving the graceful society of Lady Egerton, much to my vexation.

I shall keep this open for news of the King.

5:30 P.M.—The King dies like an old lion. He said yesterday to his physicians, "Only let me live through this glorious day!" This suggested to Munster to bring the tricolour flag which had just arrived from the Duke of Wellington, and show it to the King. William IV said, "Right, right," and afterwards, "Unfurl it and let me feel it;" then he pressed the eagle and said, "Glorious day." This may be depended on. He still lives. . . .

Carlton Club,
June 20, 1837.

Dearest,

I write in the midst of three or four hundred persons and in a sce of great excitement. The King died in the middle of the ht. Lord Lyndhurst attended the Privy Council at Kens. on and kissed the young Queen's hand, which all are a ed was remarkably sweet and soft. She read her address and was perfectly composed, though alone in the Counc. hamber, attended by no woman.

As yet there are not eve rumours; all is tumult, and like a camp. The dissolution is xpected in the course of three weeks. My prospects are bright, and I hope soon to tell you they are settled. . . .

Victoria's reign had begun.

IV. GROSVENOR GATE

"MARK my words," said Mrs. Lewis, "our Mr. Disraeli will have a brilliant career!"

Their Mr. Disraeli turned upon her a look of such utter astonishment that her husband gave a snort of laughter.

"There you are, Dizzy!" he said. "The oracle has spoken. You're going to be a great man, whether you believe or not!"

"We all believe it," said Edward Bulwer gently. "It was only a question of the right opening."

"And now," said D'Orsay, "the right opening has—opened!"

"You all make it sound very easy," murmured Disraeli, and his eyes were hidden by their drooping lids. How often had she said that, then, if Henrietta had heard it too—or did Henrietta only prophesy?—more than two years ago?

They sat in the Lewises' drawing-room in Grosvenor Gate; a high, long room furnished, according to Henrietta, all wrong. The mantelpiece was austere white Adam, and the furniture Louis Quinze; the long windows with their rose brocade curtains looked over the trees of the Park behind chaste little ironwork balconies. To Disraeli's uncritical eyes it was a bright, luxurious room, full of gilt and gesso and col-our—an expensive-looking room. There was always a fire in it when other people's rooms were slightly chilly, in the late spring and early autumn or on damp summer afternoons. Cheerful servants came in and out with food and drink on trays, and even long after midnight, if the House rose late, he had found in it a supper-table laid with French china and silver, something hot in a chafing-dish, all sorts of bottles with their accompanying glassware—and Mrs. Lewis would be sitting there on the gilt sofa doing *petit-point* exquisitely, rather like a good child with a sampler. Odd, how those juvenile similes persisted in one's thoughts of her, when she had been a housewife so many years, and such a good one too;

though D'Orsay said she kept Wyndham's establishment far
more like a mistress than a wife. Surely no man was ever so
surrounded by creature comforts and good humour at all
times of the day and night as Wyndham. And yet she looked
the soul of impractical incompetence sitting there with her
needlework. Perhaps it was those bunched brown curls,
framing her heart-shaped, untroubled face. . . .

"Oh, but it isn't just my own idea that Dizzy is a genius,"
she was saying modestly, her eyes on her quick needle. "I
have heard it on the best authority, and more than once!"

Disraeli crooked sceptical brows above a sombre gaze.

"Who says so, besides you?" he demanded quietly. "Where
have you heard that?"

She glanced round at them swiftly and back to her sewing,
and the corners of her mouth deepened before she spoke.

"Well, the last time, it was in bed," she said.

D'Orsay's great laughter rang down the room, and Wyndham's rusty chuckle conceded her charming foolishness as
always. Bulwer was surprised. But Disraeli only sat looking at
her with the slow, thoughtful smile which her most light-
hearted *gaffe* drew from him—as though she was always quite
incredible to him, but there she was, and still he wondered.

There had been twenty at dinner, and now only these five
were left together; the men nursing tumblers of brandy and
water, Mrs. Lewis in a corner of the sofa with her needlework. It was very late, and the streets were quiet, increasing
the intimate feeling of the brightly lighted drawing-room, its
pink curtains drawn against the summer night. Bulwer was
there on sufferance, as Disraeli's friend, for Mrs. Lewis
had taken Rosina's side in the past year's difficulties. Rosina's
side was all she knew, for Bulwer never spoke of it, and
Rosina had made out a very good case for herself. Mrs.
Lewis herself was incapable of making scenes, she was cosseted, adored, indulged, with always plenty of money to
spend, and she had no idea of what had gone on in that tem-
pestuous household in Hertford Street. She knew that lots of
men did not treat their wives as Wyndham treated her, but
she could not imagine what most of the wives had done to

BENJAMIN DISRAELI   *From a Portrait by Grant*

deserve it. And everybody said that Bulwer was being un-
faithful now, and with a woman who was married to someone else. It seemed to her that such things need not be. And
so Bulwer was never asked to Grosvenor Gate unless Disraeli
was coming too, for his only apparent virtue was their un-
shakable friendship.

The King had been dead a week, and election excitement
had already begun. During the spring, while the King's life
flickered out, Disraeli had received half a dozen offers to
stand for Parliament, partly as the result of his spectacular
Taunton campaign. Derby had wanted him, Chichester, and
Taunton itself, which still remembered him with delight.
He had all but settled on Barnstaple when there came a
chance to stand as Wyndham's colleague for Maidstone.
There was no doubt this time about Wyndham's being returned again as one of the two representatives. And it suddenly looked worth while to the Maidstone Conservatives
to nominate a second candidate and attempt to carry both
seats. The result of a hasty conference at the Carlton Club
was that Disraeli was off to Maidstone tomorrow with Wyndham to begin the canvass.

It was a piece of great good fortune for him to have the
chance to come in, as it were, under Wyndham's wing. All
day he had walked among the clouds, and during dinner
he had set the air about him tingling with his own suppressed
excitement. Everything was going to be all right at last. The
world was his, or would be soon. But now at the end of the
evening he suffered a reaction. The goal seemed nearer than
ever before. To fail now would be unendurable. To fail
again—*Taunton was the fourth time, wasn't it?*—to face again,
unflinching, the humiliation and derision of defeat—once
more to school his impassive face to show no sign of despair . . .

Always before he had looked forward to an election with
eagerness and confidence, longing to begin; the bustle and
stimulus of flattery and enthusiasm among his own following; the smiling rapier-work among the heckling of a hostile
crowd; the intoxication of his own inexhaustible energy,

making his points, scoring off his opponent, raising those gusts of surprised laughter from even an unfriendly audience, and feeling the slow, unwilling *give* of opinion in his direction as he went on speaking, till cheers broke through; that sense of growing triumph, of acquisition, of *power*. . . . Yes, but he lost the election.

This time he was viewing it differently. All that effort, he was thinking, all that noise and confusion, all that fatigue and intolerable strain—for a possible nothing. He felt that one more defeat would finish him, lacerate his self-esteem once too often, and destroy his self-respect forever. If he lost at Maidstone he would quit politics and they could say he had failed, and failed ridiculously. He would be a laughing-stock. No, he would be forgotten. And what then? Go on writing books, to keep a derided name before the world? No. Let it go. Let it all go, and let them forget. But what was there then to live for, and how would one fill one's days?

For the moment as he sat silent amid the voices of his friends, gazing down into the glass held between his two hands, the zest of life all drained away, and he felt old and tired and hopeless. There seemed to be nothing to go on with, if Maidstone refused him like the others. He was thirty-two, and nothing yet but half-successes; brief demi-triumphs of a book, a speech, a friendship—and a love that now was ashes. One could not go on like this. It was spirit-breaking.

Bulwer had got in at twenty-seven, Peel at twenty-one (his father bought him the seat), Stanley at twenty (he was the son of an Earl). Perhaps one should have gone in seriously for Law—as his father had wished him to. Then one would be able to come into Parliament grandly, with a respected name, as Lyndhurst had done at fifty-four. Wyndham also had been called to the Bar first. Perhaps one should have gone to one of the Universities, and known as boys the men who would be opponents and colleagues later on. Canning, whom they had called adventurer too, had nevertheless been to Christ Church with Lord Liverpool, who became his chief.

It made a difference, there was a sort of free-masonry, no matter which side you were on later. Perhaps—

"Dizzy has gone off into one of his silences," said Mrs. Lewis's voice.

"Thinking of his speech for tomorrow," said Bulwer. "What line will you take this time?"

"The same one, I suppose," he said wearily, not looking at them.

"But surely—" Mrs. Lewis raised her head and chose her words diffidently. "Surely somebody is going to do something about that dreadful new Poor Law?"

They all looked at her.

"Poor Law, my dear?" said Wyndham. "But it's feeding and housing hundreds of people."

"It's wicked," she said simply, and there were tears in her eyes. "It's cruel. It's nothing but sending them to prison, really—as though poverty was a crime!" She realized suddenly that they were all watching her, all listening, and retreated behind her needle in confusion. "Of course I know I don't know anything about politics," she apologized. "I daresay it's the best they can do, but it does seem a pity— Well, I only know what Rook was telling me—my maid," she explained, with a smile which asked their indulgence. "She has an uncle—he couldn't find work—he's getting old—they didn't mean to beg, but finally they wrote to her—we sent them money," she added simply. "But it won't last forever. You see, that new Law—they're afraid—well, you see, it separates families—" She was sewing very fast. "Surely they have a right to kindness, as well as charity?"

"My dear—" said Wyndham, and stopped, and looked round at the others.

"But eet ees your speech!" cried D'Orsay, infinitely touched, his accent quite out of control. "There, Dizzy, ees your speech! The new Poor Law ees a Wheeg law! Let them have it!"

Wyndham was pleased.

"You might do worse, Dizzy. She's a good mascot," he said.

Disraeli sat with his eyes on her profile, his slender length relaxed in his chair, his beautiful hands drooping. He seemed to return by degrees to the bright room, and the air of confident expectation which pervaded it.

"It is an appalling law," he said at last. "I've already been chopping at it a little—held a meeting in Bucks, signed a petition, and so forth. Yes—" His eyes narrowed and sharpened. He was thinking again. "Yes—I might have another go at it tomorrow." Suddenly he smiled at her. "Thank you," he said, and she smiled back encouragingly. He drained his glass and rose. "I must get some sleep," he said, and having replaced his glass on the tray on the table he stood there looking down at it blindly, trying to recapture the joy of combat which must be his tomorrow at Maidstone. No use. It was gone.

"Have another," said Wyndham helpfully, coming to his side.

"No, thanks. I must have had too much already. I'm—very tired."

"Nonsense, you thrive on the sort of thing that's ahead of us. Just a drop?" Wyndham's hand was on his shoulder. With the other he raised the decanter above Disraeli's glass.

"Let him be, Wyndham, he's got an early start tomorrow." Mrs. Lewis spoke with matronly authority. "You'll all have heads full of fluff if you don't get off to bed at once."

"Come along, Dizzy, we'll walk home with you!"

D'Orsay kissed Mrs. Lewis's fingers; Bulwer made his bow.

"Help them find their things, Wyndham, I didn't ask the servants to wait up." She smiled the three of them out of the door with a little confidential gesture, and Disraeli when he turned found her standing beside him. Her brown curls framed an earnest, lifted face—she wasn't very tall—her eyes were grave and very sweet. "It will be all right this time," she said gently. "You must go straight to sleep, mind. I always tell Wyndham it does no good at all to plan campaigns in bed."

He faced her tensely, and his long fingers found and gripped her bare arm.

"Suppose I lose?" he whispered. "I can't face it. *Suppose I lose?*"

"Why, then we must try again," she said, looking up at him, unconfused and unfrightened in the grip of his nerves. "Again—and again! They can't go on being such silly fools forever. I should hate to think there isn't one constituency in England with a majority intelligent enough to elect you!"

He relaxed with a breath of laughter, and dropped her arm and turned away, still laughing quietly, both hands held to his head, which was aching. Then he paused and looked back at her, his face still between his hands.

"You dear soul," he said wonderingly. "How good you are for me."

"Of course I am," she agreed promptly.

Voices came up the stairs—gay, confident voices, from where they waited for him.

"Dizzy! Hurry up, man—"

"Dizzy! Come queeck!"

Wyndham reappeared on the threshold, breathing a little hard from having run up the stairs.

"Are we turning you out, Dizzy? But Mary Anne is right, you know, tomorrow is coming, as sure as fate!"

"Now, Wyndham, don't depress him, just as I've managed to make him laugh again!"

Disraeli went up to her, very grave now, and laid a hand on either of her shoulders, his ringed fingers resting lightly on the short puffed sleeves of her dress.

"I shall justify your faith in me yet. I swear it," he said, and stooping swiftly he kissed her briefly on the cheek. "Good night, Wyndham. God bless you." He was gone.

She stood looking after him, astonished. It was almost as though she was his mother, that kiss—she wondered briefly about his mother, whom he rarely mentioned—there was a sister whom he dearly loved—perhaps he kissed his sister like that—and yet he seemed sometimes so solitary—so—her mind stumbled among words—so *apart*—as though nothing really reached him, and he belonged to nobody, but stood looking on at life, amused, a little contemptuous, but—lonely too.

What had he said—good *for* him, or good *to* him? It was not quite the same. But he had strange ways with words. And either way she was glad. . . .

Wyndham was putting out the candles round the room.

"I never knew Dizzy to have stage-fright before," he said, his back to her. "He's all to bits about this Maidstone election."

"Wasn't it odd of him—to say good night to me like that," she reflected aloud.

"Can't say I blame him," said Wyndham, glancing at her over his shoulder and going on to the mantelpiece candles. "You look very nice tonight."

"It wasn't because I looked nice," she discovered with conviction. She was still standing where Disraeli had left her, in the middle of the room. "I expect he misses Henrietta," she remarked then, along some obscure line of reasoning of her own.

Wyndham muttered something about "good riddance."

"Wyndham. You don't mind that he kissed me? That is, you don't think I—"

He came and took her pointed chin in his big fingers and looked into her candid eyes.

"My dear goose," he said, and kissed her himself, not on the cheek.

II

Maidstone,
July 27, 1837.
11 o'clock.

Dearest Sa,

    Lewis 707
    Disraeli 616
    Col. Thompson 412

The constituency nearly exhausted.

In haste,

DIZZY.

III

In the journal at Bradenham—

November 12, 1837.

Tomorrow I leave Bradenham to take my seat in Parliament. I have passed these three months since my election chiefly in Bucks, and in a run of desultory political reading, though chiefly on Ireland. Attended several political dinners in my County, to which I limit myself; spoke often and well.

My health wonderfully renovated; were it not for the anxiety the state of my affairs occasionally causes me, I should laugh at illness. My life for the past year has been very temperate; my nervous system consequently much stronger. I am now as one leaving a secure haven for an unknown sea. What will the next twelve months produce?

IV

London,
November 15, 1837.

My dearest,

I took my seat this morning. I went down to the House with Wyndham at two, and found it very full, the members standing in groups and chatting. About three there was a cry of "Order, order!" and all took their seats (myself on the second bench, behind Sir Robert Peel) and a messenger summoned the Commons. The Government party was very strong, in consequence of an article in the *Times* about two days back which spread panic through their ranks, but which I think was a hoax.

Shaw-Lefevre proposed, and Strutt of Derby seconded Abercromby (for Speaker). Both were brief, the first commonplace, the other commonplace and coarse; all was tame. Peel said a very little, very well. Then Abercromby, who looked like an old laundress, mumbled and moaned some dulness and was then carried to the chair, and said a little more, amid a faint, dull cheer. To me, of course, the scene was exciting enough, but none could share my feelings except new members.

Peel came to the Carlton yesterday and was there a great deal. He welcomed me very warmly, and all indeed noticed his cordial demeanour. He looks very well, and shook hands with me in the House. He asked me to join a small dinner at the Carlton on Thursday. "A House of Commons dinner purely," he said. "By that time we shall know something of the temper of the House. . . ."

V

William had contrived to live out the dreaded re ncy period after all. Victoria was less than two months p t her eighteenth birthday when he died, but she was of e, and she could occupy the throne in her own right. Nat ally she would have to rely on her ministers at first in gov rnmental questions, but in all private and household mat rs the officious Duchess of Kent was immediately relega d to an insignificance which it would have done Willia a good to behold. The German governess, Lehzen, and F ron Stockmar, Leopold's gift to his niece, were both mo influential than the Queen's mother.

The change over from William to the rl Queen somehow caused much less stir than when he hi self had taken over from his brother George. Unlike Will am, Victoria made no speeches, and was seldom seen in pub c, even after she moved from Kensington Palace into the ew Buckingham Palace, which both George and William had rebuilt and tinkered but never used. Melbourne as Prime Minister found himself suddenly in possession of almost unlimited power. And there was no one in all the Cabinet or either House better fitted to undertake the guidance of the intelligent, high-spirited, self-willed girl who stood in the feeble old King's place.

Melbourne was fifty-eight now, handsome, urbane, humorous; a man women always liked; a singularly lonely man for all that, with singularly little to love. He was too gallant to regard his new sovereign as a daughter—too old to imply anything of the lover. It was a relationship oddly fourth-dimensional, partaking of both impossibilities, and from the beginning it was firmly rooted in mutual confidence, respect and affection.

He was amazed and delighted with her dignity, prudence, and ability to learn. During that summer the little Queen daily recorded in her private journal conversations with Lord Melbourne *"alone,"* which she termed "agreeable," "satisfactory," and, above all, "comfortable." She thought him "honest, kindhearted, and very clever." And after a lifetime amid strident German garrulity she added that she liked to talk to him because he spoke so quietly. He went to Windsor with the Royal household, and always sat next the Queen at dinner, rode with her in the Park on his own beautiful black mare, joined in the simple evening diversions of letter-games, cut-up maps, and sometimes whist. Marvellously he adapted his casual, habitually profane conversation to her ears, pruned his jokes to almost school-room humour. But still his famous hearty laughter rolled through the Royal rooms, with Victoria's equally audible mirth joined to it. The two of them roared with laughter over anything. She had found a playmate. He had found—perhaps youth.

Before the year was out she could hardly bear to lose sight of him for a day, and it was said in the clubs that the Prime Minister had become the Queen's private secretary. The result of this sudden and enduring devotion between them was immediately plain—the Whigs had got a new lease on life.

Parliament was still in temporary quarters after the fire. The Commons sat now in the patched-up chamber which had once been the Lords, and the Lords were in still more incommodious accommodation. The Commons complained of draughts, and the Lords complained of smells. Both Houses were particularly unruly, distracted, and contentious.

The Government majority was a thin one, eked out again by the Irish members. There had been desertion by some of the landed interest to the growing Conservative ranks. The Radicals, dissatisfied that more concessions had not been made to them, had weakened considerably. The madness of

1832 had definitely passed. But the Whigs' best chances lay in Peel's indolence rather than in their own efforts; that, and the Queen's obvious contentment with the present régime.

There had seldom been so strong a party in Opposition. Besides the perennial Wellington, Peel was (for him) full of spirits; Lyndhurst was active and confident, and had just married again, a handsome and wealthy young Jewess; there was Stanley, whose speeches were now often full of invective toward his former associates—O'Connell's name for him, Scorpion Stanley, had stuck; and on the front bench beside Peel sat young William Ewart Gladstone, not yet twenty-eight, with five years of Parliament behind him. In the row behind these fair, florid Britons, sober in dress and unexceptional in deportment, there was the sombre, enigmatic face and imaginative tailoring of Benjamin Disraeli.

London,
December 5, 1837.

Dearest,

Yesterday was rather amusing in the House. The Sheriffs of London, Sir Bob or Tom, and Sir Moses, and no mistake, appeared at the bar in full state to present, according to the privilege of the City of London, some petitions; after which they took their place under the gallery and listened to the debate, which turned out to be the Jewish disabilities question by a side-wind. Nobody looked at me, and I was not at all uncomfortable, but voted in the majority with the utmost *sangfroid*. . . .

VI

Cold December rain streamed down on London, and the midnight streets were empty. But the drawing-room at Grosvenor Gate was bright with candles and a fire, and the small table with its lace-edged cloth stood ready with china, glass, and silver. Mrs. Lewis, in pink silk with bare arms and shoulders, sat in her corner of the French sofa, her little satin slippers crossed on a footstool, her quick needle busy at *petit-point.* Her heart-shaped face with its bunched brown curls either side was childlike and serene in the becoming light, unclouded by impatience or anxiety. The House was sitting late again with the eternal Irish question up, but when Wyndham came in he would want his supper and would have things to tell. O'Connell's behaviour was getting out of all bounds, and all the Radicals, Wyndham said, were acting like thorough ruffians these days, until the Speaker himself had had to interfere. As usual she did not pretend to understand what the trouble was about—something to do with Irish methods at the polls in the last election, she thought. It was all very confusing, but Wyndham's stories of what they said to each other were pointed and made her laugh. Privately she considered the legislators of the realm very like naughty little boys who had never outgrown their school-days' ideas of repartee.

Life was too short, she would have said if questioned, for a man to come home to a mere sleepy hump in the bed for a wife, when he was wide awake and wanted to talk and eat and have something attractive to look at. One wore one's pretty clothes and one's brightest smile, after a late night at the House. One did not even yawn over one's needlework if one had been forehanded and had a nap after dinner. Besides, Wyndham liked to bring people back with him, to a cheery fire and a hostess, while funny stories were told, rude speeches were quoted, and fine points argued, over the wine. Surely that was what a wife was for, among other things, of course—to entertain a man's guests and be amused by them. Besides, it was the best time of day, with the curtains drawn, and the candles lighted, and a sense of peace, and privacy, and comfort. . . .

Rook came in with a silver chafing-dish on a tray, and fussed about the table with a small cosy tinkle of glass and china. The footmen never did things to suit Rook, the most scrupulous of housekeepers, in a black apron with a jangle of keys at her belt. And always when Rook had quite finished, Mrs. Lewis herself would have a look, with a touch here and there.

"Something hot, I hope, Rook," she remarked across her needlework with a smile.

"Yes, madam—creamed oysters, you said."

"And what have you brought him to drink?" queried Mrs. Lewis, knowing pretty well herself, but one could always chatter aimlessly to Rook when the evenings got a bit long.

"Just the usual, madam. Would you be wanting a bottle of champagne as well? Because I'm afraid Parker's gone to bed with the keys of the cellar in his pocket again."

"Never mind, I don't think my husband will bring anyone back with him tonight, as late as this. If he does want anything, he can use his own keys."

"Well, I've brought six of everything, in case." Rook ran an efficient glance over the table, counting: salad, cruet—brandy, sherry—glasses—silver—plates—it was all there. "Will that be all, madam?"

"Yes, thank you. Go to bed. I can't have anyone waiting up later than this. Let them all go to bed."

"Thank you, madam. Good night, madam."

Rook's smile was a benediction. When the door had closed behind her Mrs. Lewis rose with a rustle of pink silk, and went herself to inspect the table. Nothing was an inch out of place. She bent to make sure of the taper, alight under the oysters, and then set the door ajar again so that she could hear Wyndham when he came in, returning with a little sigh of satisfaction to her needlework and her footstool.

Above the sizzling whisper of the fire she could hear the drip of rain at the windows. What a horrid night to be out, and the temporary building which still housed the Commons was very unhealthful. For the hundredth time it crossed her mind how pleasant it was after all to be a woman, safe at home by the fire, instead of having to rush about in all weather, making speeches and trying to govern the country. Who would be Lord Melbourne, after all, thought Mary Anne Lewis, threading her needle. But of course if one was born a man one got used to it, and even liked it. . . . Her mind drifted on whimsically, here and there, arriving nowhere, among her happy, inconsequential thoughts, while she waited, cherished and secure, for Wyndham to come home.

At last the street door closed heavily, as was his way, and in a minute she heard voices on the stairs. Someone was with him, after all.

"Is that you, Wyndham?" Foolish words, in her sweet voice—she knew the sound of him so well.

"It's two of us," said Wyndham, puffing a little, on the stairs.

"Nice hot food and a fire in here," she called back. "Come along, you must be dead."

He arrived in the drawing-room, big and kind, with the smile he kept for her. She raised her face to his kiss, and his cheek was wet with rain.

"I've brought Disraeli back with me," he said as he straightened, and Disraeli crossed the threshold slowly, closing the door behind him. He stopped her with a gesture as she started to rise.

"No, don't stir," he said gently. "You'll spoil the picture." He came down the room to her quickly, with his light, soundless tread, and bent to kiss her outstretched hand—Wyndham was still holding the other—and stood looking down at her a moment before going on to the hearthrug. He was scrupulously dressed, as always; a bottle-green coat tonight, and a white brocaded waistcoat with the usual gold chain around his neck, and pearl-grey trousers. His shirtfront was exquisite, his cravat a miracle of black silk and starched gills. Above it, his face was unusually white and tired. "You're a lucky man, Wyndham," he said, "to come home every night to a warm room, and lights, and supper—and a pretty wife."

"Different from the club, isn't it!" said Wyndham with pride. "Nobody in a pink dress there! Just brandy and tobacco smoke and more speeches! Never anything worth looking at!"

"That's very sweet of you both," she smiled, and was touched.

"Bulwer will be here soon, Mary Anne." Wyndham turned to the table, peering hungrily under dish covers. "I had to ask him."

"Oh!" she said, on a little cry of delicate horror. "That man!"

"Now, Mrs. Wyndham, be charitable," said Disraeli a trifle wearily. "Let him warm himself at your fire for my sake—even if his wife has left him!"

"Poor Rosina," said Mrs. Lewis to this. "You're not fair to her, Dizzy."

"And you're not fair to Edward Bulwer," he retorted with heat. "A man ridden by debt, and driven mad by a woman's tongue—"

"At least she was faithful to him!"

"Was she! That wasn't clever of her!"

"Dizzy!" cried Mrs. Lewis, and Wyndham chuckled as he sniffed the oysters approvingly. "Do you mean to say that if Rosina had had affairs with other men—"

"I mean that if Rosina had behaved so that any other man could possibly have been attracted to her, Bulwer would still be her slave!" he interrupted angrily. "Year by year I have watched that beautiful fiend Rosina go from sheer bad temper to hysteria to *madness,* egged on by her basilisk mother—"

"Dizzy, what words!" she objected in a very small voice.

"Never will I marry for love!" he exclaimed. "It's been a short cut to hell for half the people I know!"

"Well, how about us, eh?" Wyndham came and took his wife's hand in both his big ones. "How's this for a marriage?"

"This?" Disraeli looked round the bright room slowly. "It's heaven."

"Well, then—!" said Wyndham's wife, mollified.

"It's hard to realize that this is a marriage too," he reflected. "Poor Bulwer. Be kind to him, Mrs. Wyndham. Be generous with the peace you know how to make for a man."

"I shall never forgive him," she said, trying to look it.

"Very well. But never let him know!" They smiled at each other. "I'm sorry if I snapped at you. I'm a little tired." He relaxed on the corner of the sofa beside her, with a sigh.

"He wants cosseting tonight, my dear," suggested Wyndham. "He's just made his maiden speech."

"Oh, Dizzy, already? Why didn't you tell me at once? But how exciting! How did it go?"

"It didn't go," he said, without expression. "It was a colossal failure. Don't let's talk about it."

"It was no such thing!" said Wyndham loyally. "Those scamps of Radicals were determined you shouldn't be heard. And *my* début was a failure because I *was* heard! You can take your choice." He gave his rusty chuckle. "However, I think the situation might be improved by a little champagne."

"You'll have to fetch it yourself, Wyndham," said his wife without removing her pitying gaze from Disraeli's rigid profile. "Parker's gone to bed."

"Quite so," agreed Wyndham cheerfully. "Shan't be a second—" He escaped, strong in the hope that his wife would find a way to bring Dizzy round. He was resolved to take his time about the champagne, first because he had the Englishman's horror of scenes, and was not at all sure what Dizzy might do or say when he came out of the paralysis of despair which had kept him silent all the way from Westminster; and secondly because of his unbounded faith in a woman's ability—any woman's, but particularly his Mary Anne's—to deal with these situations.

It had been an evening Wyndham would never forget. Granted that the House was singularly unruly this session, they had made an exhibition of themselves tonight that was dumbfounding. Granted that the speaker was unusual in his appearance and his choice of words, and foolhardy in the opening he took. Granted that he was—it was a thing which Wyndham's loyalty and affection seldom allowed him to contemplate—a Jew. All this could hardly account for the reception of his maiden effort tonight.

No wonder that Dizzy was all to pieces about it, Wyndham conceded, descending the cellar steps gingerly with a candle held high. But himself, he preferred to be out of the way until Mary Anne had, as it were, got Dizzy together again. Then they could have supper, and the champagne would do the rest. Let's see now—hot wax from the candle dripped on his hand and he swore softly—Burgundy, no—hock, Chianti, Moselle, no—ah, here we are, champagne. He pottered blissfully among the cobwebby shelves.

VII

In the silence Wyndham left behind him, Disraeli rose draggingly, and went to stand in front of the fire, his elbow on the mantel, the warm light dancing on his still, white face. He seemed to have forgotten there was anyone else in the room, wrapped in his own misery, remote, withdrawn into Gethsemane. She glanced at him once or twice, and went on with her sewing. Finally—

"Was it really so bad?" she queried gently.

He spoke without moving.

"It was awful. Unbelievable. Worse than any nightmare."

"What happened?"

"They drowned me out," he said, still without turning to her. "They wouldn't listen. They hooted—they howled—they stamped and cat-called and made animal noises. It was Bedlam. I've been visiting the House for years, and nobody else has received such treatment."

She was silent a moment, thinking. *Why,* was the question she wanted to ask, but she saw that one must go carefully. She thought she knew why, a little. He did not look like the others, nor dress like them—nor think like them. He made no attempt to conform, and some people resented that. And besides—she remembered things that had been said a week ago when a Bill to remove all religious disabilities had resolved itself into a debate on Jewish emancipation only, and had been defeated—besides, there was his race. But surely England was not so uncivilized in this day and age as to hoot a man because—

"What was the debate about?" she inquired cautiously.

"The eternal Irish question, of course."

"Then it was O'Connell!" she exclaimed, enlightened.

He swung back to her suddenly, needing the comfort of words at last.

"O'Connell got up and made a long, rambling speech, dragging in the Irish Municipal Corporation question and everything else, when the discussion was purely and simply the Protection Fund for the Protestant landowners. Stanley was to answer O'Connell, and at the last minute I asked Stanley to let me take his place. Stanley doesn't like me. He was glad enough to let me walk straight into it!"

"You chose to answer O'Connell for your maiden speech?" she repeated, amazed.

"Yes, I did."

"What blind, brute courage!" she murmured into her sewing.

"More than two years ago I told him I would take the first opportunity. This was it."

"'We shall meet at Philippi,'" she said softly, and he uttered a breath of dreary laughter.

"You remember that?" He came to sit beside her again, his elbows on his knees, his ringed hands hanging. He was spent. "I was warned, of course, but that only drove me to face it sooner. Besides—I didn't want to give him time to attack me first. I suppose that might have been worse—but I never saw anything like tonight in nearly ten years of politics. It was a howling mob! Well—they have squashed me." The twist of his lips was bitter.

"Not you!" said Mrs. Lewis, threading her needle with absorbed concentration so that she need not look at him. "One day they'll come crowding in to hear you."

He glanced at her, probing her calm, sweet face for dishonesty. He saw, incredulously, that she meant it. But then, she had not been there tonight. Nothing he could say now would make her understand what that had been.

"You see," he began a little unsteadily, "one expects elections to be rough. One expects to be heckled and insulted with personal remarks and shouted down. I'd got used to yells of 'Old clothes!' and 'Bring a bit of pork for the Jew!'— that sort of thing—when I was canvassing. But I thought that once I was *in*—once I had got my seat—" He was shaking with nerves. Without raising her tactful eyes from her needle, she

knew that his hands and his knees were trembling, and she
wondered how he kept his teeth from chattering. She had
seen a lovely horse like that once—quivering with nerves, not
fear or anger—just nerves; she went on sewing. "You see—
in the House one is entitled, not exactly to courtesy, but there
is a kind of *decency*—at least, a new member is always allowed
a hearing—so it took me by surprise tonight, I—I wasn't expecting anything quite so—*barbarous*. Good God, a man can't
face it and *live!*" His head went down into his hands.

She glanced at him compassionately, without losing the
rhythm of her stitch, leaving him a long pause to master himself. She was not embarrassed or frightened by what to Wyndham would have been a scene. In her own complete simplicity
she felt no awkwardness before this naked misery. He was
overstrung, and hideously disappointed—spiritually mauled.
He needed to get it all out to someone, preferably a woman,
because men were queer about showing their emotions before one another. Men could let themselves go before women
without loss of stature. Usually his sister helped him through
his bad times, she knew, but Sarah was at Bradenham. Her
impulse was all to put her arms around him as though he
was a broken-hearted child—all men were children—and tell
him that it didn't matter, not to her, and that she believed
in him as much as ever, and to rail against the rabble who
had stoned him. But instinct told her that if she did that
now he would break down and weep, and that must not happen, with Bulwer on the way and Wyndham bringing up
champagne. That would only humiliate him the more. At
last she spoke quietly into the tense silence.

"Dizzy—what did Peel think?"

He came up from the depths slowly; slowly turned his
head.

"That's one of the things Bulwer is trying to find out now.
He'll be along in a few minutes, I should think." His eyes
sought her face again, anxiously. "You don't really mind his
coming here, do you?"

She dared to glance at him then, and smiled.

"Not if you want him."

"You're very good to me," he said simply, and leaned back against the sofa like a man who draws the first breath after an intolerable pain had passed. The worst was miraculously over, and thanks to the quiet little woman beside him. Somehow she had pulled him through, by tact, and patience, and not sympathizing too much in the wrong way. He wondered at her anew. What was there about her that soothed and comforted without words? He had very nearly made a fool of himself just now. And she had saved him. How? His eyes rested on her face again, trying to read the secret of her in the wide brow and childish lips. It was not that she didn't understand when a man was racked. Tears stung his eyelids—tears of sheer gratitude. He wanted to kiss her small, busy hands and try to tell her what she did for him, just by breathing, there beside him. Little saint—little angel of peace and good will—little guardian angel to a man's self-respect.

"You mustn't take this to heart, Dizzy," she was saying wisely, while she sewed. "After all, you've won your seat. You are in. And that's what we all wanted so badly. The rest will come."

"I used to think that," he admitted wryly. "I used to think that once I had my seat, the rest would be easy. I thought I could hold them—get them laughing—in the right way, I mean—amuse them—sway them—carry them along. I've seen it done. I've done it myself with an election crowd at the hustings. I saw myself as one of the Chiefs, and going on from there to the Cabinet. I saw myself on the front bench with Peel. I even saw myself—Prime Minister!" He tried to laugh.

"I remember the night you told Melbourne that," she said. "You stood there on the hearthrug at Caroline Norton's looking very young and beautiful, and you said—'I want to be Prime Minister'—just like that." She smiled at him as though he had been a clever child.

"What cheek," he sighed.

"Melbourne asked you what you wanted to do. I liked you for answering him. I think he did too."

"He's having a good laugh now—if he remembers!"

"He'll remember."

"I hope not!"

"Oh, Dizzy, don't! It doesn't mean anything, tonight doesn't," she assured him earnestly. "I wish you could believe that, as I do! And the next time you speak—"

She broke off, as Wyndham reappeared with a bottle of champagne under his arm and a tray of shallow glasses teetering between his two hands. She watched him, smiling, in his somewhat awkward progress to the table—dear Wyndham—she would have got the glasses herself, but one couldn't leave Dizzy like this.

Disraeli drew a long breath. Yes, the pain had eased off now. He was no longer sick and giddy, blind and dazed with what had happened to him. It was as though he felt himself all over and found that he was still alive and whole.

"I shall have to tell Sa how it was," he muttered. "The papers will make the most of this. I'll write to her tonight. Anyway, they didn't set me down, that's one thing! I was on my feet nearly as long as I had meant to be!"

"He fought through with absolutely undaunted pluck and unruffled temper," Wyndham said proudly. "And he made good isolated hits when there was a lull. The party backed him well, until it was drowned out, and Peel cheered him, which is not his custom."

Then Bulwer came, with the news that Peel had said it was anything but failure, and that Sheil, in agony with the gout, had sat the debate out anyway, and wanted to meet Disraeli.

"That's very generous of Sheil," Wyndham assured them. "You see, Dizzy, for one thing the House hates a man to arrive there a full-blown orator. They want to discover him themselves, and bring him out gradually."

"The House," said Mrs. Lewis with decision, "is a collection of hoodlums and children who ought to be spanked. Let's have something to eat."

Wyndham and Bulwer smiled at her, and at each other, over her head. She was so right, they knew. But Disraeli sat still, not looking at them.

"You've only told me the pleasant things you heard," he objected. "What about the rest. Did you talk to Stanley?"

"No."

"*He* must have been pleased!"

"Apparently the uproar was all organized by the O'Connellites and the Radicals," Bulwer was beginning.

"*Your* friends!" remarked Disraeli without animus.

"No, *not* my friends," said Bulwer, annoyed. "The attorney-general said it was a compact party at the Bar of the House over which they had no control, and that you had nothing whatever to be afraid of in future. On the whole I'm convinced it's the best thing that could have happened to you—"

Disraeli's brief, incredulous laugh cut him off.

"Edward, don't perjure yourself, please!"

"No, look here, I mean it." He glanced at Wyndham nervously. "You see, you gave them no time to get used to you. You tried to take the House by storm, just as you do everything else, headlong, at a dead run. But you're not quite what they're accustomed to, Dizzy, you—" Again his eyes sought Wyndham's, and a gleam of humour passed between them. "—you were bound to upset them. On the other hand this overwhelming catastrophe has actually created a feeling in your favour."

"Yes, that's all very comforting, my dear fellow, but don't forget—" Disraeli's impatient gesture set his rings flashing. "—*I* am the one who has to face it again!"

"But you wouldn't be Disraeli if you didn't face it again," argued Bulwer, "and soon."

Something snapped somewhere, and Disraeli shot to his feet.

"I'm *tired* of being Disraeli!" he cried out at them passionately. "I wish you'd all stop being tactful and cheerful, and admit that the speech was an ignominious failure! I wish you'd let me fail in peace!" With another of his swift, clean movements he swung away from them, toward the curtained windows, both hands to his head.

There was a stunned silence. Bulwer looked down at his

boots. Wyndham and his wife exchanged helpless glances. She had tried to save them from this, she was thinking. She *had* saved them, but they had had to go on talking, like idiots, instead of opening the champagne and having supper quickly while the air was comparatively clear. They were probably all hungry, anyway; heaven knows when the three of them had last had decent food.

"I'm sorry—my head aches," said Disraeli jerkily, his back to them. "I'd better go home."

Bulwer moved toward him, with his characteristic uncertainty, and laid a hesitating hand on his shoulder.

"I know how you feel," he said diffidently. "I've felt the same way in my daily grind. I've often been tempted to give it all up—go abroad—bury myself in some blessed climate like Italy and stay there—in peace. We're sacrificing our youth—the time of pleasure—our singing season. But we are bound to go on. We are bound. How our enemies would triumph if we retired now from the scene!"

Disraeli stayed quiet under his hand, surprisingly.

"That's a glorious inspiration you offer me, Edward—the confounding of my enemies!"

"And the gratification of your friends," said Bulwer with his rare, sweet smile, and turned away. He had done what he could.

"I suppose you're right. Only I thought I was getting used to it. It's discouraging to find I'm not." He faced them again, with an effort, his slim height gallantly held. He smiled at them. "Wyndham—did I hear something about champagne?"

Wyndham seized the bottle. Mrs. Lewis tucked her sewing away in its silk bag for the night. She was proud of him. That was very good of Dizzy, very strong, and sane, very sensible—to stay and see the evening out, as though nothing had happened. That was courage. She liked him better than ever before.

"I agree with Bulwer," Wyndham was saying, as he wrapped the neck of the bottle in a white napkin. "This clamorous reception may prove fortunate. Nothing is worse than to be heard in supercilious silence as I was! You're bound to succeed in spite of their bullying. You've shown the House that you have a fine command of language—that you have courage, temper, and wit." The cork came out with a cheery pop. "Have at them again as soon as possible. You'll be all right next time!"

"Yes, and next time try to be dull," said Mrs. Lewis unexpectedly, and they all looked at her with interest. Nobody objected, or told her she was wrong, nobody laughed. She glanced round at their three inquiring faces with her engaging innocence. She knew nothing about politics, really, she seemed to say, but— "Be very quiet, and quote figures at them, and dates and details. Read uninteresting data off little scraps of paper from various vague pockets. If possible, mislay your eyeglasses. Reason with them endlessly in words of one syllable, as though they were half-witted. Never let them laugh—not once. And then sit down. Be like them, and before long they will beg you to be different again."

They stood staring at her. In those few sentences, without guile or malice, from years of listening to men talk at home, and two or three uncomprehending attendances at election campaigns, from unnoticeable observation and eavesdropping, she had hit off the typical Parliamentary manner. Peel was in those few light words of hers, and Lyndhurst, and Melbourne, and, until he was worked up, even Grey.

Disraeli found his voice first.

"Out of the mouths of babes," he said.

"But, by Jove, she's right!" gasped Bulwer.

"She usually is," murmured Wyndham, rather proud of her.

"You always say that Dizzy is a genius." She turned to him. "But stupid people hate to have genius rammed down their throats, and the House as a whole is a prize idiot. It wants to think that Dizzy learns from it, not it from him. You said that yourself, Wyndham. And then he can be as clever as he likes. And then I can say, 'I told you so!' " She smiled round at them all, suddenly shy and apologetic, and unaware of the magnitude of her revelation.

"Give me that, Wyndham, I want to drink to your wife,"

said Disraeli abruptly, reaching for a glass. "I came here to-night feeling I had suffered the last humiliation—wanting to die like a dog in a hole in the wall and never have to face my world again. And what happens?" he demanded with a perilous sweep of the full glass. "A fire—supper on the table—two loyal men and one wise woman—and life becomes bearable again! Let us drink, Wyndham, to that dear, wise woman."

They lifted their glasses, rather solemnly, and toasted her, to her infinite confusion. Her cheeks went pink, and when she tried to thank them her throat closed, and she could not make a sound. She had not had her health drunk since her wedding. The eyes she lifted to Wyndham were embarrassed and shining. Perhaps she had been talking too much again.

Disraeli stood alone in the middle of the carpet, the forgotten glass in his fingers.

"They laughed at me tonight," he was saying, very softly, a little through his teeth. "They amused themselves at my expense. O'Connell the bully thinks he has me on the run. But I have begun several things many times, and I have often succeeded in the end. They jeered and hooted and drowned me out tonight," he ruminated softly, while the cold fighting smile settled on his lips. "But the time will come when they will hear me."

"Hear, hear," said Bulwer gently, and drank again, and with a smile Wyndham held his glass to his wife's lips that she might drink to that herself.

VIII

When Disraeli woke the next morning it was still raining drearily, and he lay looking at the ceiling with half-closed eyes, trying to pull himself round for the day. Once more he must face up to the consequences of failure, once more the mask of sardonic composure must be adjusted, once more his enigmatic silences must protect him from uttering either bravado or despair. His friends would condole more or less tactfully, his enemies would watch him with open curiosity, and his own thoughts must remain a mystery to both.

His manservant tapped at the bedroom door, looked in, and at sight of the white, strained face on the pillow withdrew again, to reappear shortly with a cup of strong black coffee which he tendered in sympathetic silence. Disraeli sat up to receive it with a twisted smile. The fellow thought he had been having a gay night, did he!

"Thank you," he said. "Get me all the newspapers."

The Press was what might have been expected, except for the *Times,* which tried to soften its account with praise of those parts of his speech which had been heard. Sa would see the *Times,* and he must write to her immediately after breakfast. He sighed. It would not be easy.

A cheerful fire was warming the room now, the low saucer-bath stood ready on the bath-sheet spread in the middle of the floor, the tin can of shaving water steamed under a towel on the wash-hand-stand; the manservant hovered solicitously over the chest of drawers choosing his fresh linen. With an expression of infinite sweet-tempered patience with a refractory world, he swung his feet to the floor and began the dandy's arduous business of dressing. Everything must be aggressively perfect today—not a crease, not a smudge, not a thread out of place—all spotlessness and glitter. Meanwhile, he stared thoughtfully at the dripping window-panes and shivered in his bath. Shaving was an ordeal. There was a long and intricate session with brush and comb and pomade, until each shining black curl lay exactly in its appointed place, the last one close against his forehead over the right eyebrow.

Standing on the hearthrug in his underclothes with his back to the blaze, he rejected two shirts, one after the other, alleging that they had not been properly ironed, and that the laundress had obviously been drinking again. The third he consented to wear, after a searching scrutiny of its frills and cuffs. Trousers of his favourite fawn colour went on next without comment, and the slender polished boots passed with only a glance, the gratified valet snapping the strap briskly under the instep.

Ten nerve-racking minutes were then consumed by the cravat, all black, lying in small neat folds to the lobes of his ears and emphasizing the clean, sharp line of his chin, with no frivolous white gills today; spreading in restrained black silk puffs and smooth disciplined billows to the edge of the high-cut red and gold brocade waistcoat—the strap nipped in at the small of his back gave him a waist like a woman's. The heavy gold watch-chain was passed over his head and under his curls at the back, and after it a fine pale gold chain with elongated links to cross the black silk delicately above the V of the waistcoat; two rings—only two today—a massive gold thing, his seal, and a diamond, modest but good. At last, with a final, unhurried scrutiny of the ensemble in the mirror, he relaxed with a sigh into a dressing-gown of mauve brocaded silk, and, like royalty dining in public, clothed and self-possessed to the last degree, sat down to his solitary breakfast.

He had found, as the years went on, that he emerged from these crises not altogether without appetite, and he viewed the sizzling Bradenham ham on the plate before him with favour. Sa kept him supplied with dainties from the country, and in the summer she sent him flowers for his rooms. He fell to wondering again, while he ate, what he was going to say to her about last night.

The old habit of preserving his countenance before the family still held. They, least of all, should know what he suffered at these times of humiliation and defeat. To them he was always a glamorous figure living a lambent existence in Town, sought after, successful, the friend of great men, the protégé of power. He knew bitterly this morning that it was not just a desire to spare Sa's feelings that made this letter difficult to write. Once more, he must try to save his own face at home. He had a boundless dread of losing that ultimate stronghold of his self-esteem, Sa's blind admiration. There was always one last ditch of comfort—Sa believed in him. He knew in the bottom of his soul that she would have gone on believing in him even if she had been in the House last night and heard the whole hideous row, but he was glad she had not. Sa need never know the worst about him. With her he could always salvage that last ounce of pride which enables a trampled, unstrung spirit to pick itself up and struggle on.

So his mind was busy while he breakfasted with phrases for Sa. The things that Bulwer had said, and Wyndham, would be useful. This brought his thoughts to Mrs. Lewis, and he sat contemplating that amazing woman over a cooling cup of coffee. She had been so right last night, as though she had made speeches in the House herself, and knew how it thought and what best defeated it. Presumably that was feminine intuition. It had to be intuition, since it could not be experience. But, then, if women could only get experience as well—why, they would be colossal! If intuition like that could be actually applied to politics, where would governments be? Women, he was sure, at least some women, knew things without trying that men never found out as long as they lived. Wyndham himself said that she could see the backside of a man's immortal soul in one glance, and that he never trusted a man she did not like. And she believed in Benjamin Disraeli. It was a very healing knowledge.

He tried to remember what he had said to her, in the first blank pain of reaction. Whatever it was, it had not disturbed her divine serenity nor shocked her childlike frankness. He thought she was the simplest creature, the most natural person he had ever known. With her one had to become natural too. Masks were no good with her, and enigmas did not mystify her, and she simply did not perceive pretenses. Her candid gaze stripped one of all social defences, left one open to her comprehension, and her quaint protectiveness, and, he supposed, to her disapproval if one was unworthy. Imagine a woman, he thought, *conceive* a woman, if you can, with whom you could be entirely yourself, before whom you need never raise barriers, to whom you could not pose— simply because when she looked at you with her grave, sweet eyes the barriers and the pose were not there at all. The simplicity of life in such circumstances, he was thinking, while his coffee cooled undrunk, was beyond conception—

and the relaxation of it—the peace! Wyndham really must
have a most uncomplicated existence. . . .

Sighing, perhaps a little enviously, he rose and went to his
writing-table. Two hours and a quarter after he had opened
his eyes on an oppressive world, he began the letter to Sa.
He tore up a good many sheets of paper, and sat for a long
period with an idle pen drying in his hand, but at last it was
finished. He signed it "Yours, D.—in very good spirits," and
was surprised to find that this was quite true. Marshalling all
the mitigating circumstances for her benefit had had a very
remedial effect on his own raw spirit. He was in, he had his
seat, he had challenged the hostile Irish element and had
faced out their hoodlum tactics without loss of temper or
dignity—and next time he would try to be dull.

The rain had gone off into a mist, though the pavement
was still shining with wet. He sealed the letter for the post,
and put on a blue coat with gold buttons, a black cloak with
a scarlet lining, and a tall black hat, and started for the Club.

IX

London,
December 18, 1837.

Dear Sa,

Nothing daunted, and acting on the advice of Sheil, I
spoke again last night, and with complete success. It was
on the Copyright Bill. The House was not very full, but
all the Cabinet Ministers and officials were there, and all
our principal men. Talfourd, who had already made a long
speech (his style flowery, with a weak and mouthing utter-
ance) proposed the Copyright Bill very briefly. Bulwer followed him, and confined himself to the point of international copyright, which called up Poulett Thomson. Then
Peel, on the copyright of art; and then I rose.

I was received with the utmost curiosity and attention.
As there had been no great discussion I determined not
to be tempted into a speech, which everyone expected of
course I rose to make. All I aimed at was to say something

pointed and to the purpose. My voice was in perfect condition. I suggested a clause to Talfourd, with the idea of which I had been furnished by Colburn. I noticed that the subject had already been done so much justice to on other occasions that I should not trouble the House, but I had been requested to support this Bill by many eminent persons interested in its success. Thus far, I was accompanied by continued "hear, hears," and I concluded thus: "I am glad to hear from Her Majesty's Government that the interests of literature have at length engaged their attention. It has been the boast of the Whig party that in many brilliant periods of our literary annals they have been the patrons of letters. ('Hear, hear' from John Russell & Co.) As for myself, I trust that the age of literary patronage has passed ('Hear, hear' from the leader of the Rads), and it will be honourable to the present government if, under its auspices, it be succeeded by an age of legislative protection." I sat down with a general cheer.

Talfourd, in reply, said he would avail himself of the "excellent suggestion of the honourable member for Maidstone, himself one of the greatest ornaments of our modern literature." Here Peel cheered loudly, and indeed throughout my remarks he backed me. So on the whole there was glorification. Everyone congratulated me, and all agree that I managed in a few minutes by my voice and manner to please everyone in the House.

I really think, on the whole, that the effect of my début, and the circumstances that attended it, will ultimately be favourable to my career. Next to undoubted success the best thing is to make a great noise, and the many articles that are daily written to announce my failure only prove that I have not failed. . . .

London,
March 15, 1838.
Dearest,

I write to say I heard yesterday of the sudden death of my colleague. I have seen Mrs. Wyndham; she is, of course, extremely overwhelmed; she was sitting in the room with him when he died. . . .

Added to his acute sorrow at Wyndham's unexpected death, Disraeli had all the harassing details of the choice and election of a successor at Maidstone—which came distressingly soon after their recent mutual triumphs in the same scene. He had only just begun to taste satisfaction in his new place. Already the House was becoming acclimatized to the exotic personality in its bewildered midst. Grudgingly it began to listen to him; cautiously it assimilated the startling creations of his tailors; involuntarily it ceased to find him ridiculous. And then, without warning, Wyndham died, and the man who had helped to get him there, who had believed in him and befriended him in every sense of the word, was no longer beside him, sharing the fun. It was shattering.

F a few dazed hours it seemed impossible to go on in th emptiness of soul which Wyndham's passing left. The copyright Bill, Bulwer's blessed censorship fight which possessed him, the New Poor Law abuses, the daily involutions of debate, all became futile and small beside the fact of a man's life snuffed out when he was enjoying himself, when his friends counted on him, and his wife loved him.

Not since that voyage home from Egypt had he come so devastatingly face to face with the immensities. He paused, sick and shaken, in the midst of life as he had dreamed it, and looked back at Wyndham, for whom there was no more endeavour; and half of him said, "What's the good?" and the other half said, "Go on—there is still time, for you."

But the now familiar scenes of the House, its easy laughter, its schoolboy rudeness, its essential enmity and fellowship, had a nightmare quality during those first days after the death of his friend. Wyndham was not Lord Liverpool or Canning, of course—but it was persistently shocking to find everything so much as usual, at Westminster, and to see how small was the void he left and how quickly it must be filled by a stranger. Disraeli saw that it would not do to dwell on it. One must get on with things. One must not fall behind. . . .

London,
March 17, 1838.

Dearest Sa,

You will hear with delight that last night, very unexpectedly, for I had given up all thought of speaking, and suffering not a little both mentally and physically, I rose and made a successful speech.

I was so disturbed by deputations from Maidstone, rival candidates for the vacant post, the arrival of Jem, &c., &c., having been twice called out of the House to the Carlton, and having nearly lost my voice which I had been cooking with so much care for days, that I had given up the affair as a bad job. About ten o'clock, I think, when I was standing behind the Speaker's Chair, Hardinge beckoned to me, and I seated myself between him and Graham. He wanted to speak about the new writ for Maidstone.

Having got a place, I did not leave it, though I ought to have done so, having answered his question, and I asked Graham whether he would speak. He said No, and recommended me, but very kindly, not to try, as he said the House was noisy, tired, and uninterested, and wanted to divide. So I gave it up forever, but just as I rose to quit my seat, Clay, who was speaking, sat down, and the Speaker, imagining that I was going to rise to speak, called my name.

I was in for it, put my hat down, advanced to the table, and dashed along. I got the House still in a minute, I was heard with the greatest attention and good humour, succeeded in all my points—and at length sat down amid loud cheers, and principally from the Government side.

Strange to say, I got Jem into the House, and missed him after my speech; I hope he heard it. Chandos detected him early in the evening.

"Disraeli, is your brother here?"

"Yes."

"I thought so; (smiling) no mistaking him."

I have scribbled all this nonsense in the most marvellous haste. . . .

Bradenham,
March 17, 1838.

My dearest,

We were grateful for your long despatch. Jem told us enough to make us desire to hear what you felt. It was Jem's début in the House so we did not know how much to trust him. He describes the rush into the House as prodigious when you began to speak, and then the profound silence, and then the cheers. He heard many people speak of you, rejoicing in your speech and your reception—and before you spoke Castlereagh rushed in, saying, "Has Disraeli been up yet?" (afraid he had missed you). It seems by Jem's account of all the sensation produced that you are quite as great a man at Westminster as at Wycombe.

God bless you, dearest!

Yours affectionately,

SA.

X

Though spared the ordeal of nursing Wyndham through a long illness, Mrs. Lewis was nearly prostrated with shock and grief. Before she was really well enough to travel, she set out bravely for Wales, to settle his estate in the West. From there her letters drifted back, sad and lost and pitiful, full of the unphilosophical pathos of a child's first sorrow. She had been so happy and so cherished and so cosy. And now Wyndham was gone. Everyone tried to tell her what to do, and most of it she did not like, and it was so hard to know what Wyndham himself would have thought about these things.

It seemed to her that next to Wyndham, Dizzy, whom Wyndham had loved and trusted, would know best. Helplessly, with tears on her cheeks which splashed down on the page and made unsightly blots, she wrote him her anxieties and her despair—alone and bereft in Wales, among bullying strangers and overbearing relations where she and Wyndham had made so gay a beginning (his first seat was Cardiff) and where every hour brought some stabbing recollection or re-

minder of lost youth and happiness. Eagerly she awaited
Dizzy's replies, humble before his masculine wisdom in
worldly affairs, profoundly grateful for the time and trouble
he took to set her right in this puzzling, tragic business of getting along without Wyndham. More and more she came to
regard Dizzy as infallible. She was so anchorless, and he told
her what to do, almost what to think. She absorbed his advice and did her best to put it into practice, and at the same
time it dawned on her comfortingly that he was really fond
of her too, as well as of Wyndham, and that she mattered to
him, not just as Wyndham's wife, but as a separate person,
as something left over, now that Wyndham was gone.

Carlton, London,
April 27, 1838.

My dear Mrs. Wyndham,

It is natural, after such severe trials as you have recently
experienced, and such petty vexations as you are now
forced to encounter, that you should give way to feelings
of loneliness and sorrow. It is natural and inevitable, but
you must not *indulge* such sentiments, and you must endeavour not to brood over the past. The future for you
may yet be full of happiness and hope. You are too young
to feel that life has not yet a fresh spring of felicity in store.

As for me, I can truly say that the severe afflictions
which you have undergone, the excellent and to me unexpected qualities with which you have met them, the talent,
firmness and sweet temper, will always make me your faithful friend; and as far as my advice and assistance and society can contribute to your welfare or solace you under
these severe trials, you may count upon them. For as you
well know, I am one of those people who feel much more
deeply than I ever express, and if I ever express feeling
of regard to anyone, my memory assures me that it is
never any fault of mine if they are not fervently cherished
and if they do not endure.

I fear you are at present in a miserable circle of narrow-
minded people, incapable of any generous emotion and

any genial sympathy; but this is an infliction which will not last, and I recommend you by all means to command your temper and watch over your interests.

I look forward now with great interest to your return. *Expedite,* but do not *hasten* it. Be active, but do not be in a hurry, or you will have to return once more to that odious place and those odious persons whom I hope will be speedily banished from our memories.

And now God bless you, and believe me,

Ever your affectionate friend,

D.

London,
May 5, 1838.

Dear Mrs. Wyndham,

Town is very agreeable, the weather soft and warm; and I suppose the fields and trees have put on their spring liveries these last few days, as well as the households of our fine people here.

All the world is talking of the grand festival which is to be given in Merchant Taylors' Hall by the Conservative members of Parliament to Sir Robert Peel. I am, of course, one of the hosts. It is to be one of the most magnificent gatherings ever witnessed. There is a gallery which will hold 70 ladies. Tickets to admit them were offered to Lady Peel, but she declined the dangerous honour, confident that the selection would create ill feeling; so the 70 ladies' tickets are to be balloted for by all the hosts. I know to whom I should venture to offer mine, were she in London or could go, but I suppose that is impossible.

The Chesterfields had the audacity to ask 5,000 guineas for the loan of their house to the Russian Ambassador Extraordinary to the Coronation, and absolutely expected to get it. Lady Jersey asked 2,000. Lady Londonderry thought all this house-letting *infra dig.,* and had the spirit to write to the Empress, who had been most hospitable to herself and Lord L. when in Russia, and offered Holdernesse House and the whole establishment to the Grand Duke, who is coming over; intending themselves to go into a hired house. The offer was declined by the Empress in a letter in English, beautifully written, in which she signs herself, 'With reiterated love, your affectionate Alexandra.'

Lyndhurst made a very successful speech the other night on Spain, and foreign politics are coming into fashion. I must cease at present all this gossip, which I thought might amuse you. Pray come back to Town cheerful and happy, and believe in a happy and brilliant future like

Your affectionate

D.

X I

That summer was a very sumptuous one in London, with the coronation of the girl Queen set for the end of June, and Disraeli's letters to Sarah were full of the splendour and pageantry he loved.

London,

June 25, 1838.

My dearest,

London is now very gay. The whole line of procession is nearly covered with galleries and raised seats; when these are clothed with carpets and coloured hangings the effect will be superb. London teems with foreigners. There are full 200 (*on dit*) of distinction attached to the different embassies, and lodged in every possible hotel.

I must give up going to the coronation, as we go in state, and all the M.P.'s *must* be in Court dress or uniforms. As I have withstood making a costume of this kind for other purposes, I will not make one now, and console myself by the conviction that to get up very early (eight o'clock) to sit dressed like a flunky in the Abbey for seven or eight hours, and to listen to a sermon by the bishop of London, can be no great enjoyment. . . .

London,

June 29, 1838.

Dearest,

I went to the coronation after all. I did not get a Court dress till 2:30 on the morning of the ceremony, but it fitted me very well. It turned out that I had a very fine leg, which I never knew before!

The pageant within the Abbey was without exception the most splendid, various, and interesting affair at which I was ever present. To describe is of course useless. I had one of the best seats in the Abbey, indeed our House had the best of everything. The Queen looked very well, and performed her part with grace and completeness, which cannot in general be said of the other performers; they were always in doubt as to what came next and you saw the want of rehearsal. Lyndhurst paid his homage with singular dignity, but committed the *faux pas* of not backing from the presence. Exmouth paid his homage very well, but complained terribly of the weight of his robes and coronet, which were made for his grandfather at George IV's coronation, and the old lord was a very tall, stout, burly man. I have got a gold medal given me as M.P., but I have presented it to Mrs. Wyndham.

O'Connell was in Court dress and looked very well, and was deeply interested in everything, but was hooted by the mob. Bulwer I did not see. He certainly was not in the House. I saw Lord Ward after the ceremony in a retiring room, drinking his champagne out of a pewter pot, his coronet cocked over his nose, his robes disordered, and his arms akimbo.

The procession was, I think, rather a failure; heavy, want of variety, and not enough music or troops. . . .

London,
July 11, 1838.

My dearest,

Yesterday, the day being perfect, there was a splendid review in Hyde Park. I saw it admirably from Mrs. Wyndham's. The Delawarrs, Rolles, Laurence Peels, and Dawsons were there, but no one was allowed to be on the drawing-room floor, lest there should be an appearance of a party, except old Lord Rolle and myself, to be his companion.

The Londonderrys after the review gave the most magnificent banquet at Holdernesse House. There were only 150 asked, and all sat down. Fanny was faithful and asked me, and I figure in the *Morning Post* accordingly. It was the finest thing of the season. Londonderry's regiment being reviewed, we had the band of the 10th playing on the staircase; the whole of the staircase (a double one) being crowded with the most splendid orange-trees and Cape jessamines; the Duke of Nemours, Soult, all the "illustrious strangers," the Duke of Wellington, and the very flower of fashion being assembled. The banquet was in the gallery of sculpture; it was so magnificent that everybody lost their presence of mind. Sir James Graham said to me that he had never in his life seen anything so gorgeous. I think it was the kindest thing possible of Fanny asking me, as it was not to be expected in any way. The splendour of the uniforms was remarkable. . . .

Mrs. Lewis had returned to Grosvenor Gate in midsummer, looking white and weary and small in her black gown. At their first meeting Disraeli advanced across the carpet to her with both hands outstretched, and impulsively bent his slim height to kiss her fingers. He had missed her, and was unaffectedly glad to get her back—even this pathetic shadow of herself, with the quivering, uncertain smile and lost vivacity. Tenderly he set himself the task of making her herself again, and soon he had her chattering, even laughing at his jokes in the old way, and the look of bewildered misery left her eyes.

In the late summer she paid a visit to Bradenham, and there she revived perceptibly in the ardent admiration of that affectionate household. She had been there twice already, with Wyndham, and they were all devoted to her, and strove to make her feel that there at least she would always be safe from loneliness and an enduring sense of loss.

Day by day he watched her fitting into the family life, unconsciously making and decorating her own little niche in the long sweet days of the Bradenham menage, getting back her confidence in the world which Wyndham's death had shaken. He was surprised at how much she had absorbed and remembered of their ways and the village life at the feet, as it were, of the manor house. She knew which was the gardener's cottage and which was the sexton's, she called the coachman by name and inquired after his old mother's rheumatism. She had apparently a long understanding with Tita, and was not surprised, as the family had been, at his prosperous courtship of Maria's maid, the exquisitely English Hughes. She visited the kitchen garden with Tita, to behold the peaches growing against the wall; nodded wisely to his talk of pruning, spraying, and mould, and admired his fat onions. Tita swelled visibly under her smile, and Sa remarked that while she had no fault to find with his manners he had never in all these years beamed at *her* like that. Mrs. Lewis said it was on account of the onions.

Spasmodically her natural gaiety reasserted itself, and her black dresses gave way in the August heat to mauve and white. Even in mourning, she knew how to spend money on her clothes, and the full skirts, big sleeves, and small waists of that season became her trim little figure ideally.

He would wake up in the morning wondering what dress she would be wearing that day. He hurried down to breakfast for fear of missing that first heart-warming glimpse of her descending the staircase. He went to bed at night smiling over things she had said—her mind was so fresh, so without inhibitions, and her similes were sometimes very apt, and her remarks as frank as a child's. She said the most shocking things, and looked surprised at laughter. The house was bright with the sound of her clear, girlish voice, and the sun seemed to seek out her white skirts in the furthest corners of the rooms. He loved to see her following Sa about the garden with a basket, asking intelligent questions about weeds and grubs and fertilizers, while Sa, who was a thorough and ambitious gardener and cut the flowers for the vases with her own hands each morning, heaped the basket with blossoms. He was glad that she and Sa were friends. He watched her playing with Jem's noisy dogs, fearless and laughing while three or four of them barked and jumped about her for sticks to be thrown, smudging her dress with their paws. He heard her reading aloud to Isaac tirelessly in her light voice, and guessed that she did not in the least understand what most of it was about. And he listened with amusement while she gravely exchanged recipes with Maria, copying out some of his favourite dishes to take home with her, and writing to Rook for the ones that Maria wanted from Grosvenor Gate.

Nothing was too dull or too unimportant to engage her rapt attention while it lasted. She played any game she could find in that household of many separate enterprises, and enjoyed them all. He perceived with the effect of a revelation that it was all new and absorbing to her, to have so many things to do, and he wondered with sudden insight if perhaps she had found life with Wyndham a little—he sought for not too harsh a word—tame. She had not known, of course, that she lacked anything—but the way she seized now on small occupations at Bradenham, opportunities of companionship, told its own story. Naturally, he said to himself. But naturally, after twenty years, and Wyndham, though kind, was an absent-minded man. She had been lonely. And now to have even Wyndham's need of her wiped out—

Poor darling, he thought, looking affectionately at her unconscious head that evening, bent over Sa's gardening books at a table in the little parlour, while she read out directions about loam and sheep manure and Sa wrote it down in the gardening journal she had kept ever since coming to Bradenham. Poor brave little darling—following the print with her small forefinger. Poor little—no, not poor. Wyndham had left her everything. She had more money than she needed, and the house in Grosvenor Gate. She was still delightful to look at, and always amusing to listen to. She was—if it came to that—a wealthy widow. People would soon be wanting to marry her. And in another revelation, he discovered that this was to him a revolting idea.

She glanced up suddenly, drawn by his steady gaze, across the table strewn with the books and catalogues, and busy with the scratch of Sa's pen—glanced up and found his sombre eyes full on her from where he sat in shadow.

"What is it?" she said, and a hand went unconsciously to her hair to make sure all its pins were in place. "Is anything wrong?"

"No," he said, and smiled.

"What were you looking at, then?"

"You," he said.

Her eyes were puzzled.

"I don't see why," she objected.

"No, you can't," he agreed. "Not from there."

Embarrassed, she felt of her hair again, and looked down anxiously at her dress.

"Behave yourself, Ben," said Sarah calmly, and went on writing. "What comes after heliotrope?"

"The lilies," said Mrs. Lewis automatically, but her mind was not on it.

Sarah turned a page and dipped her pen.

"Go on," she prodded gently.

They went on.

Disraeli rose and took his revelations out on the terrace where he could be alone with them. Everything looked so simple suddenly. He was amazed and chagrined that he had not seen it sooner. He was in love with her, apparently, and it had stolen upon him unawares. It must have been happening to him for some time, for him to come suddenly around a corner of his mind, as it were, on the established fact. Now that he looked for evidence, it was there in plenty. Both the other times when she left Bradenham after a visit the place had seemed empty, haunted of her. He had even told her so, lightly, in letters which Wyndham must have read, as lightly as they were written. He had never made any secret of his affection for her. But love—it was his love she possessed now. If Wyndham had lived, of course, things would have gone on exactly as they were. But now . . .

Pacing up and down the terrace above the village in the late twilight, he sorted out his mind with a deep and abiding satisfaction. It was so sane, so comfortable, so altogether *right,* that he should look after her now, and preserve her from fortune-hunters, attracted only by her money. Himself he did not despise her money. But even if she had had none—yes, she was good for him, she was what he needed in his life, balance, and sweetness, and a woman's intuition. This was no headlong boyish fancy, this was the sort of thing a man could build on; an association comfortable as a familiar room, solacing without distracting. This was settling down.

A few days later Isaac was moved to remark at breakfast that having her with them like this was rather like acquiring another daughter, full-grown from heaven, like Minerva; and thereby created a silence, while his eldest son smiled enigmatically, and Mrs. Lewis looked anywhere but into anybody's eyes, and Sarah spoke hastily of their simple plans for the morning.

All that day she contrived to elude him, until towards sunset he intercepted her on the lower terrace, wearing a white dress and Sa's gardening gloves which were much too big for her, and carrying a basket of fresh cut roses and heavy shears.

"City mouse," he said accusingly. "It's the wrong time of day to cut flowers. Sa always does it early in the morning." As he spoke he saw Sa herself retreating inconspicuously toward the kitchen garden, and blessed her unfailing tact.

"I know—" Her cheeks were pink with bending over the bushes, and her eyes in the opalescent shade of the big white hat she wore were wide and very clear. "But Sa said it was going to rain and these would all be spoilt, so I've been rescuing the full-blown ones for potpourri. Sa is going to show me how to make it."

He offered to take the basket from her, but her small fingers gripped it tight inside the floppy gloves, a fragrant barrier between herself and him.

"No, let me," she insisted. "I love the smell of them, hot with the sun—"

He lifted one bloom from the basket, dark red, its petals languid with the heat, revealing its golden heart, and laid it against the caressing fingers of his other hand.

"Lovely," he said softly. "Lovely things they are. I like them this way, instead of cool, hard buds—"

"The buds are the virgins," she said astonishingly. "Most people prefer them."

He raised the rose to his lips and then, blocking her path squarely, he drew the stem of it through the cameo brooch on her breast; his touch was deft and light, without fumbling.

"Superb," he murmured, and his eyes travelled slowly upward to her face, so that she stepped back and turned from him toward the house.

"I was just saying to Sa that I must go back to Town tomorrow," she said.

"Tomorrow!" he cried, surprised and horrified. "But you were going to stay here—oh, forever!"

"I can't. I can't possibly." The brim of the wide hat hid her face.

He fell into slow step beside her.

"But what has happened? There was nothing in the post—" He stepped round in front of her again, barring her way. "I know. My father frightened you at breakfast. You're running away."

"No, I—"

"I hadn't meant to speak of it quite like that—I was trying to find a way, but—I was terribly afraid of losing you by going about it clumsily myself. It's true, though—what he said this morning. You belong here—you are in our hearts, a part of our lives, forever—and I am in love with you."

"Oh, please, I—"

"Is it so surprising to you? Have I hidden it so well? Or don't you—like the idea, at all?"

"Oh, Dizzy, please—I can't think of such things, I—it's much too soon, and besides you mustn't—"

"Because of Wyndham?" He spoke the name gently, and her eyes filled.

"Oh, please—"

"I know, I know, I am always too soon!" he cried despairingly. "But life slips through our fingers every hour, and I cannot bear to mark time! Already we have forfeited days—

weeks—because I was afraid to speak! And when did Wyndham ever grudge you happiness?" He caught her by the arm and turned her firmly toward the yew walk where they would be sheltered from the windows of the house. "I'm glad we've got down to it, at last. Come, we'll have it out now, and then I shall know what is in store for me. My dearest—Mary Anne —I want to marry you, I want you with me all the days of my life, I cannot imagine an existence without you any more."

"But, Dizzy, that's impossible—I—I'm older than you are—"

"And wiser," he smiled down at her. "That's as it should be."

"No, no, not wiser. I don't know anything, really, only what Wyndham taught me. It amused him to pretend to follow my advice sometimes, but—"

"It has amused me too," he murmured, "because your advice is always right. Where would I be now without it?"

"Just where you are, of course."

"No. You and Wyndham between you have set my feet on the ladder. Wyndham is gone—but don't desert me because of that. Don't cast me out now, to make my way alone."

"But I can't possibly be your wife," she protested, and her breath came quickly. "When you are forty I shall be—an old woman. And a man is still quite young, at forty."

They had reached the further end of the two long lines of clipped yews, which cast late shadows on the green turf. He took off her absurd hat and tossed it to the grass behind her, and touched the bunched curls against her cheeks with loving fingers.

"You dear soul," he said. "How can you expect me to live without the sight of you and the sound of you, every day and any day? How can you condemn me to go on alone—"

Alone. She could understand that. She knew what it was now, to be alone. The touch of his hands on her hair ran through her disturbingly. She could not meet his smiling eyes, hers fled from the fascination of his lips, so close to her face. Standing there with the fragrance of red roses between them, she felt an impulse, impossible to contemplate, to lean against him confidingly, her cheek pressing the crisp frill of

his shirtfront, and feel his arms go round her—sanctuary—
but Wyndham was dead, and a man's possessive strength,
especially a young man's ardour, were not for her.

"I am the one who is alone," she said sadly. "You will find
someone—someone else—who can give you everything—"

"And what is there to give that you have not?" he said
patiently. "Beauty that takes away my reason—a body that
exhausts me with desire—good God, I've had all that!" he
flung at her roughly, and saw her face upturned to his again,
not startled or embarrassed, but full of comprehension. "I
don't want a mistress!" he told her brutally. "I want peace—
a home—a wife!"

"Yes, but—you have the right to children too, and I—"

"Bulwer had children!" he reminded her. "And was his
marriage happy? I could name a dozen men with flourishing
nurseries at home who could find it in their hearts to envy
Wyndham those twenty barren years with you!" And then
because she winced at the word, he bent above her tenderly.
"My darling—I shall see to it that you do not regret the
children—too much."

"It is you who will regret them, later on," she said obstinately, turning away her face from his kiss, and added very
low—"I think Wyndham did."

"Mary Anne—dear, delightful, unreasonable, mistaken
woman—you who know so much and can be so blind—" His
arms went round her, basket, shears and all. "I love you and
I want you in my life—forever. I can't do without you. What
are you going to do about that? Don't answer me now. But
promise to try to think about it sanely—impartially—without
all these conventional objections and cut-and-dried formulas. Unless of course—" His hold on her slackened. "—unless
the whole idea is hateful to you."

"No, no!" She caught at his sleeve. "It's only that I—I've
never thought of you like this—before."

"Then think of me now! And think of me like *this!*" He
kissed her suddenly, while her lips were parted on an exclamation of protest. And when after a long moment he released
her, the protest came with doubled emphasis.

"Dizzy! There might be a gardener—!"

He stood laughing down at her outraged propriety, holding her by the elbows. He was very near, and the kiss had set her tingling. The world was a dazzling blur of blue and green and gold before her eyes. But this was bewildering—it was youth again, love again, and a pounding of pulses which had been quiet a long time. Something had happened to her, something quite impossible, like being very drunk. She had not felt like this for years. Well, no, not ever. Her cheeks were hot, her knees were queer, and her heart—but it was not right, it was not decent—a woman of her age—a widow—

"Promise me you will think," he whispered, his lips in her curls. "Promise you will let me know soon—whatever you decide."

"But I can't decide!" she cried in panic. "Not for a long time! Not for—a year, at least!"

"I see." He seemed to accept it thoughtfully, as though it had not occurred to him before. "The widow's year. Yes, I suppose we must. But I can see you often?" he begged. "You will not keep me in outer darkness all that time? And sometimes when we are alone together you will let me have your hands to hold and your lips to kiss—"

"No—no—I must go back to Town tomorrow—"

"But you can't do that—you mustn't! I can't leave my father now, they are counting on me to be here the rest of the autumn—"

"Yes, of course you must stay here. But I shall go back to Town. I must try to think—I must be by myself a while and try to—"

"Look at you!" He caught her chin and raised her face to his. "One kiss, and look at you! Dear God, she's blushing! My darling, you are going to be happy again, do you hear?— gay again—and younger than ever before! That is my privilege, and I will not be denied it. Would Wyndham forbid you to be happy, do you think, just because—"

"Don't—don't speak of Wyndham!"

She broke from him and ran across the grass toward the house, the roses spilling from her basket, her brown curls bobbing—once she tripped on her skirt and he caught his breath, but she only dropped the basket and the shears and ran on down the green aisle, until her white dress disappeared around the corner.

He retrieved her hat from the grass and went on along the turf walk in the opposite direction to the end and faced westward, toward where the sun was sinking behind rain clouds, somewhere over the Isles of the Blest. His lips moved soundlessly as he stood in the rosy light, her white hat dangling from his hand by its broad mauve ribbons. Wyndham—give her leave . . .

XII

Reluctantly he had to let her go from him, back to Grosvenor Gate and its memories and loyalties. Unwilling to disappoint his family, and terrified of nagging her into flight from London or into some ultimate final refusal, he stayed on at Bradenham, and as the days passed the more remote she became the more eager he was to be near her, the greater his need.

His letters came to her nearly every day, a steadily mounting tide of impatience and devotion. She read them over and over, with doubt and rapture and despair, while single sentences printed themselves forever on her heart and brain, and came back in her wakeful nights to haunt her with their beauty and their stark necessity and their promise of companionship, security—love—in the emptiness of her widowhood. "The sun shines, and Bradenham looks beautiful; most green and fresh. But you are not here. . . . I have not been out of the house since you left it, until this afternoon, having been in a sort of apathy. . . . I would have written on Friday, but was really too unhappy; so I sauntered about thinking of you, and gleaned, for we can no longer gather, flowers which I sent to you, and which I amused myself by dexterously packing in franks; for to tell the truth, I spoilt more than one before I could stow them, which with the united aid of scissors and patience I at last contrived to succeed in. . . . I have made up my mind to leave this place tomorrow, in order that I may have the delight of a day or two with your own sweet self. . . ."

At his first entry into the drawing-room at Grosvenor Gate he snatched her up and kissed her almost before Rook had closed the door behind herself. And it was good to feel his heart beating beneath her cheek and hear his voice, choked and tender, against her hair—before she pushed him away from her firmly and made him sit down, and tried to lead the conversation safely to politics and the state of the country.

And all the time they talked, there would come silences, and she dared not look at him, but was conscious still of his probing eyes and his strong, kind hands with their splendid rings; hands that demanded so much of her, but so respectfully, and she longed weakly to lay hers in them now and confess that she was his for the taking.

And each time he rose to go and stood looking down at her questioningly, her heart cried, "Now! Tell him now!" but something in her held back and she could not, and he went away unsatisfied, with little lines of strain round his mouth. He was so patient, and so good, she thought helplessly. But the year was not up. Not till March. Oh, but it was wrong to count the weeks—!

And then she would catch sight of herself in the mirror and lean forward to look at the bright-eyed reflection which faced her there, and run anxious fingers down her smooth cheeks and along the firm line of her chin; single grey threads coming now in the brown curls—hardly visible yet, but—would he mind?—had he seen? People said she had never looked so well. It gave her a guilty feeling. And yet she knew it was true. As though she could not conceal the new excitement she lived in, day and night—as though the secret shone through. Perhaps he saw that too?

He was in Town during November, very busy with politics, much sought after. Peel was laying the foundations of a new party, and Disraeli would be in it, and the promising young man named Gladstone. Melbourne's Government was hanging on now only by the favour, the open partiality

of the little Queen. But that could not last forever. Governments had been forced out against the wishes of the sovereign
before this.

It was a wretched autumn with continuous rains and chill,
affecting everyone's nerves and health. Disraeli acknowleged
a growing restlessness, likely to sharpen into irritability over
small things. Politically, the prospect had never been so
bright for him. But his private life was full of tension and an
almost unbearable suspense. He was not sure of her yet.

And with the uncertainty his own impatience grew, until
he gazed aghast at the ruin it was in her power to make of
him. What had begun so comfortably, so logically, at Bradenham, as a sane solution to his existence had become a de-
vouring necessity. There was no longer any balance, or any
solace, in his love for her, it had become wholly distracting.
Body and soul, the idea of her had come to possess him, until
he felt that he would never know peace again until he had
from her the answer he craved. No, not even then, not until
she was his completely, to have and to hold in the sight of
the world.

He had no idea how the change had come about. For a
long time now she had amused him, cosseted him, admired
and encouraged him; and he had contemplated with infinite
pleasure a marriage which would perpetuate all those things
in his life. And then suddenly, without warning, he was
enslaved. He supposed it began that day in the garden when
he had first kissed her open lips and seen her alter between
his hands to stand trembling and blushing like a girl. He had
not expected the warmth of his very honest affection to so
transfigure her; he had not dreamed of such a gratitude as
hers for his love. It awed and intoxicated him. And from
loving, he had fallen desperately in love.

And now her eternal scruples, and her absurd personal
humility, her fears and doubts, and her precious proprieties
kept them still apart. She would give him so little to go on
with. She would not promise anything for fear what she
regarded as a madness on his part would pass and leave him
bound to her. She would not even let him argue about it

because a man they had both loved was not yet dead a year. And all he wanted was to hold her in his arms. . . .

"I am going back to Bradenham until after Christmas," he announced suddenly one day, and at her startled look he rose with a wideflung gesture of sheer distraction which set his rings flashing. "This is no good to me!" he cried. "I can't bear much more of it! You hold me off—you talk about the weather—you play with me, cat and mouse—!"

"Dizzy, *no!*" She was horrified.

"I know, I know, the widow's year!" he agreed savagely. "Very well, I shall go to Bradenham until it is up! I am not good at thinking twice before I speak to you! And I want you in my arms!" He swooped on her and she found herself where he wanted her, a little breathless. "My darling—sometimes you try me rather high. Forgive tantrums. I was never any good at waiting." He kissed her, hard, and set her down again, and left her staring at the door through which he had passed.

And then his letters came again, sometimes tender, sometimes stern and censorious, always a little frightening. She never knew how to answer them. It was hard to write and ignore everything he had said in his. Sometimes she did not write at all, because she dared not, and that drove him to a frenzy. But always his sentences stayed with her, like a song running in her head. "I can tell you nothing but that I love you. . . . I will believe that my fate is indissolubly bound up with yours, until your voice or your conduct assures me that all this time I have laboured under a miserable delusion. . . . I envy the gentlemen about you, but I am not jealous. When the eagle leaves you, the vultures return. There, that is sublime! . . . Alas, it is too much love that makes me querulous, and the suspense of affection and the pangs of separation. . . . The happiest of New Years; and, indeed, I hope and believe it will be the happiest of our lives. . . . All my hopes of happiness in life are centred in your sweet affections, and I wish only to be the solace and glory of your life. . . ."

No, one certainly could not ignore them. And yet one did not dare to stretch out a hand too confidently to such largesse:

XIII

To both Caroline and Rosina, Mary Anne Lewis seemed a woman greatly to be envied. She was honourably widowed, independently wealthy, and if Caroline pitied her for being childless, at least real flesh and blood children had not been torn from her by an insensate law.

And now there were disturbing rumours round London that she would not remain a widow for long. She was too lightminded and frivolous, people said, to feel her loss as a woman should; too pretty still to lack admirers, and much too well off to be left to enjoy her fortune in single blessedness. Some man was sure to sweep her off her feet by making love to her—especially some handsome and amusing man, such as Mr. Disraeli, who was understood to call there every day when he was in Town. That really would not do at all. Caroline decided that someone ought to speak to her. Someone ought to try to make her understand that it was sheer insanity, once you were free, with money of your own, to shackle yourself again.

Caroline's own £50 a year had remained in Norton's hands, and when he was sued for her debts he tried to attach her meagre royalties to pay them—bills for jewellery, some of them, trinkets which had remained in his possession when she left Storey's Gate. She had kept her head up and refused to mope and hide, even while the endless unseemly struggle for the unfortunate chicks went on. Her vanity insisted that if she did not go out in the evenings as she used to do, and show herself at all the usual houses, people would think it was only because she had not been asked. Norton had declared that she could write for her living or her family could support her, but he would not. She went to live with an uncle in Green Street who had always adored her, gave little dinner parties there, and during the long, quiet mornings in that empty house she drove her pen tirelessly in her chosen cause, looking to it, she said, to extricate her "as the soldier trusts to his sword to cut his way through."

She produced a pamphlet—*The Natural Claim of a Mother to the Custody of her Children as Affected by the Common Law Right of the Father*. She had to publish and circulate it privately, as Murray and the rest were too cautious to put their imprint on so unconventional and controversial a work. She moved heaven and earth to get the Infant Custody Bill introduced into Parliament, and when Talfourd tried to help her there were unkind implications about their relationship. Her friendship with Melbourne had been unspoilt by their mutual notoriety, but his new and absorbing duties at the Court of the young Queen kept him out of Town most of the time and she saw very little of him now. She was desperately lonely, and felt her anomalous position keenly—single, but married to a man's name; a devoted mother, but never permitted to see her children; expected to continu ̀ chaste and cheerful, she would say with scorn, but without ̀ ̀ress.

Her affection for Mary Anne Lewis was genuine and rather protective, for the poor little thing had no conception of life as it really was, thought Caroline, having sat in the lap of luxury all her days with a good husband, though dull, to look after her; and she was just the type, now that she had to manage her own destiny, to make a fool of herself. Caroline felt that even at the risk of seeming to interfere, one really must try to make her see how lucky she was, and encourage her to guard her liberty and independence, even in its inevitable loneliness, as her life. And so, on an afternoon in February, 1839, Caroline tied on her bonnet—she had nothing to spend on clothes, but always looked fashionable if a trifle sombre—and went to call at Grosvenor Gate. She found Rosina Bulwer already there, on more or less the same errand.

Rosina had an annuity of £400 a year from Bulwer, and her children had been put into his mother's care. Unlike Caroline, she did not miss them greatly, but she had been piteously dependent on Bulwer for her happiness, and her selfish, unreasoning love for him had all turned sour now,

and become an obsession of hatred and jealousy. Her affair
with the Neopolitan had been not much but vanity, and a
desire to show her husband that men still found her attractive, but he had mismanaged it, made too much of it, and
ever since then had considered himself free to do as he
pleased with his own life. Rosina was living with the faithful
Miss Greene, who sympathized with her inordinately, and
helped to magnify her wrongs and her resentment, until
Rosina had become more than a little unbalanced. She wrote
a novel called *Cheveley: or A Man of Honour*, which was
meant to pillory Bulwer. And she continued to levy condo-
lence from Mary Anne Lewis, whose simplicity saw only
that Bulwer was hard to live with and had behaved very
badly, and that Rosina was eating her heart out over the
separation.

Rosina too had heard things, and had come to talk sense
to Mary Anne and prevent her from wrecking her idyllic existence by persisting in a foolhardy infatuation with marriage.
No woman with money was safe. Some man was bound to try
to get his hands on it as soon as it was decently possible, and
since the man rumour named oftenest in this connection
was young Mr. Disraeli it was probable, concluded Rosina,
that not even decency would come into it; a conceited and
unjust man, who had never liked her and who was Edward's
champion.

She welcomed Caroline as an ally. Caroline knew what
men were. Just because this babe-in-the-woods had had one
lucky marriage was no sign she could get another. Especially
. . . With Rosina's bright blue skirts spreading against Caroline's sober plaid silks, the becoming flare of their bonnet
brims framing severe and disapproving faces which had once
been very beautiful, they sat together on the gilt sofa in the
drawing-room, exchanging glances, and drinking tea—they
both knew she had adopted afternoon tea because Mr. Disraeli liked it—and envying her the pleasant, spacious room,
with its fire and its effect of sumptuous expenditure; envying
most of all the fact that no man had the right to come into
it at any moment and give orders; eyeing her handsome black

silk gown, so completely up to the minute in style, full-skirted, big-sleeved, with fine lace at throat and wrists; eyeing too the fresh, sweet face above it, so unlined, so contented, so—*glowing*. Widows had no right to glow. No woman of her age had the right to look so many years less than her age. They were both younger than she was, and look at them —faded, beside her, worn out, tear-stained—*used*. The difference happiness makes to a woman's looks, they thought, eyeing her. But widows have no right to be happy. Their conviction grew that Mary Anne was up to something. They began to try to extract the truth from her.

Most unexpectedly she turned to give battle before they had well begun. She hadn't asked their advice about anything. And here they were, cautioning her, talking down to her about life, a word which they spoke with a capital L, assuming that she had no more idea how to take care of herself than a child of two. She was very easily confused and very easily bullied and she hated standing up to people. But really, this was as bad as those relations down in Wales. This was *croaking*.

"Oh, I know you think I'm frivolous and feather-headed," she announced with spirit, and they glanced at each other significantly. "But I don't see that just because a woman has been happily married it follows that she knows less about men than women who—who have been unhappy."

"No woman knows anything about men, my dear, until one of them has left the marks of his fingers in bruises on her skin," remarked Caroline drily.

"Caroline—don't!"

"You see? You don't even believe me!"

"Yes, but—"

"But don't let's talk about it!" Caroline interrupted. "I know! That's what's the matter with the world today. Unpleasant topics are taboo. Infant Custody—married women's property—divorce—don't let's talk about it!"

"Yes, and perhaps if we just pretend it isn't there, we'll wake up some beautiful morning and find that it isn't!" agreed Rosina ironically.

Mrs. Lewis looked from one to the other with rebellion surging in her gentle soul. She was no match for them, she knew. How had they got started on this silly argument? They had driven her into it, assuming loftily that she needed to be warned against men, also with a capital letter, just because they had made unfortunate choices themselves and didn't trust any man; implying, yes, actually implying that she was well out of her marriage to Wyndham, and so must never look at another man as long as she lived. What were they getting at, she wondered, even her guileless nature roused to suspicion by their very pointed remarks. Were they so stupid as to think that because their own husbands had been unkind, all husbands were like that? And did they think—more suspicion glimmered through her habitual trustfulness—that if a marriage failed it was always entirely the husband's fault? Men were difficult beings, to be sure, but she herself had solved one of them. Her self-respect, which had suffered from their superior ways, revived a little.

"I'm sick to death of being called a 'sheltered woman' and patronized and talked down to as though I was a girl barely out of the school-room," she said firmly. "I know I'm not clever. I've never written a book, or got a Bill introduced into Parliament. I'm not educated very well either. Caroline made them all laugh at me the other evening when I said I never could remember if the Greeks or the Romans came first." Caroline and Rosina exchanged amused glances. "But anyway," she swept on defensively, "I made one man very happy as long as he lived, and that's more than either of you can say!" There was a dreadful silence. Caroline buried her face in her cup, Rosina looked down at her lap, and her lips twitched. Mrs. Lewis gazed at them aghast. She had not realized quite how it would sound. "Now I've been rude," she gasped. "I'm sorry, Rosina. I'm sorry, Caroline." Caroline gave a chilly little nod which accepted the apology, and set down her cup with a clink. The facile tears hung on Rosina's long Irish eyelashes. Somehow or other they now got her hopelessly in the wrong. It was her own fault for trying to argue with them. One never knew what one might say. "I only meant," she faltered, "that no marriage is easy, not even a happy one. I learned things with Wyndham, and I—"

"Do tell us, Mrs. Lewis, your recipe for a happy marriage," mocked Rosina.

"We-ell," she began seriously, at a loss, "you share things with each other. And if something goes wrong you cheer each other up. And you let him talk about what he's interested in, and finally you know enough about it to be interested too—"

"You may have been born with a love of politics, my dear," Rosina's smile was malicious, "but it was astounding how authors bored me!"

"And his love affairs?" suggested Caroline. "Do you take a polite interest in those as well?"

"Wyndham didn't have love affairs."

"How do you know?" murmured Rosina.

"Well, he—just didn't," she maintained, embarrassed. "Once I thought he—"

"Ah, yes?" encouraged Caroline, leaning forward attentively.

"But I just—didn't seem to take any notice of it and he —it blew over."

"Did it?" murmured Caroline.

"You see, it doesn't do any good to notice things like that," she explained to them earnestly. "Crying or—getting angry or —begging him not to—that doesn't do any good. Sulking, or flirting with other men doesn't hold a husband, either. You have to be infinitely the *pleasantest* person he knows—and the chances are that *she* gets cross sometimes, and—pretty soon it wears off. That is—it does if you married for love in the beginning."

"And how if you are married for your money?" inquired Rosina. "Would the same tactics be effective, do you think? Oh, I wasn't thinking of my own case," she added hastily, at Mrs. Lewis's look of utter non-comprehension. "I hadn't a *sou!* Every time the bills came in, Edward would rave about my Irish wastefulness. We married for love, make no mistake, and look at us now!" There was an uncomfortable silence, while she found her handkerchief and wiped her eyes pathetically. "You're bound to miss Wyndham for a while, of course," she went on then, as though Wyndham had been a piece of furniture whose absence was an inconvenience. "But I can imagine far worse fates than yours!"

"I d-don't see that that's got anything to do with it," objected Mrs. Lewis logically. "It doesn't make me any less lonely."

"Good heavens!" cried Caroline. "You're free while you're still young enough to enjoy yourself! You've got this house to live in as long as you like, and money enough to do what you like! That's what she means!"

"Yes, but what shall I do?" she challenged them, confident that she had them there.

"Well, you might travel!" Rosina made an impatient gesture. "Or you might write books, or—"

"What on earth should I write books about?" Mrs. Lewis demanded with real exasperation. "I keep telling you Wyndham and I were happy together!" Caroline and Rosina turned up their eyes in despair. "You say I'm free. But I didn't want to be free. I'm not used to it. I feel stranded—lost—and I'm miserably lonely!"

"Who told you so?" queried Caroline coldly.

"Wh-what?"

"I've no patience with you, Mary Anne! A widow with your figure and your income and your state of mind is fair game for the first fortune-hunter that comes along!"

"I don't know what sort of idea you have got of my income," she said to this, with a certain dignity. "But I assure you it's nothing out of the way. A good healthy crop of masculine debts would swallow it whole."

"Take care that it doesn't, my dear," said Rosina.

"But I really haven't got enough money to be useful to anyone but myself—"

"*Any* money is useful, my innocent, to a rising M.P. who is up to his ears in debt!" said Caroline.

She looked at them with a sudden growing chill of uneasiness. They were getting at something. They had something up their sleeves. She didn't feel able to cope with them any longer, she wished they would go, she felt herself being driven further and further into a corner.

"I think you're both horrid today," she said unhappily, "and—and I don't know what you mean."

"Oh, yes, you do! That's why you think we're horrid!" smiled Caroline.

"My dear Mary Anne—" It was Rosina's turn. "I think we ought to tell you. People are saying that you will marry *the Jew!*"

So that was it. She was gazing at them, stunned, staring from one to the other piteously. It was her first encounter with public opinion in its more virulent forms. It seemed to her incredible that people should dare to speak of that secret thing, openly, as though she had given them leave by some action of hers, some word uttered even in closest confidence. She felt betrayed—outraged—stripped.

"They've no right to say such a thing!" she gasped at last. "Especially before my year is up!" she added.

"Oh, as for that," said Caroline carelessly, "it's all over Town that he proposed before the funeral!"

"Caroline, how *dare* you repeat such a thing to me!" she cried, tears of anger and disillusionment in her eyes. "Wyndham was devoted to him, and he was grateful for what we had been able to do for him. But he never—"

"She knows who we mean, anyway!" remarked Rosina, with a glance at Caroline.

"Of course I know who you mean!" All her loyalty was up in arms now she saw what they were getting at; all her passionate loyalty to Wyndham's friend, who had so bewilderingly become her own suitor. An insulting allusion to his race had always infuriated her—he went to church like anybody else. They had chosen the surest way of all to send her flying to his defence. "You're all very pleased to have the brilliant young Mr. Disraeli to dine," she accused them wildly, "but as soon as it's a matter of his falling in love with somebody else, he becomes *the Jew!*"

"Are you suggesting that we're jealous?" inquired Rosina.

"It's a very different thing, going in to dinner with a man, or marrying him," remarked Caroline.

"Mary Anne, don't be a silly little fool!" cried Rosina. "It was all very well to make a pet and a protégé out of Dizzy when Wyndham was alive—especially as everyone knew Dizzy had his hands full elsewhere." She smiled. "You knew all about *that,* didn't you, dear?"

"Of course I did! But it's been over quite some time now."

"How long?" murmured Caroline unkindly.

"I know what you're thinking, Caroline." She faced them proudly now, her chin up, and a red spot on each cheek. Now she knew where she was. "And it's really none of your business, but the break with Henrietta came long before Wyndham died. I know that, because he told me so—Wyndham did. He was very relieved. You see, all she cared about was balls and giving dinner parties and picnics—she hated the idea that Dizzy might have a serious career in the House. Wyndham was so pleased that Dizzy knew enough to choose between her and—what he wanted to do. It showed very good sense, don't you think, for a young man like that? She was so lovely," she added generously, for she had always felt like a little brown wren in the presence of Henrietta's dazzling beauty.

"Oh, Dizzy has taste, I'll grant him that!" admitted Rosina.

Mrs. Lewis shot a long, demure glance at her, and then looked down at her clasped hands in her lap. The corners of her mouth deepened before she spoke.

"Thank you, Rosina," she murmured, and knew she had scored.

"Mary Anne, you're not thinking of this *seriously?*"

"I'd rather not talk about it, Caroline," she said much too late, and added unwisely, "At least not yet."

"Oh, nonsense, don't split hairs! Your year is nearly up. What do you intend to do?"

"I don't think you've any right to question me like this!" she cried out, her back against the wall.

"My poor little goose," purred Rosina. "We're only trying to save you from making a dreadful mistake. The man is a mountebank—a charlatan—an adventurer! He wouldn't look twice at you if you weren't a rich widow!"

"As though people never fell in love with widows unless they had money!" she objected futilely.

"As though men ever fell in love with anyone unless there was something in it for them!" corrected Caroline. Her eyes ran over the neat little figure and soft brown hair dispassionately. "You're not as young as you were. Of course it's the money."

That got home.

"I know I'm older than he is," she admitted humbly. "I've told him so. But—"

"Have you told him how much older?" insisted Caroline.

"He wouldn't listen." The colour had all drained away from her face now. Her small hands were cold and shaking, winding her limp handkerchief round and round her thumb. She was abject with nerves and fatigue and doubt. They had worn her out, found the weak place in her defence. She began to plead. "But you say yourself that I've kept my figure—and my skin was always nice—and I've got all my teeth—"

"My God, Mary Anne, you talk as though you were a horse!" exclaimed Caroline, and she turned on them passionately, sweeping aside their sarcasm and their worldly wisdom and their patronizing airs, throwing herself on their mercy with the recklessness of despair.

"Do you think I *wanted* to fall in love with Dizzy?" she demanded. "It seemed cruel and heartless to care about anyone else so soon after dear Wyndham died. But there is no *suttee* in England! I have to go on living, and the best of living is loving—especially if one is a woman, and not very clever!"

"That all sounds very much like our Dizzy somehow," observed Rosina, unmoved.

"Well, why shouldn't it? Why shouldn't I listen to Dizzy? After Wyndham died like that, so suddenly, it seemed as though everything I had in the world was swept out from under my feet, and I was alone, and afraid. And then I had to go all the way down to Wales to look after the estate—and somehow I felt buried alive down there, and it looked as though nothing would ever be any fun again, and I wished I was dead like poor Wyndham! And Dizzy kept writing me such kind letters, as though he knew how I felt, and meant me to keep in touch with things here, so I could come back some day and have friends again, and good times—" She caught the bright flicker of ironical glances between them, and stumbled hastily into further justification and defence. "Oh, I don't mean they were love letters! They weren't. Not at first. They were all about politics, and things Wyndham had taught me to understand and care about—they made me laugh—they made me homesick. And when I tried to tell him in my letters what he was doing for me, and how I felt about things—tried to thank him for taking the trouble to be so kind to me—he wrote that I mustn't brood over the past, and that I was still young enough to—" She broke off again in embarrassment, with a nightmarish feeling that she was pleading for her life before some relentless tribunal, striving against time and hopeless odds to state her case before the black cap went on and the verdict was given. "Oh, please, *please*—you needn't look like that! If it wasn't for Dizzy I should still be down there in Wales eating my heart out—as good as in my own grave! And I *am* too young for that!" Her breath caught on a sob. She could not bear to look at them any more, at their small surprised smiles at such nakedness as she had shown them, and their bright, astonished eyes that watched her as though she was a play. They weren't human, they had no hearts, they weren't her friends any more, they didn't even try to understand, they were all wrapped up in their own bitterness and defeat, they weren't generous, they didn't want her to be happy when they were not, they were cruel and hard and unforgiving—

"Well, of all the transparent ninnies I ever listened to," said Caroline lightly into the silence. "And you're angry with us when we talk to you as though you were a school-girl!"

She made one last attempt.

"You don't understand Dizzy, either of you," she began.

"Oh, heavens, even that?" murmured Rosina.

"You don't understand, I tell you! Underneath all that sarcasm and queerness of his, he's often lonely and discouraged, and that only makes him wittier and more maddening on the outside. Oh, I've seen! I've watched it over and over again! Women like you dancing on his raw nerves, and he only smiled and looked bored, and so you thought he hadn't realized the hateful things you were trying to stab him with! I'm not clever, but I know how to amuse him!"

"Well, upon my word—!" gasped Caroline.

"Just because neither of you succeeded in holding on to your own husbands, you choose to think all men are odious!" She was crying now, defencelessly, like a child, hitting out right and left blindly for the sake of the man she had come to love with all the passionate protectiveness of her ardent nature. "Just because you're both lonely and wretched is no reason why *I* should be! I don't see why a respectable woman can't love twice in a lifetime! And even if I don't know all about Infant Custody and the Greeks and the Romans, *I* know how to make a home, and *I* don't bore the man you call Jew!" Once more the quality of their silence struck her like a blow, and she realized that she had said hateful things with intent to wound, things the more fatal because they were so terribly true. Her sobs were checked in her throat by the enormity of her crime. She looked up fearfully, bitting her lip. Their faces had not changed. Still those small, cold smiles, still those bright, attentive eyes, waiting for what she would do next. It was disconcerting to have them be so— cold-blooded about it. A word flashed through her tumbled thoughts, and left a streak of wonder behind it—*bear-baiting*. They had set the dogs of their worldly, disillusioned sentences tearing at her vitals and now sat back to watch— Her mind sheered off the metaphor in horror. They were waiting. For what? She swallowed, and words came out somehow.

"And now I suppose I have mortally offended you both and you'll never speak to me again!" she said.

"My dear," said Caroline, and her laugh was mirthless, "we are struck dumb with admiration! Such a power of hero-worship is beyond us entirely!"

"You've no right to call it that," she argued with dignity. "I said he would be a great man in politics, and he is! It wouldn't surprise me to see him in the Cabinet one day!"

"With that name?" said Rosina, and laughed.

"A Jew in the Cabinet?" said Caroline incredulously. "Oh, my dear—!"

"He's Church of England, the same as you or me!" she blurted desperately, and was driven on again by their raised, humorous eyebrows. "I said that one day they would come crowding into the House to hear him, and they do! The benches always fill up now, when word goes round that Dizzy is going to speak!"

"Mary Anne Lewis," began Caroline with exaggerated patience, "will you stop this spate of idolatry long enough for me to get a word in edgeways? Why we bother with you I can't think, but for the last time, listen to me. Your precious Dizzy may be all you think he is, and he may even love you for yourself alone, who knows? But what about ten years from now?"

"And no matter how true all this you've said may be," added Rosina, "you know what the world will think to its dying day, don't you—that Disraeli married a rich widow for her money!"

"But—" She sat looking at them, dazed and shaken, shrunk back into her chair. "But that would be bad for him—wouldn't it?"

"Oh, yes," shrugged Caroline. "If that matters."

"But it does matter! It's the only thing that matters! Oh, but I—I hadn't thought of it like that before. You mean—even if we were perfectly happy together—even if he went on loving me always—only a very few people would ever know that. And to everybody else it would look as though—as though he had sold himself."

"Quite so," nodded Caroline. "The world is quick enough to see a flaw in one's private life! If there aren't any flaws, the world doesn't believe it! And the world is usually right!"

They had won. Inadvertently, almost, at the last minute, they had beaten her. She sat very still, realizing that she was beaten, taking in the fact that it wasn't any good holding out against them any longer, because this time they were right.

"I don't know what to do," she was saying dully to herself. "Oh, poor Dizzy—I don't know what to do—"

"We've told you what to do," said Rosina competently. "Send him packing. Don't tempt Providence!"

"It isn't as though I looked older," she went on dully to herself. "It isn't as though I *felt* older—I don't know what to do—"

And just then Rook appeared in the doorway, smiling and pleased.

"Mr. Disraeli is here, madam," she said.

XIV

He had been at Bradenham for Christmas, and an illness of Isaac's had detained him there. He arrived at Grosvenor Gate that afternoon in a mood to deal with the situation as he saw it. Letters were futile, unsatisfactory things at best, cooling off before they reached their destination, or somehow by the time they arrived not meaning quite what they had seemed to say when they started. And with letters she had always the refuge of not answering questions. Sometimes she did not write at all for days.

He could bear it no longer. Today, before he left the house, he meant to know the answer to the one question that really mattered. If only he could *know*, he told himself on the way to Town, then he could wait if he must. He was so sure, most of the time, that she loved him. Today he would get at the roots of her persistent doubts and vaccilations, and put an end to a suspense which was wrecking his nerves and his work. His new book, *Alarcos*, was suffering— he could not keep his mind on it. He could not sleep, he lay about on sofas, his appetite was not what it should have been—he was in love. But this time he meant to marry. This time . . .

It was a grey and chilly day, and he wore, to keep up his spirits, a velvet frock coat the colour of old claret, with the high rolling collar and pouter-pigeon breast of fashion subtly exaggerated and shown off by his very slender waist and long legs encased in narrow fawn-coloured trousers, strapped under the instep of his polished boots. His cravat was severely black, very high, without white gills as he preferred it, and it filled the V of his silver brocade waistcoat with no gleam of shirt frill to relieve its immaculate austerity, though a rim of white cuff was permitted to show at his wrists. His high hat and his gloves matched his trousers. He looked superb, a walking argument against the sombre trend of blacks and dull browns in men's clothes these days. If you regarded life as a tragedy, like poor Bulwer, well, yes, go into mourning about it. But until then . . .

He was so at home in that house now, and he knew so well just what he meant to do and say when he saw her, that he ran lightly up the stairs behind Rook and arrived on the drawing-room threshold only a few seconds after the announcement of his name. And he found the room full of women.

Instantly the mask of saturnine indifference slipped into place. Only his eyes showed through it, flickering with impatience, bright with the things that were bottled up inside him. His heels came together, he bowed to each of them separately, with murder in his heart. One glance at the face of the woman he loved showed him that she was unhappy, pale, and tired. What right had they to come here, croaking, these two sad remnants of women; each with a broken life, dripping gloom, demanding endless sympathy, using up other people's vitality and happiness by forcing them to condole and to contemplate such dismal wreckage? All very well to be sorry for them, yes—but not, as it were, at the point of a gun. The atmosphere they brought with them was unhealthy, they lived in an odour of disaster. Their sorrows, he concluded, never at a loss for words, making his punctilious bows, pervaded the room like a stench. It wanted airing out when they had gone. He would see to it that they went very soon.

They had imposed on Mary Anne long enough, setting out their woes before her as a beggar exhibits sores, his terrible, articulate thoughts continued behind his pleasant smile, while he refused tea on the ground that he had just come from the club. When Mary Anne was his, as she must be, so that he had the right to protect her, he would see that she was not depleted of all her lovely natural gaiety by the nagging misfortunes of others. Let Rosina and Caroline consort together by all means, enlarging on their symptoms and misfortunes to each other by the hour if it amused them—but let them do it somewhere else, not darkening the sunny places where Mary Anne existed in innocence and goodness, without grievances.

And so he remained politely on his feet, his face a miracle of courteous regret, while they remarked that they were just going. And because he stood there in the middle of the carpet waiting to open the door for them and bow them out of it with his own impeccable grace, they rose together with a rustle of silk and found themselves moving toward it, while at Mary Anne's request he rang the bell for Rook to escort them downstairs. And so here was the man, after all, who took upon himself to enter that house which was apparently masterless, and somehow impose his authority on its inmates and its guests. Rosina and Caroline exchanged glances, on their way to the door. How far had this thing gone? Were they too late? They had understood that he was in the country until the end of the week. . . .

Amid a tinkle of wholly cordial chatter they kissed Mary Anne's soft cheek, Caroline reminded him that she would see him at the Salisburys' on Thursday, he bowed—and finally closed the door behind them, his mouth gone a little tight at the corners, his expressive brows a little aslant. Then he whirled and snatched up the precious black-clad figure in an ardent embrace, striving by his own urgency to warm her back to life again, relieved to find that she surrendered utterly to his kiss, her arms sliding up around his neck. But almost at once she drew back, and glanced past him at the door.

"Dizzy, do be careful—"

"The cats have gone, now the mice can play," he remarked, still holding her, and stooped to look into her face. "My dearest, you've been crying!"

"N-no, I—it's nothing." She pulled away from him gently, and went to the sofa and sat down, not looking at him, her hands clasped tight in her lap.

"Merciful God, how I've missed you!" he said, and his voice was startling to hear, so changed it was, so charged with feeling, as he stood where she had left him, looking down at her. "I've been away from you a lifetime, and it's convinced me of one thing—there is no hell on earth like separation from the being you love best! I want to be with you, to live with you—never again to be away from you. We must be together, I care not where—nothing else is possible!" She did not answer, looking down at her clasped hands, and swiftly he was beside her on the sofa, his fingers closing over hers, his lips against her curls. "Never send me away, my good angel—health, my clear brain, and your love, and I can conquer the world!"

He was waiting for her to answer. The silence stretched tight between them. Her throat had closed and her mouth was dry. She wasn't ready for this, she had had no time to think what to say to him, she did not know where or how to begin. This would not do, and yet she was powerless to stop him. And the comfort of him, the infinite well-being of his mere presence, the delight of his hands on hers and his voice in her ears! She sat choked and wordless with the enormity of what was before her.

"Ah, now we come to it," he said quietly. "This is why I came back the minute I could get away. Why are you like this? Why have you withheld all hope from me in your letters? What have I done? Why don't you answer?"

"It's nothing you've done, Dizzy," she answered weakly. "I—it's too soon—you hurry me so—"

"I don't mean to hurry you, dearest. I've tried to be patient. But we can't go on like this, can we? These constant partings and odd, inopportune reunions will be the death of us. And the inevitable result will be fading emotion and final estrangement."

"No!" She caught at the hands which held hers. "Oh, no, no—!"

"You see, I can't reconcile love and separation," he reasoned with her gently. "My idea of love is to share every thought and every fancy, every charm and every care. And if that is an illusion—it is an illusion worthy of the gods! But is it so impossible? Is it?" His lips were in her curls again. "When I am away from you I am ill and stale and stupid. My zest for living goes. My days are aimless and empty. Do you enjoy making me miserable? Do you keep me waiting just to show your power over me? Because God knows I never wish to deny it!" He kissed her cheek, his lips slid down it to her throat. "I love you," he whispered, "and each day more!"

"Dizzy, I can't!" she cried desperately with a gesture that flung him from her. "Don't, *don't,* I can't marry you!"

Slowly he rose to his full height, withdrawing from her entirely, looking down at her on the sofa.

"I don't understand," he said at last.

"I c-can't put it any plainer than that. I can't marry you."

"I don't mean to be dull." He passed a hand across his eyes like a man blinded. "It's just four words that don't seem to mean anything. I suppose now I must say—why?"

"I'm older than you are," she said wretchedly, distinctly, like a child repeating its lesson. "People will say that you married me for my money."

"Do you believe that is the reason?" he demanded with an icy reasonableness.

"*No,* but—"

"Then does it matter?" he said.

"For you, yes!"

"You might allow me to be the judge of what concerns myself," he objected coldly, encased in his own pain. "It is you who will mind their saying that—isn't it! You will be ashamed."

"No, no, I—" She began to cry now, helplessly, for she felt him receding from her, and dared not try to bring him back. "But you could have a title and five times my income, and youth besides—"

"Doubtless some such paragon exists," he conceded politely. "But I have chosen you."

"But *why*, Dizzy—when I'm such a dunce?"

"How can I tell why?" he cried, with a flashing gesture of utter exasperation. "I am in love with you! Call it an Act of God and don't quarrel with it, *I* don't!" He stood looking down at her bent head a moment while she sobbed softly into her hands. Then his eyes went back to the door through which Caroline and Rosina had passed. He began to see. "So people will say I was after your money, you think," he reflected softly.

"I didn't think so," she defended herself instantly. "That was Caroline."

"And she convinced you," he suggested, watching her.

"I told her it wasn't true!" she gulped.

"You seem to have discussed the matter pretty freely with your friends," he observed, and it was suddenly abominable to him that they had sat there with his love for her defenceless and naked on their tongues. "I suppose you realize that everything you said will be all over London tomorrow!"

"I said it wasn't true," she repeated doggedly.

"And what else do they think?" he demanded, raw with horror of them and the things they represented. "Didn't it occur to them also that possibly I was after my friend's wife?"

"Oh, Dizzy—!" She turned from him, her face hidden in her hands.

"Yes, I was sure they wouldn't overlook that!" he said with a dreadful satisfaction.

"But I told them—"

"Well, suppose it was true!" he cried out roughly, and she stared up at him, tear-stained and terrified, so that his voice dropped again to the tone of icy reasoning she had never heard before. "Does that surprise you so much? Now you have opened this question, and you shall have the answer. First of all, I admit that situated as I am, I could not be blind to the advantages of a wealthy marriage. My father wishes to see me settled before he dies. And I myself was getting sick of bachelor chambers—I wanted a home—love—companionship—without all the nervous wear and tear of an intrigue. I've had enough of that sort of thing, as you know very well! And so I, shall we say, envied Wyndham—"

"Dizzy, I'd rather not hear any more," she begged in panic.

"—*envied* Wyndham, I say, perhaps half unconsciously! This house came to stand for all I had not, that was charming and kind and restful—and complete. Then we lost him. Before God, the shock to me was nearly as great as to you! It meant the end of a friendship I had counted on like my own right arm. And then I realized that coming here would have to be different. We had to be more to each other—or less. I couldn't give you up—so I meant it to be more. And because it is my nature never to do things by halves, I began to make love to you—too soon for convention, perhaps, but not too soon for a miracle to happen."

"Dizzy, please don't go on like this—"

"It was a miracle, wasn't it," he insisted, leaning over her. "Each day you grew lovelier—because you were happy again. Happier, I think, than you had ever been. I watched you blooming under my hands with incredulous delight—in your black gown and your second flowering. And so I awoke one morning and found myself Pygmalion—I had fashioned a woman out of love. And from that day to this you have not been an hour out of my thoughts."

She was calmer now, and sat plaiting her damp handkerchief in fingers that shook. She had much to think about.

"You—didn't love me in the beginning," she said.

"I have been recklessly honest with you," he admitted, and his voice was natural again, the voice that he used for her, warm and vibrant and caressing. "And even as it was in the beginning we might have been very happy together. But the love I know now, that nags at my heart night and day with my need of you—the longing to have the right always to find you no further away than the next room—are you angry that it was born of your love for me?"

It was so disarming a question, in his beautiful voice— those rich, rare tones like velvet, that never failed to lull and possess her—his voice had colour, texture, temperature, it was almost a tangible thing, enfolding as the clasp of his hands, a thing one could hold to in the dark. . . .

"You see," she began all over again bravely, and stiffened herself against the magnetism flowing all round her, turning her will-power and her very bones soft with submission to his least wish—who could resist him, when he spoke like that? —and why was she the one marked down to disappoint him when all she wanted in the world was to shut her eyes and be swept away? "You see, if we were the same age they wouldn't have so much room to talk about the money. But I'm—"

"God in heaven, are we back to *that* again?" he cried, but without anger, and he caught her unceremoniously by one hand and jerked her to her feet facing the mantelpiece mirror, both his hands squaring her shoulders to it, making her look. "Look at your face in that mirror!" he commanded. "Is it the face of a woman too old for love? *Is* it?" And he gave her a little shake so that her brown curls bobbed childishly, and the quivering smile that could not help breaking round her mouth when she met his eyes in the glass took off approximately twenty years and left her, tear-stained and troubled as she was, looking like a girl in her first season and shy of her lover. He bent forward with an incredulous catch of laughter, and turned her slowly in his arms to face him and not the mirror. "I never saw a woman before who was charming when she cried," he marvelled. "Usually their noses get pink! Your tears are like a baby's, made to be caught on someone's lips—"

Almost he had her then. She was worn out and frightened, and she was never good at standing up to people, and she could not bear to see him angry with her, and she only wanted him to have what he wanted, forever and ever. . . . But she must do what was best for him, and one day he would thank her. So she put him from her firmly, while he watched her in new astonishment, and she walked away so that the sofa was between them.

"You'd better go now, Dizzy," she said.

For once he was lost. For once he guessed wrong.

"Because of the money?" he said, very low, and she nodded, her back to him.

The pain that engulfed him then made him insensible to everything else. He could not think, he could not reason, he could not even see. He was for the time a single tortured nerve, containing just enough intelligence to direct the terrible retaliation his tongue could always inflict. She might have been O'Connell or the devil himself for all he knew or cared as he spoke, possessed by a molten fury of words which came out of their own volition and dropped one by one with dreadful distinctness on the shrinking air of that kind, cherished room which had never heard such things before; ignoring interruption, impervious to sanity or mercy. He heard himself speaking and could not stop until he had done.

"The money," he began, through his teeth. "Let me tell you the truth about that too, before I go. Your fortune proved to be much less than I or the world supposed. It is not a thing which could benefit me in the slightest. It is merely a jointure sufficient to maintain this establishment and gratify your private wishes. Do you think I am ambitious to eat and sleep in this house and call it mine?"

"Oh, please, please, I didn't mean—"

The cold, hard, metallic words did not swerve for any plea of hers.

"That could only appeal to a penniless adventurer!" he went on. "It is no inducement to a man in my position to sacrifice his dear liberty and mortgage his future! I can live as I live now, without disgrace—until inevitably I come into a substantial inheritance."

"No, no, I never implied a word about money, I only—"

"You only feared what the world would say about us! This perfect love, grown out of an old companionship, means so little to you that at the first whiff of public opinion you order me out of the house because of what your precious friends will say!"

"I didn't! *I didn't!* Dizzy, please—"

"Those dreadful, cruel women who have made such a mess of their own personal relationships they can never again believe in an honest emotion! Very well, I'll go—but you have left me no refuge in the world. I have no home at all now. Bradenham is forever haunted of you!"

"Oh, don't be angry with me—please forgive me—"

"Forgive you, yes—when I am old and ready to die! Forgive the woman I loved for being a coward and a sycophant, after it can no longer matter to me that she wasted my life, and made me a jest in the mouths of her witty friends! *The upstart Jew,* who failed to marry the rich widow of his benefactor! You have made me *that!*"

"Dizzy—!" Her face was hidden now from the sight of him, white and rigid and cruel, beside himself with rage and hatred of her, unable to see that she had only tried to do what was best and that her own heart was breaking as she stood there.

He found himself at the door, the knob turned in his hand, he paused there, while words went on dropping from his lips in a silence that winced and shuddered under the lash.

"Good-bye," he said, and thought how softly he spoke, how calm he was, how collected, how carefully he weighed his words, and how still the room was, listening to him. "I don't wish you happiness, it is not in your timid nature to attain it. Keep your poisonous, stuffy friendships with sour, unwanted women! Grow like them yourself, so that love is a bitterness on your tongue, and your heart rots away in your

living body! Grow old like them, alone, cast off, *wasted!* And
I hope you will remember until you die one man whose
honest passion was poured upon sand!"

And then he was on the stairs—another door opened before him—he felt his way, shaking and sweating, out of the
house, his hat still in his hand—cool air blew on his face—
he shivered, and remembered to put on the hat he carried—
odd, his face was wet with perspiration—his legs worked jerkily, as though after an illness—where was he going?—the
club?—no, he must dress—home, then, to his rooms—a man
thought very clearly in a crisis—he must go home, and
dress. . . .

X V

His rooms in Park Street were only five minutes away;
around the corner and across the road—there was a clatter of
hooves and a shout as he stepped off the kerb, but he did not
look up or alter his pace—and up the steps to his own door
by blind instinct. He pulled the bell and stood leaning
against the wall until his manservant opened the door.

"Brandy," he said as he entered.

It appeared silently before him on a salver. He sank into
a chair with the empty glass in his hand, and found himself
at his writing-table, staring at pens and notepaper. No good
writing to her now. It was finished. She had asked him to go.

"Brandy!" he said savagely, because the glass was empty.
"Bring the bottle, can't you? And what's the matter with the
fire? I'm cold."

The bottle was placed on the table beside him—not a full
bottle by any means. He emptied half of what was left into
the tumbler—the neck of the bottle chattered against the
rim as he did so—splashed in a little water, and drank. That
was better. He wondered dimly if he had caught a chill, and
decided that he wasn't ill, only angry. Angrier than he had
ever been in his life before. And she had done this thing to
him, the woman he had trusted above all other women.
You'd better go now, Dizzy. He would never forget the sound
of it. Never trust a woman again. Remember that, my boy.

Never give one power again. They were created solely to amuse. Never count on them. That was fatal.

The brandy had begun to reach him, and he felt steadier, and very clear-headed. She had asked him to go, but what had he said to her? He could not quite remember, but he had been very calm, very self-contained, he was sure. Still, there was a great deal she ought to know, the woman who had turned him out of her house. His eyes rested thoughtfully on his writing materials. Why, if he had wanted to marry for money there were far better opportunities open to him than herself. Had he told her that? Her fortune, which she had thrown in his face, was comparatively small. He would inherit money too, when that time came. Meanwhile, although he had debts, his position was no longer embarrassing. Had he told her that?

In a few days, when it became known round London that he no longer went there, and that their association was at an end, people would begin to jeer at him, a rejected suitor, and then his humiliation would be complete. Election defeats, political snubs and buffets, he had borne—the fortunes of war. But now, just as he had begun to figure at Westminster as he had dreamed of doing, through all those bitter years of failure and ridicule, just when they had begun to listen to him as one of themselves—this. She had contrived to do what all his enemies could not do. She had broken his spirit. She had left him nothing. Had he told her that? She was shallow, like the rest, worthless, frivolous, a slave to convention, a coward before public opinion, a traitor to his years of misplaced confidence. She cared more, after all, for what a few back-biting women might say than for what became of him, and for the shining, triumphant thing they might have made of life together—if only she had been the woman he had thought her, mistakenly, for so long. He would tell her so, in cold, plainly written words that she must read, that she could not interrupt by asking him to go.

He reached for the pen. Driven by his terrible, lacerated pride, the double pride of a young man and a Jew; tortured by his outraged, bleeding faith in her which seemed to have come up by the roots; sick with nerves and reaction, he wrote for the better part of an hour, without knowing that he repeated himself. When he finished, the brandy bottle was empty and he was still quite sober. He gave the letter to his manservant to be taken round to Grosvenor Gate at once, and then went out of the house again just as he was, after all, bound for the club.

"I must get drunk," he thought clearly, as he emerged into the early winter twilight. "One can't get drunk alone."

Walking down St. James's Street, he fell in with D'Orsay, and they wound up at Crockford's, where he played whist all night with a bottle and a tumbler on the table beside him. Inevitably he held all the cards, and could not lose. As the night wore on, men noticed his white, rigid face and the way he held his liquor, and murmured behind their hands. "The little widow is coy," was the general surmise.

He got home somehow in the small hours, numbed with fatigue but still quite steady on his legs; crawled into bed, and fell asleep with the lamp still burning. At eleven the next morning he returned slowly to consciousness and realized at last that he had been drinking. His manservant attended him in sympathetic silence.

Peevishly the complicated business of dressing went forward. Nothing was right. The bath water was not hot enough, the shaving water scalded him. The towels had not been changed, and there was a mark on the tip of one boot. The particular shirt he wanted to wear had not come back from the laundress, and two cravats were wrecked in the tying. After long consideration he chose pearl-grey trousers with a narrow black stripe down the outside seam, and swore because the cord of his dressing-gown did not knot itself unaided. At last, with every fold and every hair in place, he sat down most unwillingly to breakfast.

One glance at the letter on the top of the pile beside his plate ran through him like a cold douche.

"How long has this been here? Why didn't you wake me?" he demanded unreasonably.

"It arrived by hand after you had left the house last night, sir."

"*Last night!*"

"Quite late it was, sir—just as I was going. I put it in the usual place against the lamp, sir. You must have missed it when you came in, sir."

"But this morning! Why on earth didn't you tell me this morning!"

"You don't usually open your letters until breakfast, sir." This was perfectly true.

Somehow it had not occurred to him that she might answer his letter. *You'd better go now, Dizzy.* What was there for her to say—after that? His fingers fumbled as he broke the seal.

> For God's sake come to me. I am ill and almost distracted. . . .

The rest of it blurred before his incredulous eyes. The paper shook in his hand.

> . . . I will answer all you wish. . . . I never desired you to leave the house, or implied or thought a word about money. . : . I often feel the apparent impropriety of my present position. . . . I am devoted to you. . . .

The light Sheraton chair he was sitting in went over backwards as he rose.

"My coat," he said, stripping off the dressing-gown.

"Yes, sir. I thought perhaps the dark blue this morning, sir—?"

"Don't stand there, man, *any* coat! Hurry up!"

The dressing-gown lay in a pool of silk on the floor where it fell. He thrust his arms into the garment the man held for him, snatched the first hat his eye fell on. The door banged behind him. Breakfastless, with pounding temples, bright-eyed, with the tenderest smile curving his lips, he was on his way to Grosvenor Gate.

For God's sake come to me. And with that, everything else was wiped out. She was ill—worrying—crying—he had been unkind—he had hurt her, his darling. And it was never her own doing which had brought about that dreadful quarrel. It was entirely those interfering women, yesterday—upsetting her, confusing her honest, loyal mind with their criminal insinuations. But she had sent for him in spite of them, she knew in her heart where her own happiness lay, and his. And this time she would come into his arms without any more doubts and reservations, and there would be no more scenes.

What a day, he thought, sniffing the raw February morning as though it was purest June. What a world to be alive in, gazing rapturously at the grey street wreathed in fog, with muddy gutters and a slatternly maid swabbing down the steps across the way, her fat arms red with cold. Spring, he decided, as he turned the corner and caught sight of the bare, dripping trees in the Park.

Always from now on she would be there in his life, with her gay chatter and her wise, sweet eyes; always there to turn to, no matter what happened now, encouraging him, helping him, believing in his ultimate success as firmly as he ever had himself, sure that he would be a great man, really great, as he meant to be, for her. With her beside him, his wife, they would receive important invitations, they would entertain Royalty, they would have a country house of their own, and carriages, they would travel. She was a charming hostess, a most expert housekeeper, a discriminating judge of men. She would make his life a rich thing, a happy and glorious thing, without loneliness or despair or anxiety. There was nothing he could not do under the benediction of her love, freely given before the world.

He would repay, oh, a hundredfold. She would be proud of him yet, really proud, for his would be a name worth having before he had done. Already Peel was counting on him, and the next time the Conservatives came in, which they must do before long, he would hold a sound position in the Government. Wellington said the country was on its legs again, Melbourne said things were soothing down. But Ireland was still with them, of course, and another bad harvest would make the Corn Laws controversy acute. Fresher issues such as the agitation for factory reform and popular education would provide golden opportunities for a new Government. Would Peel make the most of them when his chance came?

A few years ago Peel had stood for the younger generation against Wellington's High Tory colleagues. But now Peel seemed almost imperceptibly to have crossed the line to the side of the oldsters—or perhaps the line itself had moved and left him static, on the wrong side. If Peel kept on as he was, he would soon be an old fogey with the rest of them, dependent on formulas, seeking always the easiest way. Who was now the younger generation, and where was its leader? Why, any man with foresight and a decent regard for humanity, a man willing to move with the times, could gather round him a new party, a *young* party, without factious tendencies, scorning the limitations of political dogma, and combining the best of both Tory and Radical tenets. . . .

And the sovereign? What could be predicted about the mysterious, virtuous, strong-willed little woman who could scarcely get through a single day without consulting Lord Melbourne, and how would she get on with Peel? Wellington had once explained the old Tory difficulties by remarking that he himself had no small talk and that Peel had no manners. And after Melbourne's jovial ways and easy laughter, what woman—Queen or no Queen—would welcome Peel's frigid personality and ponderous language? It was a disturbing and illuminating idea: the Queen could not keep Melbourne forever, and she was not going to like Peel. Peel would never have the sense to humour her or the wit to flatter her, and to him it would not matter that she could be charming and affectionate. A female sovereign would be wasted on Peel. But a man who chose to exert himself to win her regard, a man who understood women, and who could be a little charming himself. . . .

Suppose by the time Peel came into office again his ideas had become hopelessly old-fashioned. Suppose it looked as though Peel was going to make a mess of things, after he was in a position to do so. He could never bear criticism from his supporters. If one disagreed with him one must be strong enough to stand alone, and go on without him. No. To secede from a party was not enough. One must have a party of one's own.

Disraeli drew a long, exultant breath of the foggy winter air. *Young enough to wait*—the light words, in a voice he had come to love, returned to him from that evening at Caroline Norton's, how many years ago? Younger than Peel, anyway, and willing to learn, which Peel was not. Peel's foreign policy would want bolstering up; he was a bit short-sighted, a bit the Home Secretary still. Canning had begun at the Foreign Office, Canning had been able to see as far as the frontiers of the Empire. Europe was quiet enough now, but the East was always on the boil, and Russia was always on the prowl. In the Peel Ministry which was sure to come before long, who would be given that most delectable portfolio, for the Foreign Office? Surely a man who had travelled, a man who knew something of the East, and who realized, like Canning, the immense importance of Empire. . . .

His eyes were bright with visions. His life had turned the corner, into the straightaway. He could not be beaten now. He would do great things, not just for himself, not even just for her, but for England, whose very cobblestones he loved this raw, dim morning which was bringing him his heart's desire; the slow, sure, canny, lovable land which his spirit embraced with a passionate protectiveness. He saw himself contributing, through the years to come, his own small greatness, achieved with endless care and unremitting toil, to the greatness of England. He was England's debtor, he would be its servant, and to the last ounce of jealous effort its guardian. But he must have place, position, power. Perhaps he would be in Peel's Cabinet; if not at once, before very long. Perhaps an under-secretaryship first, Peel himself had started that way. And then perhaps a portfolio—perhaps even the Chancellorship, Lyndhurst talked of retiring—perhaps—yes, nothing was inconceivable now—perhaps one day he would be Prime Minister. . . .

He arrived on her doorstep, and pulled the bell.

NOTES

ALL quotations from letters, diaries, and political speeches, and all excerpts from Disraeli's published works are authentic. It is a great pity that more of Sarah's letters and Mrs. Lewis's have not been preserved, but Disraeli himself is doubtless to blame for that. Fortunately he was loved by two women, his sister and his wife, who never destroyed a piece of paper he had written on. In this book, therefore, he is allowed to tell his own story in his own words as far as possible, and the surrounding text has been adjusted so as not to reiterate his account. Each sentence of his own thus becomes a necessary link in the chain of his eventful days.

Footnotes and references have been purposely omitted, though a short bibliography follows; both facts and inferences can all be found in the monumental *Life of Benjamin Disraeli* by Monypenny and Buckle. Most of the more informal chapters, such as the scene with Melbourne in Caroline Norton's drawing-room, and the quarrel with Mrs. Lewis, are based on recorded incidents and actual letters.

The book ends twenty-nine years before Disraeli became Prime Minister in 1868. His wife died in 1872, after thirty-three years of unblemished devotion between them.

Kebble, who is one of the soberest of party historians of the last century, writes of Disraeli: "The story of his entry into public life has been told so often that marvellous as it is I shall not repeat it here. Not the wildest romance that ever entered into the brain of poet, dramatist, or novelist, can equal the unvarnished facts of that astounding history. Distinguished by peculiarities singularly trying to English tastes and habits; enjoying the rare bad fortune of being both hated and ridiculed at the same moment and by the same persons; pelted with libels and caricatures; the object of a thousand enmities which he took no pains to conciliate; without money, without interest, without patrons, the young man who replied to Melbourne's good-natured inquiry whether he could be of any service to him, that 'he wished to be Prime Minister,' actually lived to realize his heart's desire, to trample on the prejudice, malignity, and jealousy which impeded his early rise, to overcome obstacles which, in a country like England, seemed absolutely insuperable,

> To mould a mighty State's decrees,
> And shape the whisper of a Throne,

and to die amid the lamentations of the English people, who felt, perhaps, with some twinges of self-reproach that they had recognized his genius too late."

In the beginning "it was not believed possible that one with such antecedents as his could ever become a genuine English statesman. His first appearance in the House of Commons; the strange costume, the black curls, the unaccustomed language, the eccentric daring that seemed like puerile conceit; the defiance of the House, which then looked like theatrical bravado; his very wit, humour, and sarcasm, even his birth and origin, were all remembered against him. . . . Through all this array of envy, hatred, malice, and uncharitableness Mr. Disraeli fought his way to victory, but not without receiving wounds of which the traces long remained, if indeed they ever totally disappeared."

BIBLIOGRAPHY

History of Europe from Napoleon I to Louis Napoleon, by A. Alison

Cambridge Modern History

History of the Peace, by Harriet Martineau

England in 1835, by F. Raumer

Early Victorian England, Ed. by G. M. Young

Modes and Manners of the 19th Century, Ed. by G. Thompson

Old and New London, by E. Walford

Greville's Journals

Croker's Correspondence and Diaries

The Creevey Papers

History of Toryism, by T. Kebble

History of the Whig Ministry, by J. Roebuck

Recollections of Captain Gronow

England Since Waterloo, by J. Marriott

Life of Benjamin Disraeli, by Monypenny and Buckle

Disraeli's Works

Home Letters, Ed. by Ralph Disraeli

The Genius of Judaism, by Isaac Disraeli

Commentaries on Charles I, by Isaac Disraeli

Random Recollections of the House of Commons, by J. Grant

Random Recollections of the House of Lords, by J. Grant

Leaders of Public Opinion in Ireland, by W. Lecky

Louis XVIII, by M. Sandars

The Patriot King, by G. Thompson

Grey of the Reform Bill, by G. Trevelyan

Peel and the Conservative Party, by G. Clark

Life of Lockhart, by A. Lang

Life of Murray, by S. Smiles

Life of Edward Stanley, Earl of Derby, by T. Kebble

Life of Bulwer, by V. Lytton

Life of Melbourne, by McCullough

The Most Gorgeous Lady Blessington, by J. Molloy

Mrs. Norton, by J. Perkins

Royal Dukes, by Roger Fulford

The Girlhood of Queen Victoria, by Viscount Esher